SOFTWARE DEFINED RADIO
FOR AMATEUR RADIO OPERATORS
AND SHORTWAVE LISTENERS

by

Andrew Barron, ZL3DW

Published by Radio Society of Great Britain of 3 Abbey Court, Priory Business Park, Bedford MK44 3WH, United Kingdom
www.rsgb.org.uk

First Edition 2016

Second Edition 2017

ISBN: 9781 9101 9346 4

Cover design: Kevin Williams, M6CYB
Typography and design: Andrew Barron ZL3DW
Production and revisions: Mark Allgar, M1MPA

Printed in Great Britain by Hobbs the Printers Ltd. of Totton, Hampshire

Any amendments or updates to this book can be found at:
www.rsgb.org/booksextra

Table of Contents

ACKNOWLEDGMENTS

Thanks to my wife Carol for her love and support and to my sons James and Alexander for their support and their insight into this modern world.

Thanks also to everyone who has ever helped with the design or production of software defined radios for radio hams and shortwave listeners, and to the hundreds of software developers who spend thousands of hours writing SDR software and then make it available to the community for free!

Finally many thanks to you, for taking a chance and buying my book.

Andrew Barron, ZL3DW
December 2017

AUTHORS NOTE

The information contained in this book is my own analysis of software defined radio as used by amateur radio operators and shortwave listeners worldwide. It intends no criticism of any particular brand or model of radio equipment or any software application. The author has no association with any equipment manufacturer or SDR software developer. Research material for the creation of this document has been sourced from variety of public domain Internet sites. The author accepts no responsibility for the accuracy of any information presented herein. It is to the best of my knowledge accurate but no guarantee is given or implied. Use the information contained in this document at your own risk.

The book refers to software and software defined radios created by many individuals and companies. All such software and intellectual property relating to hardware mentioned in this book is copyright by their respective authors..

INTRODUCTION

Everyone is talking about software defined radios. But is an SDR right for you? This book explains the basics without getting too technical. It will help you to get the most out of your new software defined radio or decide whether you want to buy one. The use of software defined radio by amateur radio operators and shortwave listeners is rapidly growing in popularity as people become aware of their great features and performance. What used to be the domain of a few dedicated hackers and experimenters has now reached the 'mainstream' ham population.

To many hams, software defined radio, conjures up images of circuit boards, tricky software, and black box radios without any knobs or buttons. But that is not how it is anymore. Many of these radios are just as easy to setup and use as any other ham radio or shortwave receiver. Some even have all of the buttons, switches, knobs, and controls you are used to. These SDRs "with knobs" do not need to be connected to a personal computer (PC) for their operation. You might not even know that you are using an SDR. They are "the same on the outside, but different on the inside." Take a look at the Elecraft KX3 QRP radio or the Icom IC-7300. They look just like other amateur radio transceivers, but they are both software defined radio transceivers. However, software defined radios with knobs are not the real focus of this book. The most interesting stuff is happening with the SDRs that don't have knobs on the front panel.

Who would want a radio without any knobs! Certainly not me! I never thought I would end up using a radio with a nearly blank front panel. I got into software defined radio because I wanted one of those fancy band scopes like the ones on the latest high end transceivers. My first SDR was a SoftRock kit on 9 MHz, wired into the receiver I.F. stage of a transceiver. I liked it... a lot. I found it amazing to be able to see the signals on the band as well as hearing them. The SoftRock experience was so positive that I bought a FLEX-1500 QRP radio. I used it to drive a 100 W linear amplifier made from the power amp block of a surplus Yaesu FT-301 transceiver. Within a couple of months, I was hooked on the SDR experience. Now I have moved on to one of the new 100 W SDR transceivers. My old HF transceiver sits gathering dust. Now, when I use a conventional radio, I feel deprived of the band scope. It feels like I am operating blind.

The improved audio quality and ease of use are great, but for me, the best thing about using an SDR is being able to see all of the signals across the band. With the SDR, I can set my receiver filter to exactly the right width, avoiding unwanted noise and I can see and often eliminate any interfering signals. There are other benefits too, such as the ability to watch a net frequency on the 80m band while working a PSK station on 20m. Contest and DX stations can monitor other bands for an opening without moving off their run frequency.

I firmly believe that if you make a commitment to using a software defined radio as your main receiver or transceiver for a couple of weeks, rather than just casually observing a few QSOs and shortwave stations for an hour or two, you will quickly find that using an SDR becomes truly addictive. It takes a while to get used to the idea that the radio interface is on the computer and learning how to operate the radio with a mouse, but it is really no different to using any other computer application such as browsing the Internet, sending an email, or operating a digital mode program.

Software defined radios offer a new way to operate and some amazing new features, including remote operation, looking at several bands at the same time, and improved transmitter performance by using new techniques. In many cases, you can use your radio with several different software packages. It is like getting a brand new radio just by loading a new computer program. A lot of SDR software is free, not shareware or limited in some essential way. It is created under the open source rules by amateur software developers or groups. These programs are fully featured and can be downloaded and used completely free of charge. Not only that, they are usually very well written and well supported. You do need a PC to use black box (no knobs) software defined receivers and transceivers. If you already use a PC in your shack and you have connected it to a radio for digital mode operation, monitoring CW signals, logging calls, or remote control, then you should have no difficulty adjusting to life with a software defined radio. It is different and it does take a bit of getting used to. But operating a software defined radio quickly becomes just like using any other computer application.

Software defined radio is a logical extension of the digital signal processing (DSP) found in many amateur radio transceivers and some shortwave receivers. Digital signal processing in conventional receivers and transceivers is performed by specialized DSP chips in the radio. They are programmable devices running software ('firmware') like a microprocessor but they are specially designed to manage radio, audio, or video, signals. AF (audio frequency) DSP works by converting the audio output from the demodulator into a digital signal. The digital signal is manipulated to apply filtering and noise blanking and then it is converted back into an audio signal and passed on to the audio amplifier stage. With I.F. (intermediate frequency), DSP the I.F. output of the first or second mixer of the receiver is converted into a digital signal. Features like I.F. shift and I.F. width control are performed using firmware code running on the DSP chips. Often a band scope is provided so that you can see a display of signals above and below the receiver's frequency. After the DSP stage, the digital signal is converted back into an analog signal and passed on to the demodulator. A software defined radio receiver takes the DSP process further by performing the demodulation on the digital signal, as well providing the traditional DSP band scope, filters, and noise reduction. Software defined radio transmitters use digital signal processing to modulate and shape the radio signal.

Software defined radio is a merging of radio technology and computer technology. Some of the radio is still hardware circuits but the operating panel and DSP becomes a software application, usually running on a personal computer.

This book covers the many things that an SDR can do better than your old technology receiver or transceiver. I think there is something for everyone. Here are some of the features and benefits that you can expect from a software defined radio. Not all of these functions are available with all software defined radios, or software. But these eight items will give you a taste of what you can gain by buying an SDR.

1. Generally, SDRs have very good receiver performance. This is mostly due to the fundamental difference in technology. Digital down conversion HF receivers have no mixers (in hardware) so they don't suffer from the intermodulation distortion effects and 'birdies' that mixers and oscillators contribute to standard Superheterodyne receivers. Of course, the manufacturers of conventional radios do go to great lengths to try to eliminate these problems by using excellent designs, quality components and by picking I.F. frequencies that place image signals outside the ham bands. Great performance comes at the cost of increased complexity and a higher price.

2. The panadapter screen of a software defined radio displays the signals across a ham or shortwave band. A simple mouse click tunes the radio to any signal that you can see. The panadapter will also show other interesting things such as interfering signals or the effect of poor quality transmissions. CW key clicks, over-modulated digital mode signals, and linear amp splatter are all easy to spot.

3. Tuning around the band with a conventional receiver you might easily miss a station making occasional CQ calls. With an SDR, you will see the signal pop up on the waterfall or spectrum display. When your QSO is finished, you can click to move directly to the next station without having to tune up and down the band. This is fantastic during contests because you can click on each station in turn as you work up or down the band.

4. With some software defined radios, you can listen to two VFOs (receivers) at the same time, to hear a DX station and also the station they are working in the pileup. The panadapter can show both the DX station and the pileup of calling stations. This lets you pick a relatively quiet spot to transmit or work out which way the DX station is progressing through the calling stations. You can easily see when the DX station is transmitting and time your call appropriately.

5. Being able to monitor several bands at the same time is useful as well. You can quickly see which bands are open. If you are changing bands, to work a station on another band you can see their signal come up on the new frequency, without moving off the old frequency. No more

changing bands only to find the frequency is in use or you can't hear the other station. With a software defined radio, you can watch and hear your old frequency and your new frequency at the same time. You can watch a frequency for the Net to begin, or for a DX station, while working or listening to another station on a different band.

6. You won't need cables to connect the PC sound card to your transceiver. Audio cross connections are done with special PC software. You will not need a CAT cable for computer control either, since the radio software is already running on the PC. Generally, you will need to load some shareware or freeware utility programs onto your PC to perform these tasks.

7. You won't need external audio equalizers either since the SDR software usually includes microphone and receive audio equalizers.

8. The CW Skimmer program is very popular with CW DX stations and contesters. It can decode many Morse Code signals at the same time. A software defined radio can send the entire CW band segment, or even multiple bands, to CW Skimmer, so that all of the CW signals can be identified. With conventional receivers, only signals within the relatively narrow 3 kHz receiver bandwidth can be seen by the CW Skimmer application.

I notice that many articles in amateur radio magazines now feature screenshots of SDR receiver displays. It seems that the people who are interested in the development of new digital modes, EME, propagation, shortwave signals, weather satellites, ham satellites, contesting, interference detection, and monitoring intruders on our bands are finding that software defined radios are very useful for their particular interest. An SDR receiver can be used as a spectrum analyzer to observe different types of modulation or interference signals. You can even see the frequency response of the audio modulation on a single sideband signal. You can also use the panadapter to monitor your own transmit signal to ensure that your transmission is clean and legal.

The ham radio and SWL software defined radio world is developing so fast that much of the information online and many of the products for sale are already out of date. It can be quite confusing deciding what radio to buy. This book explains the merits of different types of SDR and there is a comprehensive list of the key parameters of many of the currently available models. I hope that this book will convince you to buy a software defined radio and will help you to get the most out of using one.

One of the joys of software defined radio is that it is evolving rapidly. New features are being developed continuously. This is great for those who like to tinker with new technology and be at the bleeding edge in learning what is possible with these new radios. Others may be more interested in the competitive edge that using an SDR can provide.

WHAT TO LOOK FOR WHEN BUYING AN SDR

Firstly, you need to decide whether you are looking for a transceiver or a receiver and often your budget will be another major factor. Kit builders and those looking to connect a cheap band scope to the I.F. output of a conventional receiver may prefer a SoftRock, Genesis, or similar kit. The RTL dongles are a very cheap way to have a play with SDR and they are tremendously popular. But I am not a fan, because the performance of these devices is quite limited. The RTL dongles were designed primarily as a cheap way to receive digital TV signals and display the channels on portable computers. I believe that the FUNcube Dongle Pro+ USB dongle receiver is a better choice. They are a bit more expensive, but they have dedicated front end filters with excellent SAW filters on the 2m and 70cm ham bands. The frequency coverage is amazing and they were specifically designed to be a receiver for amateur operators and for schools involved with the FUNcube satellite project. At the other end of the scale are the direct digital synthesis 100 W HF transceivers. It is important to evaluate the SDR software as well as the hardware because it is your interface with the radio. Some radios can use a range of software applications. Others are limited to a particular program that comes bundled with the radio. If you are interested in VHF, UHF or microwave frequencies there are radios and development boards that work up into the GHz range.

What you buy is up to you. The choices are a bit like buying a car. An RTL dongle is like a 'Go-kart.' It is technically a car but it is lacking some of the capability and features that you might prefer. My fear is that you might be disappointed with the performance of one of these little radios and that this might disillusion you about software defined radios in general. The older QSD based receivers and transceivers are like a 'Model T.' Again they have many of the features of a modern car but nowhere near the performance that is available from a newer model. Of course, many people love the cheap price of the Go-kart or they only need the capabilities of the Model T and that is fine. Owning either of them can be loads of fun. As with everything that you choose to buy for your ham shack or hobby room the purchase of an SDR comes down to a careful analysis of what you want to achieve balanced by an equally careful analysis of your available funds.

There are a myriad of different SDR types. USB dongles, small box QSD based receivers and transceivers, SDR kits (usually QSD), VHF/UHF/SHF boards that use a mixer to get an I.F. frequency low enough for direct sampling, HF transceivers using direct digital synthesis, SDRs with knobs and on-board DSP, Superheterodyne radios with IQ output (at audio) from their DSP stages, and commercial or military radios that use digital sampling and DSP chips.

Check out the glossary of software defined radios near the end of the book. It contains basic details on many of the software defined radios that are currently available.

Whether you want a receiver, a QRP transceiver, a radio for VHF, UHF, or microwave frequencies, or a 100W HF transceiver, you should be able to find a software defined radio that meets your needs. If not…, buy two!

RECEIVERS

As well as the glossary, the compatibility list of SDR software later in the book includes some of the many small box SDR receivers available. You need to be careful in your selection. Some receivers use older QSD designs and the price is not necessarily a good indicator of their performance. Check out the specifications online at the manufacturer's web site and check for reviews on eHam reviews http://www.eham.net/reviews/. It is not a good sign if there is sketchy or no data available online. Some advertised radios are not yet actually available for sale. I call this 'vaporware.' SDR forums are also a great source of information and news.

Modern software defined radio receivers use digital down conversion. Make sure that the receiver covers the bands that you want. Some SDR on a chip designs only cover VHF and up. Designs that use QSD (quadrature sampling detectors) and PC or USB sound cards are based on old technology.

Designs using 8 bit analog to digital converters are likely to have poor dynamic range, but they may be adequate to play with. 14 bit designs can have excellent performance. They are often just as good as 16 bit radios, but they usually have a lower sampling rate, which means reduced frequency coverage. For example, an HF receiver using a 14 bit ADC may not include coverage of the 6m amateur band.

There are several specialist experimenters' boards with huge frequency ranges extending from as low as 10 MHz to as high as 6 GHz. Some have dual receivers and some are 'sub QRP' transceivers. Some of the major manufacturers are making SDR or conventional radios with coverage up to around 3.5 GHz, but they are generally quite expensive.

100 WATT HF TRANSCEIVERS

Sixteen bit, direct digital synthesis (DDS) radios, with two or more analog to digital converters represent the top of the heap for HF software defined transceivers. If you are in the market for a commercially produced 100 Watt direct sampling HF transceiver, there are limited choices. You can pick one of the new Signature 6000 series radios from FlexRadio Systems, or an ANAN series radio from Apache Labs. If you want a 100W SDR transceiver with knobs, Icom has just released the IC-7300 and Expert Electronics offers the MB1 HF transceiver. I am sure there will be other 100 W options available soon. DDS radios use digital down conversion (DDC) for the receiver and digital up conversion (DUC) for the transmitter.

The older FlexRadio Systems, 'Flex series' radios such as the FLEX-1000, FLEX-3000 and FLEX-5000 are quadrature detector and exciter (QSD/QSE) designs. They require an unusual FireWire interface card to be installed in your PC. Their performance is good, but the technology is old. The FLEX-1000 was the first commercially available SDR transceiver for amateur radio. It is long gone. The FLEX-5000 and the FLEX-3000 are discontinued models but they are still available on the second hand market. The FLEX-1500 radio is still available new, but it is not a 100W radio.

Hybrid or 'Superheterodyne + SDR' 100 W SDR transceivers are available from a variety of established radio manufacturers. Be warned! Even though they may have a direct IQ output or IQ via a USB connection to the PC, their usability as a software defined radio may be very limited.

These 'hybrid' transceivers are not software defined radios at all. They are conventional Superheterodyne architecture radios with DSP. The IQ outputs are usually audio frequency streams taken from the DSP stage or a CODEC. This means that the bandwidth available to the SDR software panadapter display will be much less, than what you get from a DDC based software defined radio. Since the IQ output from the radio is at audio frequencies, the panadapter display is limited to a maximum bandwidth of about 192 kHz. It is usually only 96 kHz or 48 kHz. The resulting spectrum display is narrow, similar to what you would expect from a QSD based generation one, or generation two, SDR receiver. Also, the panadapter may function like a band scope with no point and click mouse style operation.

The Apache Labs ANAN and the FlexRadio Signature radios use 'state of the art' direct digital synthesis technology. But their technical design and their sales philosophy differs. Your choice comes down to a comparison of the specifications, performance figures, and software features, balanced against the cost for each model.

The FlexRadio Signature 6000 series of radios have digital signal processing performed within the radio and this dramatically reduces the requirements for the Ethernet connection between the radio and the computer. Because the digital signal processing, is not being done by the software running on the PC, you can use less powerful devices like tablets and Netbooks to control the radio and display the receiver panadapters. The FlexRadio SmartSDR operating program, which comes bundled with the radio, is proprietary 'closed source' software. Its capabilities are amazing!

The Apache Labs ANAN series radios have been developed in conjunction with the OpenHPSDR group of amateur radio and SDR enthusiasts. When you buy an Apache Labs radio, it does not ship with any PC software. However, several excellent SDR programs have been developed under the 'open source' rules and they are made available to radio users for free. With the Apache radios, the frequency selection, decimation and filtering, is done by the FPGA inside the radio. The modulation, demodulation, and DSP functions are done by PC software. You need a faster more powerful PC because there is much more data being processed by the computer software.

Any modern PC should be easily able to support either type of radio. I initially used a fairly old 'dual core' PC running Windows XP and I didn't have any issues running my ANAN-100 transceiver. There are advantages with both methods. The FlexRadio Systems approach allows the use of less powerful computers and operation over a network, but the resulting internal complexity makes the radios more expensive.

Overall, the SDR world seems to be moving towards the 'server – client' approach adopted by FlexRadio Systems. Members of the OpenHPSDR group in conjunction with the team at Apache Labs are working on the integration of a powerful single board computer with the ANAN series radios. The single board computer will take high speed data from the radio over a dedicated Ethernet connection and perform DSP functions in much the same way as the Flex radios do. This would allow the Apache radios to display more panadapters and panadapters of differing sizes. At the moment, all of the panadapters must use the same sample rate. It is possible that future releases from Apache Labs will have similar computer hardware or dedicated DSP inside the radio.

The approach taken by the Expert Electronics team for their Expert Electronics MB1 transceiver is closer the Apache Labs design. The radio can be operated completely stand-alone with no connection to an external PC because it has a Linux or Windows based PC built into the box alongside the radio board. As well as running the SDR program, the internal PC can be used for other computing tasks such as your station log or digital mode software.

QRP TRANSCEIVERS

There is a bigger range of QRP transceivers available. For the HF bands, I recommend a direct digital synthesis (DUC/DDC) radio with at least 5 Watts of output power and either a USB or an Ethernet connection. There are quite a few options including the Apache ANAN-10 or 10E, the ELAD FDM-Duo, and the Sun SDR2 pro. For VHF and above, there are 'sub QRP' very low power transceivers like the Ettus USRP, HackRF, and BladeRF. These UHF/SHF radios and boards are very low power transceivers designed for experimenters. They have extremely wide frequency coverage.

The FlexRadio FLEX-1500 transceiver is an old design but it is still fun to use and cheaper to buy than some SDR receivers. It uses a USB interface so there is no FireWire interface problem, but the older QSD/QSE technology only supports a single 48 kHz wide panadapter. Other options range from SoftRock, mcHF, and Genesis kits to transceivers like the SDR Cube.

There is a trap for the unwary in buying any QRP radio. By all means, buy one if you really want to operate a QRP station or if you want a low cost introduction to software defined radio. But, if you are planning on adding a 100 W linear amplifier, you might find that the combined cost of the QRP radio plus the linear amplifier is more expensive than simply buying a 100 W SDR transceiver.

SHOPPING CHECK LIST

Work out exactly what you want from an SDR receiver or transceiver. Do you want a cheap toy to play with, or a serious amateur radio station? Do you want a kit to build? Is an unboxed circuit board OK, or do you want a fully cased model? How much of an experimenter are you? Finally, do you want a transceiver or just a receiver?

Generally, there is a strong correlation between price and performance, but you still have to be careful.

Some points to consider:

- Some older models still carry high price tags.

- You may have to factor in freight costs, import duty, and taxes.

- Some websites offer radios that are not 'currently' available.

- Some websites look good but have very little technical information about their radios. You might be disappointed with your purchase. Good manufacturer's web sites have specification sheets, which include the most important features. Often you can download a user manual.

- Radios with 8 bit analog to digital converters (ADC) will have reduced dynamic range compared to radios that use 14 or 16 bit ADCs. This might be OK on boards that cover VHF to SHF, but may be a problem at HF frequencies.

- Radios with no filters before the ADC may suffer from ADC gain compression, aliased image signals, and possible overload. Unlike conventional receivers, a software defined radio receiver is affected by all of the signals being sampled, right across the input spectrum, not just the signals that you can see on the panadapter.

- Does the radio use a QSD design, or does it use direct sampling? Direct sampling is better, but QSD based radios are often cheaper.

- What is the sampling frequency? For direct sampling HF radios, higher sampling rates are better because you get a wider frequency range.

- What is the interface to the PC? They are typically USB or Ethernet. Some old designs used the obsolete FireWire interface.

- What software can be used with the radio? More than one program?

- What frequencies does the radio cover? Buy a radio that covers the bands that you want.

The best software defined radios use direct digital synthesis. Radios using QSD designs are OK and usually cheaper, but don't expect the same level of performance.

Here are some more key facts:

- Direct digital synthesis (DDC/DUC) radios are better. You get wider panadapters, often multiple panadapters, and better performance.

- Don't buy a kit unless you want to build a kit. There are ready built options at around the same prices. Most kits are based around outdated QSD/QSE technology.

- QRP transmitters are fine if you want to operate QRP. But by the time you add in the cost of an external 100 W power amplifier, it might be more cost effective, to simply buy a 100 W radio.

- An advertised bandwidth of 48 kHz, 96 kHz, or 192 kHz indicates that the analog to digital conversion is being done at audio frequencies. Digital down conversion radios have more bandwidth and hence wider panadapters. The FlexRadio Signature 6000 series can display 14 MHz panadapters. Some of the microwave frequency SDR boards are even wider.

- With direct sampling radios, "more bits is better." But as far as signal to noise performance and dynamic range is concerned, 14 bits is just as good as 16 bits. This is because the ENOB (effective number of bits) of a 16 bit ADC is pretty much the same as a 14 bit ADC.

- The ADC sampling rate is very important if you are buying a direct digital synthesis HF radio. It governs the maximum bandwidth that can be passed to the DSP stage of the receiver. In some cases that is equal to the maximum amount of spectrum that can be displayed on the panadapter. In other cases, the panadapter can only display sections of the sampled spectrum.

- With QSD radios, the analog to digital conversion is done at audio so the number of bits is less important. Most sound cards can manage 16 bits at a 96 ksps sample rate. Some are 24 bit and a few can sample at 192 ksps. It does not matter if the PC or USB sound card has 24 bit analog to digital conversion, the displayed bandwidth and the dynamic range will be much less than what you get using a 16 bit or 14 bit direct sampling receiver.

- Most cheap software defined receivers can only display one panadapter. More expensive software defined radios can display several panadapters, which means that you can see multiple bands at the same time. Some radios can only support one receiver, with other models you can listen to several receivers simultaneously.

WHAT IS DIFFERENT ABOUT SDR?

The internal construction of software defined radios is completely different to the traditional Superheterodyne receiver and transmitter architecture found in 'conventional' amateur radio or shortwave receivers and transceivers. When you look at the circuit board there are no adjustable tuned circuits in little cans, just a few large surface mounted integrated circuits. Some components do look familiar though. You can spot the low pass and high pass filters, with their toroid cores and the transmitter power amplifier looks just the same.

SDRs are really a logical extension of the introduction of digital signal processing. Most recent ham radio transceivers and some shortwave receivers feature DSP. In a DSP equipped radio, the signal is converted from analog to digital. DSP magic is performed using mathematics and software code and then the signal is converted back to analog again so you can hear it from the speaker. Software defined radio is essentially the same. The main difference is in how soon the signal is converted to a digital signal.

In an SDR receiver the signal is converted to digital as close to the antenna as possible. In the SDR transmitter the same thing occurs. The speech audio signal from your microphone, or digital mode tones, are converted to digital bits and processed using DSP software. The digital signal is up-converted or generated directly at the final transmit signal and converted back to an analog signal just before the power amplifier and low pass filters. CW signals are either generated in the same way as in most SSB transceivers, by SSB modulating a keyed audio tone, or keyed directly at the RF output frequency by simply generating or not generating a carrier signal. In the receiver, it is good to convert the RF signals arriving at the antenna into a digital signal as soon as possible. Digital signals can be manipulated, filtered, amplified, modulated, and demodulated without adding noise to the signal.

SDR receivers are relatively immune to intermodulation distortion (IMD). In a conventional receiver, large signals within the I.F. pass band can mix with local oscillator signals in the mixers and I.F. amplifiers. This causes unwanted signals known as intermodulation products, which can interfere with the signals that you want to hear. Susceptibility to receiver IMD is one of the main differentiators between an average receiver and a 'good' receiver. If you can't pick out individual stations working a busy contest and everything sounds mushy and distorted, then don't blame the contesters. Poor receiver IMD is the most likely reason. It is easy to measure in conventional Superheterodyne receivers using the well-established 'two tone' test method. Software defined radios generally don't have mixers (in hardware) so the causes and effects of intermodulation distortion are completely different. In an SDR receiver, the IMD performance is not predictable and in many cases, large signals near the operating frequency can actually improve the receiver's performance.

Software defined radios don't necessarily perform better than conventional radios and like conventional architecture radios you generally pay more for radios with higher levels of performance. What SDRs do provide is many new features and continual development.

TABLE 1: SDR VS CONVENTIONAL AMATEUR RADIOS		
Feature	*Superheterodyne conventional radio*	*Software defined radio*
Band scope (panadapter display)	Top end radios only, small display	Nearly all SDRs, large display
Waterfall signal display	Top end radios	Nearly all SDRs
Band scope / waterfall display of multiple bands at the same time	No	Some SDRs
Wideband band scope / waterfall display of entire HF spectrum or higher	No	Some SDRs
Listen to two signals on same band	Yes – some transceivers	Most SDRs
Listen to more than two signals on same band	No	Some SDRs
Listen to signals on multiple bands at the same time	Yes on some VHF/UHF radios but not usually on HF radios	Most SDRs
Split transceiver operation	Yes – HF transceivers	Yes – HF transceivers
CAT (CI-V) control for PC applications	Yes – most HF transceivers	Yes – most HF SDR transceivers. Depends on PC software.
Change look and functions of radio by changing software	No – but can use different CAT based programs	Many SDRs
Transmitter pre-distortion to improve transmitter IMD performance	No	Some SDRs – one brand currently
Operate different bands / modes using different computer devices simultaneously	No	Some SDRs – one brand currently
Firmware or software updates to the control software and DSP	Yes – most HF transceivers	Yes
Transmit power level	Most 100 W some are higher power or QRP	Most are QRP some are 100 W

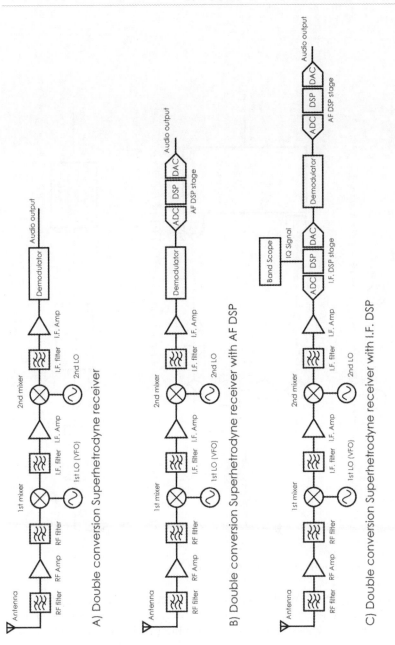

Figure 1: progression of receiver technology (part 1)

Digital to analog conversion and digital signal processing is not new. These block diagrams show the progression of receiver technology towards software defined radio. Picture A is a typical Superheterodyne receiver. Picture B shows the introduction of AF DSP following the demodulator. Picture C shows the introduction of I.F. DSP.

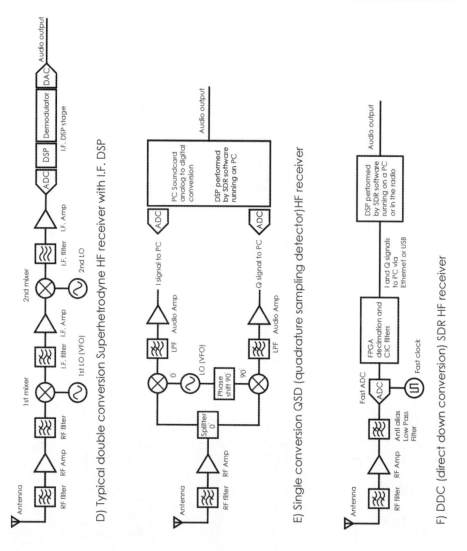

Figure 2: progression of receiver technology (part 2)

These block diagrams show the progression of receiver technology from the conventional Superheterodyne to software defined radio. Picture D is a typical Superheterodyne receiver with DSP. Picture E shows a QSD based software defined radio. Picture F shows a direct digital synthesis software defined radio for the HF bands. It uses digital down conversion (DDC).

As the designs progress from AF DSP, to I.F. DSP, then to the QSD based SDR and finally the direct sampling SDR, the analog to digital conversion is performed closer to the antenna. Converting the signal to digital as early as possible produces better receiver performance. You get less internal noise and intermodulation products, and better features like multiple receivers and panadapters.

WHAT COMPUTER SKILLS DO YOU NEED?

Operating one of the SDR radios that have knobs, and which don't need to be connected to a computer doesn't require any computer skills at all. But those radios are not the focus of this book. Most amateur radio operators use a computer for emails and accessing the Internet and many also use a computer in their ham shack as a part of their amateur radio activities. But strangely, many hams recoil from the idea of operating their radio using a PC display, keyboard, and mouse. In reality, operating a radio in this way is not much different to browsing the Internet. 'Point and click' to listen to a station. Fine-tuning is done with the little wheel between the left and right buttons on the mouse and you 'click and drag' the image on the screen to change the size of filters. Your amateur radio transceiver or receiver becomes just another PC application and you quickly become used to using it. If you really must have a knob for tuning, there are options available. Control knobs can be purchased from WoodBox Radio or other suppliers and some people use 'Midi' controllers such as the Hercules DJ console. We have been able to use CAT commands to remote control our transceivers for many years and a lot of amateur operators and SWLs use PC software to send or receive digital modes, such as RTTY, PSK, JT65, and CW. If you already use a PC in the shack, you probably won't have any difficulty using a software defined radio.

My advice is to give it a real chance. Some folks try an SDR and give up after a few days. Like any new radio, an SDR does take some getting used to. Use the SDR like you would use your normal transceiver or receiver. If you are a contester, use it in a contest. If you are a CW operator, make a few CW QSOs. Experiment with the filters and settings. I found that I very quickly became addicted to the band scope display. Being able to see the signals and precisely filter out interference was a revelation to me. If I ever do go back to using a conventional architecture transceiver, I would be sure to add a band scope.

Initially while you are setting up your new radio and software, you do need to be able to run the installation program and you might have to download software from the Internet. Also, if you want to run digital modes you will probably have to download a 'com port manager' and a 'virtual audio cable.' These topics are covered later in the book. Once the software has been loaded, making the radio work is pretty easy and after that, it is all plain sailing! You just have to learn how to use the radio software. I have included plenty of information on the major SDR software applications and some tips, which will make using the radio even more enjoyable.

Most software defined radios use either a USB or an Ethernet connection. Typical configurations are on the next page. Generation one 'sound card' type SDRs will need a stereo connection to the PC sound card for the audio IQ signals. A mono 'mic input' won't work. You need two channels, one for the I signal and one for the Q signal.

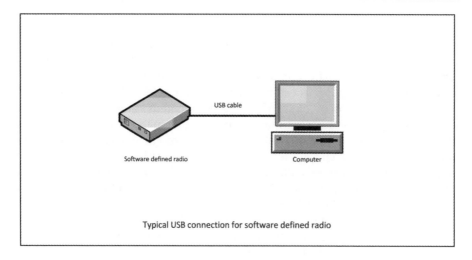

Figure 3: USB connection is usually plug-n-play

Most USB connected radios are plug-n-play. You plug them into the USB port on your PC, start up the SDR software application and everything should be fine. To use some receivers with programs that were initially designed for different SDR hardware, you may have to download a file called extio.dll and copy it into the same directory on your computer as the program files. If in doubt about how to do that, ask a teenager!

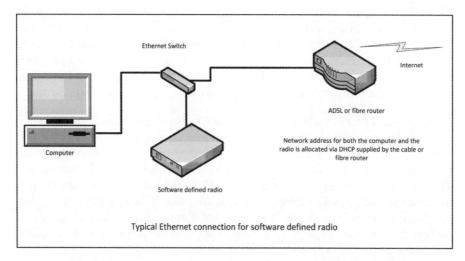

Figure 4: Ethernet connection is easier using a Gigabyte Ethernet switch

To use an SDR that uses an Ethernet interface, you will probably have to buy a CAT5e cable and a Gigabit Ethernet Switch (not a hub). These typically have four or six Ethernet ports and should cost less than $100. In this configuration, Network addresses are allocated by your Internet router.

WHAT IS DIGITAL?

I guess most readers will be familiar with what I mean when I talk about digital and analog signals. But just to make sure, I will include a quick refresher.

Sound waves that travel through the air and the radio waves that carry our conversations or music out to the world are examples of analog waveforms. When sound is converted into an electrical signal by the microphone, it becomes an electrical analog signal. An analog signal is characterized by having a constantly changing instantaneous level. You can display an electrical analog voltage signal on an oscilloscope.

An analog or analogue signal is any continuous signal for which the time varying feature (variable) of the signal is a representation of some other time varying quantity, i.e., analogous to another time varying signal.

https://en.wikipedia.org/wiki/Analog_signal.

In the case of the electrical signal from your microphone, the electrical signal is an analog of the sound waves that the microphone picks up.

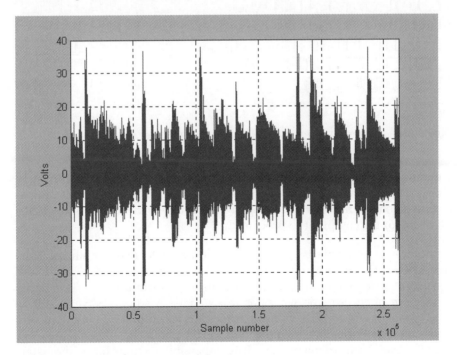

Figure 5: analog signal – an Oscilloscope trace of speech from a microphone.

Image from www.rocketroberts.com

Digital signals are discrete and finite, meaning there is a limited set of values that they can be. This could mean just two total possible integer values (0 or 1), or it could be a range of 256, 65536, or more individual values. Digital signals are always discrete. That does not mean they are careful about what they say, it means that each digital number is fixed for a known period of time. Analog signals vary continuously.

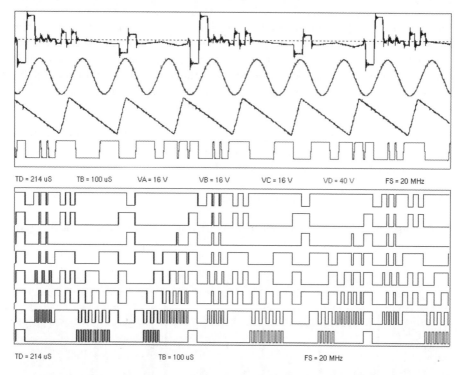

Figure 6: analog signals at top – digital signals below [www.bitscope.com]

Humans can't process digital signals directly. The digital signals must be converted into analog signals for us to see or hear. Computers can't process analog signals directly. The analog signals must be converted into digital numbers for the computer to process.

Complex analog signals like speech or music are made up of the sum of many frequencies at varying levels. The purest analog signal is a sine wave, which consists of a single tone frequency at a constant maximum level. This purity is why we often use sine waves as test signals. A square wave is still an analogue signal. It consists of a sine wave plus an infinite number of its odd harmonic frequencies all added together. I.e. the frequency of the square wave plus 3x, 5x, 7x that frequency etc. It is impossible to transmit a completely square wave over a radio system because you would need an infinite radio bandwidth to include all of the harmonics. So compromises have to be made and some distortion of the square wave shape occurs.

Most digital signals are binary which means that only two voltage levels are used. The signal is either a high level known as a 'one', or a low level known as a 'zero'. The actual one and zero voltages depend on the type of circuit and chips being used. This is known as a 'logic family' and the high and low logic levels are called 'logic states'. Some digital systems use three or more voltage levels but that does not apply to the SDR systems discussed in this book. Digital signals are used in two different ways. They are used in hardware circuits to perform logic decisions or they are grouped together to represent numbers, forming the basis of digital computing.

Hardware digital circuits, using switches, latches, counters, registers and other CMOS or TTL logic family devices, can be used to control things. You might design a circuit to turn on the lights and open the gate when you arrive home, but not turn on the lights when it is daytime. This type of digital circuit uses a set of logical rules. AND, OR, EXCLUSIVE OR, NAND, and NOR are the most common. Devices like the FPGA (field programmable gate array) are computer chips that can be programmed to rearrange themselves into complex arrays of these simple logic elements.

Computers also use digital signals and they can also be used to control things. But computers, microcontrollers, and so on, have the added advantage of programmability. You can make them perform operations on the digital signals in predefined sequences. This adaptability makes computers seem like they have intelligence. But so far, they don't. What you actually experience is a result of the intelligence of the hardware designers and the software developers. Fixed logic using non programmable logic gates cannot be changed without altering the physical wiring or circuit. But, computers can be re-programmed, which means that you can change what the computer does with the digital information. Many digital logic circuits are now constructed using programmable devices in order to provide the ability to reconfigure the logic without having to redesign the circuit board.

Using only two voltage levels for the data signals makes the information easier for a computer to process. Computers are very stupid. They can only manage data streams and groups of binary bits. They can add binary numbers together, shift their bits left and right using shift registers, compare a number with another number, or store numbers into a memory device and retrieve them later. They can do all of those functions extremely quickly, performing millions of operations a second.

Computers can't use analog signals directly. They have to turn them into digital numbers before they can be processed. This is done with an analog to digital converter. After the computer processing has been performed, the data can be turned back into an analog signal using a digital to analog converter. The PC sound card is a good example of this process. It converts analog audio signals from the line or microphone input to the digital signals used in your PC applications. On the output side, it converts the digital data stream into an analog audio signal for you to listen to on your amplified speakers.

CLOCK SIGNALS

Digital signals need to be read at the right time. Reading the data at a time when it is changing from the high state to the low state or vice versa is likely to cause an error in the data or logic system. The circuit must also avoid the possibility of missing a change of level, or reading the same level twice. Reading the level of the data signal is called sampling. The best thing to do is to synchronize the system so that the sampling occurs when the data signal is stable at either the high or low logic state. This is achieved by using a clock signal to control the sampling times. The clock signal is a regular string of data pulses. It may be a square wave signal or it may be a string of more narrow pulses. The logic chips are designed so that they read the level of input signals at the time that the clock signal changes, (usually from a high to a low state). Outputs from the logic chips are synchronized as well. The output transition is often triggered by the rising edge of the clock pulse (from a low to a high logic state).

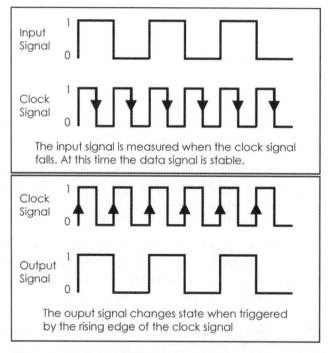

Figure 7: the clock signal controls the timing of a digital network

USING DIGITAL LOGIC TO REPRESENT NUMBERS

At any particular sample time, the digital input or output of a digital logic hardware device can only be at a 'high' logic level or at a 'low' logic level. You can use this information to represent numbers. Normally the 'high' logic level represents a binary number 1 and the low logic level represents a binary number 0. At the next sample time, you can look at the digital level again. It might have stayed the same or it might have changed state.

Each time the data is sampled in this way the result is referred to as a binary 'bit'. A bit is a logic level at a particular instant in time. A single bit cannot convey very much information, only 0 or 1. But eight bits read together or in order can convey the 256 different combinations between 0000 0000 and 1111 1111. For example, an 8 bit binary sequence of 1000 0001 is equivalent to the decimal number 129.

Technical TIP: Our normal number system is called the 'base 10' or decimal system. It uses ten numbers from 0 to 9. Binary is a 'base 2' number system. It only uses two numbers, 0 and 1. Binary numbers are easier for computers to handle because the microprocessor and other digital circuits only have to work with two voltage levels. To manage decimal numbers directly the circuitry would need to be able to detect and calculate with ten voltage levels. This is far too complex for computers, so in a computer the decimal numbers are converted to binary.

Eight bits grouped together is known as a byte. A byte is much more useful that a bit because it can represent any integer between 0 and 255.

If we decide that in some situations the number 65 (0100 0001 in binary) is equivalent to an 'A' and the number 66 (0100 0010 in binary) is equivalent to a 'B' we can start to use the computer to manage text. It goes on from there but this is not a book on computers.

Technical TIP: You may have noticed that I separated the binary numbers into groups of four. This makes them easier to read. But even grouped, long strings of binary digits are difficult to read and to write down. We could convert the numbers to decimal but this is inconvenient and not particularly easy, so another numbering system is commonly used.

The problem is that the range from 0000 to 1111 represents the numbers 0 to 15. The binary number 1001 1100 1101 0010 is 40146 in the decimal system. It is not easy to convert a number like that from binary to decimal, or back to binary again. We could break the number down to 9, 12, 13, 2 but that is a bit clumsy as well. The answer is to use a base 16 numbering system called 'Hexadecimal.' This is often shortened to 'Hex.' Hex uses the digits 0 to 9 and A to F to represent the 16 binary numbers between 0000 and 1111. In the example above 1001 1100 1101 0010 becomes 9CD2 in Hex. This is much easier to convert back to binary, so it is the preferred way to write down binary numbers. Of course, Hex is just a notation system for humans. The computer can't work in Hexadecimal it always uses binary.

Sometimes you need more detail or a bigger number and 8 bits is not enough. For example, an 8 bit analog to digital converter can only sample the incoming analog signal at 256 individual levels. If the analog input signal ranges between 0 and 1 Volt, each of the digital output numbers represents an input voltage step of 3.9 millivolts. At the instant that the ADC looks at the input signal, the incoming signal is almost never at exactly one of the sampling steps. So, the ADC outputs the closest number. This results in small sampling errors, which can't be fixed. The best way to reduce these sampling level errors is to describe smaller voltage steps between each input level and to do that you need more bits. The sampling errors are called 'quantization' errors because they are errors in the measuring the quantity (level) of the signal.

Sixteen bits grouped together is called a word, it is two bytes long. A 16-bit binary word can store 65,536 distinct values. This is enough for a computer to do complex floating point mathematics. A 16 bit analog to digital converter can sample the incoming analog signal at 65,536 levels. So now, if the analog signal ranges between 0 and 1 Volt, the digital output levels are only 0.015 millivolts apart. The sampling is much more accurate and the sampling error levels are much smaller. Sometimes 16 bits is still not enough. Modern computers use 64 bit data words. This is done so that the computer can perform calculations on very large amounts of data very quickly.

Digital signals are simple in that they only have two voltage levels. But you need a large number of individual bits to accurately, represent the analog signal levels. The other thing is that the analog input signals are changing continuously but the digital signals coming out of the analog to digital converter represent the analog signal at distinct points in time. Not only is the level represented by each digital number not exactly the same as the original analog level, but each sample only represents the input level at a particular time. We minimized the voltage sampling errors by using more bits. Now we need to keep the sampling rate fast enough to minimize the time errors. Faster sampling is better, but the faster we sample the analog signal, the more 16 bit numbers we create each second. This creates more data for our computer or digital signal processing chip to manage.

Harry Nyquist (1889-1976) determined the fundamental rules for analog to digital conversion. He found that as long as the sample rate was at least twice the rate of the highest frequency in the analog signal, the original analog signal could be recreated accurately from the digital data.

This means that to accurately, recreate a radio signal at 50 MHz, we would need to sample at a minimum of 100 Msps, (one hundred million samples per second). Multiply that by 16 bits and we have a data rate of 1,600,000,000 bits per second at the output of the ADC chip. The DSP stage in a direct sampling software defined radio has to work very hard to manage that much continuous data. In most software defined radio models, the task is made easier by only using parts of the initially sampled data and also by parallel processing. Parallel processing involves splitting tasks so that different parts of the computer can work on them at the same time.

One way to route data from the 16 bit ADC to the computer is to have a wire carrying a continuous 'serial' data stream of 16 bit numbers represented by binary bits. Another way is to use 16 'parallel' wires. That way a computer buffer can be presented with the entire 16 bit word at once. The required computer processing rate is much lower using 16 wires.

This parallel structure used inside the computer to speed up operation. For example, the data that is stored in computer memory is routed to the computer processor in parallel. Fast 16 bit ADCs like the one in the example above actually have 16 output lines. The parallel data lines on a computer motherboard that link internal parts of the computer together are called a digital bus. You can think of the bus as a computer data highway, with 16 lanes in each direction.

The data bus in your PC is either 32 bits or 64 bits wide. Some microprocessors and other computing devices like DSP chips may use an 8 bit or 16 bit data bus. Intel introduced the 4004, its first microprocessor in 1971. It was a 4 bit device, which used a 4 bit data bus.

Conversely, most external connections between computers or between your software defined radio and the computer, are serial connections where the data signal is sent one bit at a time over one wire with an earth return. USB, Ethernet, RS232, and HDMI are examples of serial connections. The old outdated Centronics printer cable is an example of a parallel external connection.

Software defined radios and the DSP stages in conventional receivers convert analog signals to digital data streams of numbers. The idea is to keep the signal in digital format through as much of the radio as possible. In the receiver, the signal is converted back to analog just before the audio amplifier and speakers. In the transmitter, the signal stays digital until just before the RF power amplifier and low pass filters.

Understanding that the signals that you receive are converted into strings of numbers and then back into audio for you to listen to is initially an odd concept. But it has been happening in the DSP stage of your old radio for years. It also happens in your CD player, video recorder, cell phone, and television. There are good reasons for doing things this way and they are discussed in the next chapter and throughout the book.

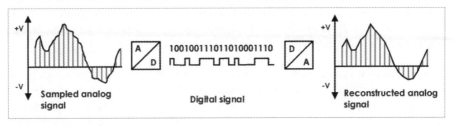

Figure 8: analog and digital signals

Most people don't think of their PC sound card, as being an analog to digital and digital to analog converter, but that is exactly what it is. You plug your speakers into the sound card analog output, never considering that the other side of the sound card is a digital connection to the computer bus.

WHY IS DIGITAL BETTER?

The whole world seems to be going digital. Your cell phone has used digital modulation since the old AMPS networks were phased out in favor of GSM and CDMA networks in the 1990s. Microwave and satellite radio links went digital even earlier, in the 1980s. Those radios are digital, but not software defined. Cassette tapes and vinyl records were made virtually obsolete by digital compact discs. The first commercial music CD was Billy Joel with '52nd Street', released in October 1982. Soon after that, CDs started to be used to store data. In most places, your television receiver uses digital technology and receives a digital signal as well. All of these things use digital rather than analog technology. So it must be better. But why?

The first and most important reason is noise. As far as possible, we want to stop any noise being generated inside the radio. All active analog circuits add noise. Digital signals can be amplified, filtered, shifted in frequency, modulated, or demodulated without adding any extra noise.

The second reason is interference. Conventional hardware mixers and oscillators can mix oscillator phase noise onto your wanted signal and the non-linear mixing process can introduce unwanted intermodulation signals and images. Software DSP, which is performed by manipulating numbers in data buffers, can perform the same functions as the hardware devices without introducing intermodulation distortion and unwanted signals.

The third reason is performance. Narrow hardware filters are difficult to make and very careful circuit design is required to get good performance. Narrow filters are prone to ringing and they are usually fixed in bandwidth. Digital filters implemented in software can be variable and they don't exhibit ringing. Features like auto notch filters, high and low audio frequency cut, I.F. width and I.F. shift controls, and band-scopes are common on radios, which use digital signal processing.

Another reason is cost vs performance. It is very difficult and quite expensive to create a top class conventional receiver, but the DSP part of a software defined radio is really just a few computer chips, which can be mass produced relatively cheaply. Firmware loaded into a DSP chip or a software defined radio's FPGA can be easily updated, improved, and revised. With a hardware radio, the performance is fixed as a part of the initial design. Your 1970s transceiver may have a terrific receiver, but it cannot be improved further without adding more hardware such as INRAD filters.

It is true that early DSP filters did introduce a variety of weird sounding artifacts, but the technology is much more developed now. You may still be able to adjust DSP filters to the point where the wanted audio becomes distorted, but you don't have to.

It can be a trade-off. In some cases, a small amount of audio distortion is still far preferable to listening to the noise or interference that the filter has managed to eliminate.

With an analog signal, virtually everything that you do to the signal adds noise and once it is in there it is difficult to remove without adversely affecting the quality of the signal. In a typical radio system comprising a transmitter, a radio path and a receiver, there are many places where unwanted noise becomes added to the signal that you want to hear at the far end of the path. The big problem is active devices like amplifiers, oscillators and mixers, but even passive devices like resisters add thermal noise. With digital signals, so long as it is possible to determine whether each bit is a zero, or a one, even a noise damaged signal can be re-created perfectly with no noise added.

Audiophiles point accusingly at the quantization noise that is a byproduct of any analog to digital conversion process, but this is very small compared to the noise created elsewhere in your stereo equipment. They say that the audio from digital signals sounds harsh, but I expect that this is more to do with the hugely improved dynamic range and frequency response, of audio from a CD compared to the audio from an LP record or an analog tape. Quantization noise is one place where a digital system does add noise to the signal. It is a result of the error signal that occurs when you sample an analog signal with an analog to digital converter. The more bits that are used to sample a signal the smaller the steps in signal level. So sampling with more bits results in lower quantization noise. *There is more about this topic in the ADC chapter*. After the signal has been converted to a digital stream of data bits, the DSP firmware code can modify the signal without adding any additional noise.

Getting back to radio systems, the optimal system would be a digital up conversion transmitter using a digital audio modulation scheme. At the receiver a digital down conversion, possibly software defined, radio would receive and decode the digital audio transmission. The only analog parts would be the microphone and its preamplifier plus the audio amplifier and speakers in the receiver. Well actually, the RF radio signal is usually amplified with a standard analog power amplifier followed by a low pass filter network and this does inevitably add some distortion. Also, there may be some filters and a low noise preamp before the analog to digital conversion in the receiver. In a VHF or UHF receiver, there is often a tuner chip or a hardware mixer and oscillator as well.

Reducing the amount of noise and distortion being created inside the radio is a major advantage. The primary aim of software defined radio is to keep the signal in a digital format for as long as possible in the transmitter and sample it back into a digital signal as soon as possible in the receiver. This maximizes the number of stages and processes performed on digital signals. Digital signal processing is at the core of software defined radio.

Of course, there is still noise being introduced to the signal as it traverses the long radio path between the transmitter and your receiver station. This can be overcome by using digital modulation, but there is a trade-off because digital signals usually require a higher received signal level.

Most amateur radio and a lot of shortwave signals still use analog modulation modes like; SSB, SSTV, AM, or FM. But we also use digital modulation such as; digital voice, digital modes, and CW. Shortwave broadcast radio stations are migrating towards using digital modulation, often DAB or DRM. Point to point radio links such as, satellite links, microwave radio links, cellular and even Wi-Fi all use digital modulation, usually variants of QAM, which is a modulation type that uses both phase and amplitude modulation to send digital data signals.

Morse code is a binary digital mode. Yes it really is! When the key is down the carrier is on. You can consider this as equivalent to sending a digital 'one' signal. When the key is up the carrier is off. This is equivalent to sending a digital 'zero' signal. It is a good example of what I am talking about. We all know that you can copy and decode (in your head) very weak and noisy CW signals. Just like other digital signals, as long as you can hear a tone or no tone you can decode the message with no errors.

Technical TIP: I have noted some confusion in online forums about what is digital and what is analog. I have seen comments stating that various components like inductors in the low pass filter were "analog." This is rubbish! Individual components are neither analog nor digital. There is no such thing as a digital capacitor, or an analog inductor. If you don't believe me, I have some digital resistors I can sell you, cheap! There are circuits that are designed to manage digital signals and circuits that are designed to manage analog signals. Some like the analog to digital converter manage both. An RF signal is analog but the modulation imposed on it may be digital.

Digital signal processing has other advantages over using analog circuits. These have to do with elimination of interference signals commonly created inside the radio and the ability to manipulate the signal without adding distortion or noise. *There is more on this topic in the DSP section.*

In a conventional Superheterodyne HF radio, the received radio signal is converted to an I.F. signal by mixing the incoming signal with a signal from an oscillator. In many receivers, this happens twice (double conversion) or three times (triple conversion). In most transmitters the modulated signal is mixed up to, the final transmit frequency in the same way. Mixers are non-linear devices and they create all sorts of unwanted signals. These are often noted as 'birdies' or whistles at some frequencies. Noise and any frequency variation on the oscillators, gets mixed into the wanted signals and degrades the receiver's performance. In a direct digital synthesis HF software defined radio, the frequency conversions are performed using mathematics on the digital representation of the incoming signal. You don't get any unwanted noise or mixing products. This is the main reason that cheap SDRs can produce audio quality that is as good as expensive conventional receivers.

DEFINITION OF SOFTWARE DEFINED RADIO

The definition of 'software defined radio' is a bit vague and is open to interpretation. These days it is usually used to describe radios, which use analog to digital converters to sample the radio spectrum as close as possible to the antenna input. The signal remains in the 'digital domain' through all of the digital signal processing and is not converted back into an analog signal until just before it is passed to the audio amplifier and speaker. In the transmitter, the reverse applies. The microphone or modulating signal is converted into a digital signal, processed in DSP, and it is not converted back to an analog signal until it is sent to the RF power amplifier. The panadapter spectrum and waterfall displays are representations of the analog signals being received by the radio, but they are just data displayed as dots on a display screen.

The ITU definition is not really adequate. In fact, in my opinion it describes any radio with any kind of computer control, including CAT (Icom CI-V).

"Software-defined radio (SDR): A radio transmitter and/or receiver employing a technology that allows the RF operating parameters including, but not limited to, frequency range, modulation type, or output power to be set or altered by software, excluding changes to operating parameters which occur during the normal pre-installed and predetermined operation of a radio according to a system specification or standard." ITU-R SM.2152 (09/2009).

The FCC manages the radio spectrum in the USA. It is primarily interested in devices that emit signals on radio frequencies. Their definition says software defined radios must always include a transmitter. There is no FCC definition for software defined radio receivers.

"Software defined radio. A radio that includes a transmitter in which the operating parameters of frequency range, modulation type or maximum output power (either radiated or conducted), or the circumstances under which the transmitter operates in accordance with Commission rules, can be altered by making a change in software without making any changes to hardware components that affect the radio frequency emissions". Spectrum Use Employing Cognitive Radio Technologies, ET Docket No. 03-108, Report and Order, 20 FCC Rcd 5486 (2005).

I prefer a definition that I found on Wikipedia.

"Software-defined radio (SDR) is a radio communication system where components that have been typically implemented in hardware (e.g. mixers, filters, amplifiers, modulators/demodulators, detectors, etc.) are instead implemented by means of software on a personal computer or embedded system."

'Software Defined Radio: Architectures, Systems and Functions (Markus Dillinger, Kambiz Madani, Nancy Alonistioti). See http://en.wikipedia.org/wiki/Software-defined_radio.

So definitions vary, but in general terms, if the filtering and demodulation in a receiver or the filtering and modulation in a transmitter, is done using software which is re-configurable without replacing chips in the radio, then the radio is 'Software Defined'. In other words if the signal is converted to a digital signal and processed using reconfigurable software or firmware running on a PC, embedded computer processor, programmable DSP chip, or FPGA (field programmable gate array) it is a software defined radio. But if the signal is converted to a digital signal and processed in a dedicated (not reconfigurable in the radio) DSP chip it is not a software defined radio.

Even that definition is not really adequate anymore because the lines are blurred. Many recent conventional radios can have firmware updates, making them at least partially field upgradable. Often, the firmware running on DSP chips can be updated without removing the chips from the radio, so in some respects those radios could be considered 'software defined'. But most folks don't refer to them as software defined radios. On the 'flip side', radios like the Elecraft KX3 and the new FlexRadio Signature 6000 series are usually considered to be SDRs even though they use dedicated DSP chips and a microcomputer inside the radio to perform the modulation, demodulation, and other DSP functions.

These days what is, and what is not, an SDR is more usually defined by the hardware architecture. Conventional radios typically use a double or triple conversion Superheterodyne design with front end filters, hardware oscillators, mixers, and I.F. amplifiers, which are usually followed by dedicated DSP chips. Software defined radios use Direct digital synthesis or Quadrature Sampling Detectors and Exciters.

Technical TIP: Some FPGA chips include a microcomputer, which runs on the FPGA chip hardware as a software emulation of a microprocessor. These are called 'soft processors.' Some FPGA chips are large enough to host several soft processors.

DSP chips are specialized computer processors that are based on the same type of structure as microprocessors. Some dedicated DSP chips include ARM or multicore processors. You could program these chips to manage the control aspects of the radio. That could include real knobs and switches like the KX3, a GUI interface like the FlexRadio or a mixture of both, like the ELAD and Expert Electronics MB1 radios.

Even more technical TIP: By the way, an ARM processor is an example of an acronym inside an acronym! ARM stands for 'Advanced RISC Machine.' RISC stands for 'Reduced Instruction Set Computer' or 'Reduced Instruction Set Computing'. An 'instruction set' is the list of commands or instructions that the microprocessor is able to perform. Computer programs ask the microprocessor to perform these instructions in a particular order. RISC computers are often used in embedded systems where the full complex instruction set that is required for your PC is not needed. Simpler instructions means more instructions can be performed per clock cycle, so RISC computers are faster. The microprocessor inside your PC is a CISC (Complex Instruction Set Computing) device.

To add a little more confusion to the story, some manufacturers claim that their radio is an SDR in spite of the fact that it uses completely standard receiver and transmitter architecture. These radios actually have double conversion Superheterodyne receivers, with an audio frequency IQ signal output from the DSP stage available on the back panel. You can use SDR programs to display a band scope of the signals that are within the I.F. pass band. But the radio itself is not a software defined radio. I think it is best to use the new term 'Superheterodyne + SDR' to describe this kind of receiver.

It's not even safe to assume that a radio with no front panel controls that is controlled using PC software is a software defined radio. Some WiNRADiO and Icom receivers are standard configuration Superheterodyne receivers, which use PC control, instead of having knobs and buttons.

Finally, radios like your new hand held portable or mobile, may have a radio chip inside and be completely digital, and they may use IQ streams and DSP internally. But unless the software code that performs the modulation, demodulation, and DSP filtering can be updated without removing the chips from the radio, they are digital radios, but not software defined radios.

SDR is a logical extension of the DSP that has been inside our radios for years. I laugh at the 'grizzlers' online who say that they would never touch a SDR because they don't like the whole "digital thing." They are probably using a radio with I.F. or AF DSP and they probably have no idea that their radios contain digital to analog and analog to digital converters. I suspect that they prefer to have their CDs 12 inches wide with the audio scratched on with a nail. I know that there are some 'die hards' who use boat anchor radios from the 50's, 60's, 70's, or 80's and that is absolutely fine. It is great to collect and use antiques. Some of the early models without synthesized oscillators have excellent receivers. There is no doubt about that.

In the end, the definition of software defined radio is unimportant. What is important is that we have a new breed of radio with new features, including:

- Very wide frequency coverage compared to older technologies. Some SDRs cover from the LF to SHF bands, which is much wider than most conventional radios.

- The ability to see signals as well as hear them and the ability to monitor several bands at the same time.

- Very good receiver performance, often at a fairly low cost.

- Very sharp, constantly variable, receive passband filters which don't introduce ringing distortion.

- New techniques for noise reduction when receiving and new techniques for improving transmitter intermodulation performance.

GENERATIONS AND TYPES OF SDR

It is possible to buy software defined radios for frequencies ranging from 10 kHz up to 6 GHz or more. The aim of SDR receiver designs is to take a range of frequencies, for example, the entire HF band and convert the whole range to a digital signal. After that, digital signal processing either on the receiver board or in computer software is used to provide the unique displays and functions that make operating a software defined radio exciting.

The latest SDR radio receivers for the HF bands use digital down conversion (DDC) where the RF band is sampled using an analog to digital converter close to the antenna, normally immediately after a preamplifier and band pass or low pass filter. In the case of VHF, UHF, or SHF radios, the analog to digital converter may be placed after a hardware mixer and oscillator acting as a down conversion stage. Earlier SDR radio receiver designs use a quadrature sampling detector (QSD) followed by an audio frequency analog to digital converter. Most SDR transmitters use the same kind of arrangement as the receiver. Digital up conversion (DUC) when the receiver uses digital down conversion or a quadrature sampling exciter (QSE) when the receiver uses a quadrature sampling detector. It is also possible to use an SDR receiver in conjunction with a conventional transmitter arrangement. Some people use an SDR receiver to add a band scope function to their conventional transceiver or receiver. This can be achieved by feeding the SDR receiver from the I.F. output. Some new transceivers provide access to the I.F. output on the rear panel especially for this purpose. Other radios require a hardware modification.

There is a strong trend towards moving the digital signal processing functions into dedicated DSP chips inside the radio or to a dedicated computer within or near the radio. This simplifies the SDR software on the PC and more importantly, it dramatically reduces the processing demands on the PC and the data flow between the radio and the PC. The FlexRadio Signature 6000 series of radios already use this type of design, employing DSP chips and computer processing inside the radio.

The OpenHPSDR group, of volunteer SDR developers, is currently working on the integration of a single board computer with the OpenHPSDR and Apache ANAN radios. The current firmware allows between up to seven 384 kHz wide panadapter displays. The new method using a single board computer to perform DSP functions, will allow more panadapters to be displayed and panadapters with differing bandwidths. You would be able to display the ham or shortwave bands on panadapters specifically tailored to fit the size of the bands. Or perhaps you might want to display just the CW or SSB portions of several HF bands at the same time.

Using computer power inside, or near, the radio to perform the DSP functions, means that only the data for the audio from each receiver and the graphics required to display the panadapters has to be sent to the PC.

The PC does not need to be as powerful, opening the way for SDR operation via Netbook computers, tablets, and mobile phones. The lower data requirement also makes it easier to operate your SDR transceiver remotely over your local Wi-Fi network or the Internet.

The older QSD based software defined radios are usually, cheaper and they are fine for getting a taste of SDR or as a band scope. But you only get a part of the full SDR experience because you only get one panadapter. If you really want to get the most out of using a software defined radio, there is no substitute for a direct digital synthesis 'direct sampling' radio.

Some people are very happy using an SDR receiver in conjunction with a conventional transmitter. CAT control manages tracking of the frequencies. This arrangement gives you the advantages of an SDR panadapter and the comfort of using a familiar transmitter.

Shortwave listeners and anyone who only wants a receiver should look for a receiver with digital down conversion, which covers the bands of interest. Conventional Superheterodyne HF receivers often have a maximum frequency of around 32 MHz with some having 6m band coverage as well. But many software defined radios have a much wider frequency coverage.

The VHF and higher amateur radio bands are several MHz wide. To display wide sections of the VHF and UHF bands, you need a receiver capable of displaying a wide panadapter. Options include SDRs designed for the high bands or transverters for HF software defined radios. Many of the VHF to SHF software defined receivers that use digital tuner chips do not cover the HF bands. Be aware that using a receiver covering 60 MHz to 6 GHz may not be particularly interesting compared to an HF receiver. But they can be used for plotting aircraft beacons, looking at satellite weather maps, doing weak signal VHF or UHF work, and for EME or satellite reception.

Some of the new software defined radios; for example, the FUNcube Dongle, BladeRF, and HackRF radios are specifically designed for VHF to microwave coverage. The RTL dongles vary, from a maximum frequency of 948 MHz up to a maximum of 2200 MHz, with most models working down to around 22 MHz. The FUNcube Dongle Pro Plus is unusual in that it covers bands from low frequency (LF) 150 kHz up to super high frequency (SHF) 2050 MHz, (with a gap between about 260 and 410 MHz). Software defined radios are not really ideal for monitoring the local repeater. Often the panadapter display is too narrow to cover all of the local repeaters at the same time.

The following table describes my interpretation of the definition of each SDR generation. Other interpretations probably exist, but this definition makes sense to me.

TABLE 2: SDR GENERATIONS	
Generation	*Definition*
Generation 1 SDR	Software defined radio, usually employing a QSD (quadrature sampling detector) such as a Tayloe detector. It uses the sound card in a PC to perform the analog to digital conversion of the two audio streams from the QSD detector. Control, DSP, and demodulation are performed by PC software. If the device is capable of transmitting, it will probably employ a QSE (quadrature sampling exciter) such as a Tayloe detector and will use the sound card in a PC to perform the digital to analog conversion.
Generation 2 SDR	Software defined radio usually employing a QSD (quadrature sampling detector) such as a Tayloe detector. It uses an on board ADC (analog to digital converter) chip to perform the analog to digital conversion of the two audio streams from the QSD detector. Control, DSP, and demodulation are performed by PC software. If the device is capable of transmitting, it will probably employ a QSE (quadrature sampling exciter) such as a Tayloe detector and use an on board DAC (digital to analog converter) to perform the digital to analog conversion. VHF/UHF/SHF SDRs are often generation 2 SDRs.
Generation 3 SDR	Software defined radio, usually employing a QSD (quadrature sampling detector) such as a Tayloe detector. It uses an on board ADC (analog to digital converter) chip to perform the analog to digital conversion. DSP and demodulation is performed by chips or a computer inside the radio. If the device is capable of transmitting, it will employ a QSE (quadrature sampling exciter) such as a Tayloe detector or conventional transmitter architecture. If it is a QSE, it will use an on board DAC (digital to analog converter) to perform the digital to analog conversion. DSP and modulation is performed by chips in the radio. Many SDRs "with knobs" which can work as stand-alone radios without connection to a PC are generation 3 SDRs.
Generation 4 SDR	Direct digital synthesis SDR, using DDC (digital down conversion) in the receiver and DUC (digital up conversion) in the transmitter. The ADC and DAC are on board the radio and an FPGA is normally used to perform decimation and filtering to limit the data bandwidth requirement to the DSP stage, which may be on either the radio circuit board, or running on software inside the PC.

CONVENTIONAL RECEIVERS

Conventional receivers are usually double or triple conversion Superheterodyne designs, with hardware oscillators and mixers. They have I.F. amplifiers and some sort of AGC circuit. Often they have DSP stages after the final mixer and I.F. amplifier. The I.F. signal is converted from analog to digital and processed within the DSP chip. DSP functions usually include noise and notch filtering, I.F. width and shift control, and often a band scope. Demodulation may be performed by the DSP, or the signal may be converted back to an analog signal and passed through a hardware demodulator. This might be followed by an AF DSP stage, which shapes the audio response and provides noise filters. Even if the DSP firmware can be updated by downloading a file and sending it to the radio, we don't consider these radios to be 'software defined.'

CONVENTIONAL TRANSMITTERS

Conventional transmitters often use the same local oscillator as the receiver. The microphone, other audio, or CW signal is converted into a digital signal, shaped and filtered using DSP processes and then converted back to an analog signal. It is amplified and mixed up to the wanted RF frequency. Then it is amplified up to the final output power, passed through a low pass filter to remove harmonic frequencies, and sent out to the antenna port. An older transmitter does the same but without the DSP stage. The modulation may be performed by a hardware modulator stage or by the DSP stage.

SDR RECEIVERS

HF software defined radio receivers are usually based on one of two common architectures. Generation one, two, and three SDR receivers are QSD designs which use a Tayloe detector as a direct conversion mixer to create I and Q audio streams that are passed on to two analog to digital converters. Generation 4 SDR receivers use digital down conversion. The RF signal is sampled with a high speed analog to digital converter and then the digital signal is split into I and Q signals. This is often done in an FPGA, but it can be done in a dedicated receiver chip, or by an embedded microprocessor, or a DSP chip.

Receivers working at VHF and higher frequencies often use a slightly different design. Typically a hardware oscillator and mixer is used to mix the RF signal down to an I.F. channel and then a digital down conversion SDR performs the analog to digital conversion and DSP functions. Some of these radios use a dedicated receiver chip rather than an FPGA.

These receiver tuner chips have internal hardware oscillators and mixers followed by analog to digital conversion. A variety of methods can be used to produce the IQ data output streams for the DSP stage. The RTL dongles use a Realtek 2832U tuner chip and the Afedri receivers use a Texas Instruments front end chip. The HackRF board uses a Xilinx CPLD and an ARM Cortex processor. The BladeRF board uses an ARM9 general purpose processor and an FPGA.

Technical TIP: A CPLD is a Complex Programmable Logic Device. It is another field programmable logic device like an FPGA. CPLD chips tend to have fewer programmable gates than FPGA chips and their internal structure is different. The main practical difference apart from size is that an FPGA does not usually have any non-volatile memory. It needs a program stored in a separate EPROM, which is loaded when the device is powered up. A CPLD does have non-volatile memory so it is ready to go as soon as power is applied. A big CPLD will have around the same number of programmable logic gates as a very small FPGA.

SDR TRANSMITTERS

There are not very many commercial generation one or generation two transmitters and almost all of them are QRP low power radios. The FLEX-1500, FLEX-3000, SoftRock, SDR Cube, and the Genesis G59 spring to mind. They use a Tayloe detector in reverse as a quadrature sampling exciter (QSE). The digital (IQ) signals carry the modulated audio frequency signal. The QSE mixes the audio up to the final RF frequency, which is amplified and passed through low pass harmonic filters to the antenna. Generation three SDR transmitters are radios, which use a QSE plus on-board digital to analog conversion and DSP. Often these are software defined radios with knobs like the Elecraft KX3. There even are some SDR transceivers, which use an SDR receiver in conjunction with a conventional transmitter.

Then there are generation four, digital up-conversion (DUC) transmitters. The DSP stage creates a modulated digital IQ signal, which is up-converted to the final frequency as a digital signal and then converted to an analog signal using a fast digital to analog converter. This is followed by a power amplifier and low pass filter.

VHF transmitters might be straight DUC designs or hybrids. For UHF and SHF frequencies, the transmitters are typically similar to the equivalent receivers. A direct up-conversion SDR creates an I.F. frequency, which is mixed up to the final RF frequency by a hardware mixer and oscillator. Almost all of the software defined radios that work at UHF and above are very low power 'sub QRP' transceivers and boards.

COMMERCIAL (NON AMATEUR) SDRS

Software defined radio is well established in the commercial world. SDR technology is very common in cellular base stations and military radios. It is rapidly becoming common for mobile and hand-held radios as well. These types of radios are probably better described as 'digital' rather than software defined, because the internal firmware is not usually user upgradeable.

Many of the manufacturers of software defined radios for the amateur radio and hobby market also make radios for the commercial and military market.

HYBRID SDRS (+ SDR)

There are quite a few radios that advertise 'SDR' as a feature. Some manufacturers are now using terms like 'Superheterodyne + SDR.' This partly due to the fact that SDR features are fashionable and partly because it is quite difficult to define exactly what software defined radios are. These radios are often called hybrids because you do get some SDR functionality, even if it is only a band scope. It is not the knobs, or the lack of them that makes the difference.

Some examples of + SDR radios are the Elecraft K3S, the Alinco DX SR9T/E and the AOR AR-2300 / AR-5001D. These radios all output IQ streams at audio frequencies that can be used for a band scope display with a bandwidth of up to around 200 kHz.

Less easy to quantify are radios like the Comm Radio CR1a, the Elecraft KX3 and the SDR Cube, which use QSD technology. They are not traditional Superheterodyne receivers. These radios have on-board DSP, their modulation, demodulation and filtering is performed inside the radio and they have limited or no ability to display a band-scope or panadapter. Most people do refer to these radios as software defined radios, but in some respects, they are hybrids. It seems that using QSD rather than Superheterodyne architecture is enough to ensure their status as software defined.

Not many people would be brave enough to suggest that the new FlexRadio Systems 6000 series radios are hybrids. They use direct digital synthesis and can support several very wide panadapters. In fact, they are at the pinnacle of SDR design. But they too have all of their DSP performed in hardware by DSP chips and embedded processors. Certainly this is field upgradable firmware but then so is the firmware used in conventional receivers.

So, I'm not very fond of the term 'hybrid SDR', I prefer the new 'Superheterodyne + SDR' terminology, which at least lets you, know what you are dealing with. The fact is; direct sampling SDR and Superheterodyne 'conventional' technologies are going to continue to merge and fairly soon, "a radio will be a radio." It might have knobs or it might not. It will probably use some direct sampling technology and it will probably offer at least a band scope. Nearly all hand held radios and most mobile radios are already fully digital inside. But digital does not necessarily mean software defined.

Consider the following three scenarios:

1. A Superheterodyne single, double, or triple conversion receiver, with I.F. DSP that outputs an audio frequency IQ stream for a panadapter. The panadapter could be displayed on the radio, on an external unit, or on a PC screen.

2. As above but, the demodulation and filtering is done by firmware in a dedicated DSP chip.

3. As above but, the demodulation and filtering is done by firmware in a dedicated DSP chip or embedded computer processor that can be firmware updated without changing the DSP chip.

Are any of the radios above a true software defined radio?

I don't believe that any of them are. They are all conventional radios, which support a band scope. But by some definitions number three is an SDR, because you can change the modulation / demodulation and filtering software in the field without replacing any hardware.

Radios that fit into this category include most of the radios which include an internal band scope and also the '+ SDR' radios which can support an external panadapter.

OK let's try some tricky examples. What about a single conversion receiver, which uses a tuner chip that outputs an IQ stream over a USB connection for external demodulation, filtering and a panadapter display, all performed by PC software. A large number of receivers that are usually referred to as SDRs fall into this group, for example the RTL dongle and the Fun Cube dongle. I believe that even though these radios have a conversion stage before the analog to digital converter, they are software defined radios, because the demodulation and filtering is done by software inside the PC.

What about the case of a radio which uses a QSD quadrature sampling detector, like the SoftRock or one of the many other generation one, two or three software defined radios. They are software defined radios, because the demodulation and filtering is done by software inside the PC. But what if the DSP and control functions are done inside the radio, as is the case for the Elecraft KX3 and the SDR Cube? Most people consider the SDR Cube and the KX3 to be software defined radios because they use a QSD instead of a conventional Superheterodyne arrangement. But the functions of the modulation, demodulation, and much of the filtering is locked inside the DSP chip, which is only firmware upgradable.

I don't know the answer to what fully defines an SDR and I don't think it matters, except to the flat earth guys. I believe that the two technologies will continue to merge. We will see Superheterodyne receivers with digital up conversion transmitters and radios that include both direct sampling and Superheterodyne receivers. Or, there might be radios with conventional transmitters and direct sampling receivers.

But right now, if we narrow the focus right down to just include 100 W HF transceivers. There are two distinct camps.

- Conventional Superheterodyne architecture radios or + SDR radios with onboard I.F. DSP. They may offer an internal band-scope or a narrow bandwidth, 200 kHz or less, IQ audio output, for an external SDR program and panadapter.

- Direct digital synthesis radios with onboard or external DSP, which offer multiple wide panadapters or wideband IQ data streams. These are high performance software defined radios.

If you want a true SDR experience with all of the amazing features that this new technology offers, then go for a direct sampling QRP or 100 W SDR transceiver. Once you get used to it and you actually use the radio, on the air, you won't want to go back to the old way. Other radios may have excellent performance and the comfort of being able to adjust all of the knobs, but a single narrow band scope is just not the same as a fully featured panadapter. A radio with a built in band scope or a +SDR radio with an external panadapter display will still be great. Much better than not having a band scope at all, but you will be missing out on the really good stuff.

WEB SDR

You can get a taste of what it is like to use an SDR without buying a radio. The ability of software defined radios to run more than one receiver 'slice' on the same or multiple bands 'panadapters' at the same time has created a new opportunity for remote radio operation. All around the world, people have connected software defined radio receivers to Internet servers. Anyone can operate these remote radios via a standard web browser (with Java activated). WebSDR.org currently lists 113 servers with receivers covering a total of 306 MHz of radio spectrum.

*'A **WebSDR receiver** is a Software-Defined Radio receiver connected to the internet, allowing many listeners to listen and tune it simultaneously. SDR technology makes it possible that all listeners tune independently, and thus listen to different signals; this is in contrast to the many classical receivers that are already available via the internet.' Websdr.org*

*'A **WebSDR server** consists of a PC running Linux and the WebSDR server software, a fast internet connection (about a hundred kbit/s uplink bandwidth per listener), and some radio hardware to feed antenna signals into the PC. This radio hardware is typically a quadrature mixer connected to the PC's sound card, like the popular SoftRock kits.' Websdr.org*

Using WebSDR, several users can operate receivers on the same wide band panadapter, spectrum display at the same time. Many of the sites have multiple bands available. This is different to web sites where you can take over the operation of a conventional receiver or transceiver. In that case, only one person can take remote control at a time. Most of the WebSDR receivers operate in the HF spectrum but a few offer VHF and UHF coverage. There are even receivers operating on the 10 GHz band or dedicated to receiving signals from amateur satellites.

It can be interesting to tune around the band using a receiver located in another country, especially when propagation means the bands are dead at your location. You could use the technology to find out what regions have good propagation, or to listen to a station, which is blocked by noise or interference at your place. Or you may be able use a remote receiver to overcome antenna restrictions at your location.

Unfortunately, the majority of HF band WebSDR sites have wire or vertical antennas because with multiple users connected, it is not practical to use directional antennas. Everyone would want to point the beam in different directions.

One of the cool things that you can do with WebSDR is to listen to your own transmissions as they are being received in another country. Have you ever wondered what your signal sounds like? Or if you can be heard in Europe or Australia? With WebSDR, you can find out. Be aware though, that there is often significant latency in these systems. The signal you hear from the remote receiver may be several seconds delayed.

WebSDR is a way of using software defined radio technology, but the user experience is not the same as operating a real software defined radio at home. SDR-Radio.com offers another online way to operate a software defined radio over the Internet.

SDR-RADIO.COM / SDRSPACE.COM

If you want to get a different view of what to expect from operating an SDR before you buy one, you can download the SDR Console V2 software at http://v2.sdr-radio.com/Software/Download1. This software will allow you to operate remote SDR receivers as if the radio was attached to your own computer.

SDR Console V2 will work with a receiver that you have at home or with a receiver connected to one of the many remote servers around the world. That means that you can try the software out by connecting to a radio over the Internet and then continue to use it after you have purchased your own software defined radio. The program was written by Simon Brown, HB9DRV who was the author of the very popular 'Ham Radio Deluxe' software. It supports a wide range of SDR receivers including the RFSpace radios, AirSpy, most dongles, and Softrock receivers. Version 3, which is scheduled for release in 2016, will support transmitting using the Apache labs ANAN series of transceivers and possibly other software defined radio transceivers.

When you have installed the software, you can connect to one of the online servers. Press the 'Browse' button on the 'Connect' screen to get a list. I found that several of the radios listed were not active and some sites need a password for access. There is a list on the status.sdrspace.com/onair.xml website, which shows which sites are active and other useful information.

If you want to, you can configure your computer as a server and add your receiver to the world wide list of radios that others can use. The server software installs itself at the same time as it installs SDR Console V2. See http://v2.sdrspace.com/. To operate an SDR server you will need to open ports through your firewall to allow others to access the radio. There are instructions on the web site explaining how to setup the system.

BENEFITS OF INTERNET BASED SDR

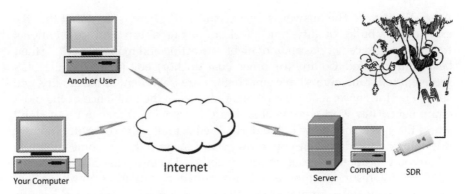

Figure 9: Internet based SDR allows several people to share the same radio

Internet based software defined radio servers allow several users to operate 'receivers' on the same SDR panadapter at the same time. You need a PC with an Internet connection but you don't need a radio. All of the online users can tune to any signal that is displayed on the panadapter. Often, each user can select their own mode and receive filter bandwidth. The SDR-Radio.com system even lets you configure the remote radio's panadapter bandwidth.

Internet SDR allows you to monitor your own signal and it can allow you to work stations when you can't receive them at your location. It is up to you whether you consider this kind of remote operating to be 'cheating.' It is still illegal in most contests and I don't think that contacts made in this way are valid for certificates like DXCC. Maybe they are, since the transmitter is still at your house. You are only extending the reach of the receiver. This type of remote operation is good for shortwave listeners since they can continue to tune the bands when the propagation is poor at home. But, again... is it cheating? It's up to you.

You might be able to combine the signals from a remote server with those that you receive at home. But I suspect that the latency from the remote radio would make this type of operation impractical.

Using a remote radio, either a receiver or a full transceiver, may be the only way that you can continue with your hobby. Many residential developments have strict restrictive covenants that ban any kind of antenna system. You can also use remote radio to operate when you are away from home, while on holiday or at work.

If you set up a server at your home, you would be able operate your own radio from anywhere that has a fast Internet connection. You can arrange this to be either a private connection just for you, or a publicly listed server.

ARE SDRS BETTER?

Are SDRs better? The answer is "yes... and no." There is no doubt that the ergonomics, build quality, and 'feel' of using a top end conventional transceiver or receiver has an undeniable attraction and many hams love their beautifully crafted Collins (or other boat anchor) equipment. While SDR receivers and transceivers have amazing features, excellent audio quality, and superb performance, using them sometimes lacks the ambience of the older equipment. They work very well and can do amazing things but they don't warm the shack and 'glow in the dark.' Well actually, the computer monitor does glow in the dark, but you know what I mean. When it comes down to what you can do and actual on-air capability, I believe that SDRs have the edge. It is interesting that more and more conventional radios now have SDR like features and even computer mouse control. A recent Icom model has two band scopes, one for each receiver.

As with most things, the more expensive the radio is, the more you can expect in the way of features and performance. Top end conventional radios are better than cheap software defined radios. But a cheap SDR may be able to do some things that the expensive transceiver can't. Dollar for dollar, I believe an SDR will outperform a conventional architecture radio on some key tests. On the other hand, there are other tests where a conventional radio may be better. For example, a radio with a 50 Volt power amplifier might have better transmit intermodulation performance. Most conventional radios have a faster transmit to receive switching time. SDRs often have significant latency which makes sending CW with a side-tone irritating. Many of these issues have now been overcome in the latest generation of software defined radios. One thing that is sure is that SDR technology is undergoing rapid development with new performance advancements every few months. If you own an SDR, you can take advantage of the new developments simply by updating the software and firmware programs. A conventional radio gets left behind when each new model is released. I was interested to see just how poorly some of the older elite class transceivers like the FT-1000MP compare with the new radios produced by the same manufacturer.

Technical TIP: The new top end transceivers are significantly better than 'elite' and 'contest' grade radios from the early 2000s. In fact, recent mid-range radios are usually better as well. Direct sampling software defined transceivers are also significantly better than 'elite' and 'contest' grade radios from the early 2000s.

There are two ways to measure whether software defined radios are better than conventional ones. You can measure the technical performance, using test equipment and on air evaluations or you can compare the way they operate, the things they can do, and whether you like the new features. In the end it comes down to; "do I like using this new radio?"

Online reviews and videos do add some value but they are very subjective. People tend to like the brands they are familiar with and they almost always strongly approve of a radio in which they have just invested a lot of their hard earned cash. Some people will turn a blind eye to truly appalling equipment out of pure brand loyalty. However, cumulative reviews do show-up equipment with poor reliability or customer support and that can be valuable information when you are making a decision about what radio to buy.

Software defined radios use a completely different technology to that used in conventional Superheterodyne receivers and transceivers. So you need different tests to measure their performance. Measuring SDR performance using the old tests that were developed for conventional radio designs can produce unreliable results. In spite of this, SDRs usually score very well in the lab tests published by ham radio magazines. The new methods used to test SDRs are interesting so I have included a section on performance testing later in the book.

SDR FEATURES

Software defined radios have some great features that are unavailable or less well implemented on conventional radios.

1. SDRs can monitor several bands at the same time. The latest HF SDR transceivers can place as many as eight panadapters on one or sometimes multiple computer screens.

2. You can see the signals on the panadapter, which lets you precisely adjust filters and see interference or distorted transmissions.

3. SDR filters created in DSP software are exceptionally sharp and they don't 'ring' causing distortion to the received audio. They are also fully variable.

4. Once the signal has been converted to digital, it does not suffer from noise addition within the receiver stages. A purely analog receiver adds noise and intermodulation distortion at each mixer and amplifier stage.

5. SDR receivers are less affected by other signals on the band. The receiver's intermodulation performance may actually be improved when there are other signals on the bands.

6. You don't need cables to connect up the radio for digital modes. Your logging and digital mode software can run on the same PC as the SDR software.

7. Changing the SDR software can add new features keeping the radio up to date. You can change how the radio looks and works. While you can update the DSP firmware on conventional radios, they still tend to get out of date when a new model is released.

8. Using the latest technology is a cool part of being a radio hobbyist.

CONVENTIONAL (NON SDR) RADIO FEATURES

1. Knobs and buttons are tactile and nice to play with. You get to tune across the band using the big VFO knob. It feels nice.

2. Non SDR radios are better for mobile operation because you don't need to look at a screen. SDRs are very visual devices and that is not useful when you are operating mobile. Also, it is inconvenient if you need a PC as well as the radio to operate the SDR.

3. People used to say that non SDR radios are better for CW. This used to be true, but not anymore. The latest SDR transceivers create CW by keying the data signal in the FPGA, rather than by generating a tone at the start of the transmit chain. This provides low latency and very fast QSK operation.

THE TOP 20 RECEIVERS AND TRANSCEIVERS

The top 20 receiver and top 20 transceiver charts are based on a wide range of receiver and transceiver, performance test data mostly from QST reviews. In my opinion, they represent a balanced survey of performance, but it is only my personal ranking. As new radios are tested, more data will be recorded and the coveted top spots may change.

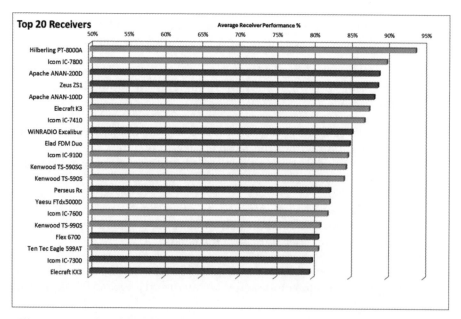

Figure 10: Andrew's list of top 20 receivers

Other excellent performance resources include reviews by Adam Farson VA7OJ/AB4OJ, the comparison of CW keying spectra and phase noise published by Jim Brown K9YC, reviews in RSGB Radcom mostly by Peter Hart G3SJX and the Sherwood Engineering tables by Rob Sherwood NC0B.

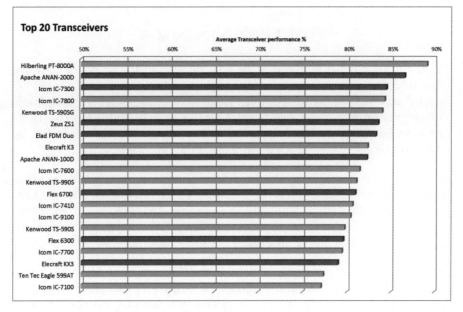

Figure 11: Andrew's list of top 20 transceivers

Nine of the top twenty receivers and eight of the top twenty transceivers are SDRs. Considering how few SDR transceivers are available that's quite an achievement. The receiver tests include; sensitivity (MDS) 500 Hz BW preamp off, blocking dynamic range (BDR) 20m at 20 kHz and 2 kHz, noise figure, reciprocal mixing dynamic range (RMDR), S meter calibration, Receiver 3rd order IMD at 2 kHz, 5 kHz and 20 kHz, white noise (NPR), and image rejection. The transmitter tests include; Transmitter 3rd 5th 7th 9th and worst order IMD, CW keying spectrum (narrow 0.5-1 kHz and wide 2-5 kHz), worst harmonic on 20m and 6m, transmit composite noise at 100 Hz and at 10 kHz, SSB relay TR switching time, carrier suppression, and sideband suppression. I don't have results for all of these tests on all of the radios. Radios are not penalized for tests, which have not been measured.

WHAT'S BEST FOR YOU?

This chapter described some of the features that SDRs have, that other radios don't have. I believe that these things make software defined radio the right choice for my shack. I have tried both and I like using the SDR better. You might decide otherwise. Nevertheless, I urge you to give it a real chance. Use the SDR in the same way you would normally use your old radio. Don't let the online forums put you off. There are many, many, online posts from hams who go to great lengths to tell you that SDRs are bad and that they would not touch one. My guess is that 99% of these pundits have never actually used an SDR, but they have an opinion and they don't mind sharing it. I have a hunch they are the same people who complained endlessly about the introduction of SSB and elimination of the Morse Code requirement for a license.

FUTURE TRENDS IN SDR

The most obvious future trend is the continuation of the tendency to move away from simple hardware solutions with complex software running on an external computer, towards complex hardware solutions with more simple software running on a variety of computer like devices and networks. There seems to be an evolution happening as the capabilities of what can be achieved using software defined radio expands.

SDR hardware has already evolved from simple narrow-band SoftRock devices to complex HF transceivers and very wideband radios. We now have 100 Watt software defined transceivers and radios that can cover frequencies from as low as 100 kHz up to around 6 GHz. The bandwidth that can be passed on to the DSP processing stage is also increasing greatly.

The SDR software is maturing as well. As the DSP functions are moved from software running on your PC to software running on a processor, or firmware running on a DSP chip inside the radio, the loading on the Ethernet connection between the devices is reduced. The saved bandwidth can be used for advanced capabilities like; multiple panadapters with differing bandwidths, more receiver slices, and multiple narrow band IQ streams for connection to external applications such as CW Skimmer. You can run SDR client software on several computers at the same time, or control your radio via WI-FI connected devices like Android phones, netbooks, and notebooks. In the near future, this will extend to the ability to use your radio remotely over the Internet from virtually anywhere.

Modern direct sampling software defined receivers and transceivers may have several layers of software:

- FPGA software (usually Verilog) to perform mixing, decimation and filtering. (Firmware updatable by download from the host PC).

- RISC software running on an ARM microprocessor, soft-processor, or micro-controller, to manage control functions and switching. (Firmware updatable by download from the host PC).

- DSP software running on dedicated DSP processor chips in the radio. (Firmware may be updatable by download from the host PC).

- DSP 'server' software running on a built-in computer or external single board computer. This would probably be Linux based software but it can be Windows based like the SUN MB-1. (Software updates directly downloadable or downloaded via a host PC).

- SDR 'client' software running on a computer, tablet, or phone. (Software updates directly downloadable from the Internet).

You might have different client software running on different devices for different modes of operation. For example, one program might be good for listening to digital broadcast stations, while another might have better filters or a built in PSK decoder. Your digital modes program might be another application controlling the radio directly rather than through an intermediary program. They can all connect to the same radio via the same 'server' application.

Another trend is the adoption of software defined radio by the 'Maker' and 'Hacker' communities. These enthusiasts are developing software defined radios with very wide frequency ranges, well into the GHz region. Their activities include receiving signals from things like high altitude balloons, aircraft, ships, and satellites. The signals might be; video, telemetry, beacons, GPS, APRS position information, or data communications. They might be interested in controlling machines, 3D printers, or robots. Most importantly, this is a growing group of young, intelligent, people who are becoming interested in radio. Some of them are becoming licensed amateur radio operators, so that they can legally transmit RF signals on the amateur bands. These enthusiasts are creating new software defined radios capable of working on the VHF, UHF, and microwave amateur radio bands. The new radios and software that they create can also be used for more traditional ham radio activities such as amateur TV, digital voice modes, repeater operation, weather stations, monitoring weather satellites, satellite operation, EME, and microwave DX.

ADAPTIVE TRANSMITTER PRE-DISTORTION

At least three SDR radio manufacturers already offer adaptive transmitter pre-distortion. This is a technique where a sample of your transmitted signal is taken back into the radio and compared with the modulating signal. By doing this it is possible to alter the phase and amplitude of the modulation in such a way that the effects of nonlinearity in the transmitter power amplifier are taken into account. The result is a significantly improved transmission with a typical improvement of 20 dBc in transmitted intermodulation performance. The improvement is so significant that you can easily see the improved spectrum of a radio, which is using adaptive pre-distortion on your panadapter display. Full duplex operation and wide transmit bandwidth capability makes this dynamic technology much easier to implement in a software defined radio than in a conventional radio.

NEW MODES LIKE DIGITAL VOICE

Because software defined radios are computer like devices it is relatively easy to extend the software to include additional modulation types and modes. Some software defined radios can decode CW, RTTY and PSK and some can decode stereo FM and DRM digital signals. There is also an add-on for SmartSDR that uses the FlexRadio API (application programming interface) to add the FreeDV digital voice mode. Extendibility like this is a major advantage of software defined radio.

DIRECT DIGITAL MODES

At present, there is a separation between the SDR radio software and the digital mode software used for RTTY, PSK, Packet, APRS, SSTV, and so on. The digital mode software modulates the mode onto an audio signal or sends audio tones in preset patterns. Then the audio is sent to the radio and used to modulate the RF signal, usually using single sideband or FM. But if the digital mode software was integrated with the SDR software, the digital modes could be created as IQ signals and used directly. The SDR software would be able to send and receive digital modes without having to use a separate digital mode program. It should also be possible to invent new modes by manipulating the I and Q data rather than using tones.

The ability to send the digital mode program a wideband IQ signal rather than a 3 kHz wide audio signal promises the ability to decode digital signals from several bands at once. Imagine having PSK from four bands on the same waterfall display. Just click on any signal to work the one you want.

In the latest SDR transceivers, CW modulation is created in the FPGA rather than switching an audio tone on and off. The same techniques can be applied to phase modulation schemes like BPSK. To create a PSK31 signal you just to switch the phase of the signal by 180 degrees rather than turn it on and off. This should be fairly easy to implement in the FPGA. QPSK could be implemented in the same way, by using 90 degree phase changes.

BETTER ADCS

There will be better ADC chips, but the trend is more likely to be towards higher sample rates allowing for a wider Nyquist bandwidth rather than a larger number of bits. This is because noise performance is less important than bandwidth in the commercial world. But it is impractical to sample at super-fast rates, so radios working in the UHF and SHF regions will always need some sort of down conversion before the ADC. This is increasingly likely to be in the form of a tuner chip or a dedicated down conversion chip.

MULTIPLE ADCS

There are significant advantages to having more than one ADC in the software defined receiver front end. In radios with down conversion stages, having two ADCs can double the usable bandwidth of the radio. For example, you could have a receiver capable of receiving HF and VHF, or VHF and UHF. Phase coherent receivers can be used with multiple antennas to artificially steer their directivity, boost a signal, or cancel noise and interference.

If both ADCs have individual front end filters, you can monitor multiple bands with a reduced risk of dynamic gain compression or ADC overload. This technique is used in the FLEX-6700, ANAN-7000DLE and ANAN-8000DLE, but not in the Apache ANAN-100 / 200. You can monitor multiple bands with a single ADC, but you may have to bypass the pre-selecting bandpass filters.

STANDARDIZATION

A lot of software defined radios are able to work with more than one SDR software program. Conversely, some applications can work with a variety of software defined radios. Standardization of the interface requirements and data protocols can extend this capability. Wouldn't it be nice if you could buy any SDR hardware and use any SDR software with it?

The server / client model can further extend the opportunity for standardization. Functions like the DSP are done inside the radio or by a server program and the display functions are performed by a separate client application. The client program might be on the same PC as the server, or on another computer connected via LAN or Wi-Fi, or it could be a computer connected over the Internet. A radio and server could simultaneously serve several different clients performing different functions in different places. For example, a client that supports DRM could play music in the lounge while you use a completely different program to operate PSK in the shack.

REMOTE OPERATION OVER INTERNET

A lot of people are very interested in using the Internet to operate their radio from a remote location. There are some methods already being used to achieve this and they are not limited to software defined radios. But a software defined radio that already sends its data over an Ethernet connection is ideally suited to remote operation. The only requirement is to extend the connection through a firewall and router to the Internet.

There are many reasons for remote operation. You might have restrictions on the size of antennas that you can have at home, or you may have a lot of electrical noise to deal with. People that travel a lot may be interested in operating their home station from another city or another country. Club stations may allow members to operate the club station from home. Or geography may block transmission in the direction that you want to use. This could be situations like; not being able to see down to the horizon for satellite or EME operation, needing a high site for VHF DX, or a mountain blocking the short path to Europe.

Many software defined radios use an Ethernet connection to the PC, which is essentially the same method that computers use to talk to each other. So there is no technical reason why the Ethernet connection can't be extended over the Internet. The main barriers to remote operation over the Internet are unpredictable delays in receiving data packets and the need for security. Data latency causes slow control operation, intermittent panadapter display, and broken audio. The need for security is evident. You don't want to open your local network to unscrupulous individuals or allow your transceiver to be operated by unlicensed individuals. Radios that include the server are ideally suited for direct connection to the Internet. The thin client connection between the server software and the client software requires less continuous data, so the connection is less affected by latency problems.

COMMON QUESTIONS ABOUT SDRS

There are many very vocal and uninformed knockers inhabiting the online forums. Most of what they say is outdated or incorrect. These are probably the same people who believed that eliminating the CW requirement for the amateur radio license would lead to the destruction of the hobby. They may also believe that the Earth is flat, DSP sounds bad, and that vinyl is better. Many of the criticisms leveled at SDRs are no longer valid, because the technology and software is continually being improved. Some of the criticisms are just plain wrong, being based on an incomplete understanding of how software defined radios work. For every 'real problem,' there is a solution available now or coming soon.

ARE SDRS ANY GOOD FOR CW?

Initially many CW operators didn't like using SDRs because of the delay between pressing the Morse key and the side-tone being heard. This delay, known as latency, is due to the time taken for the CW tone to be processed in the SDR software and then sent to the radio. The problem can be avoided to some extent by using a keyer that generates its own side-tone, or by not listening to your side-tone at all. Another issue was the ability to work QSK at high CW speeds. QSK operation allows a proficient operator to listen to the receiver in between the Morse code 'dits' and 'dahs' that they are sending. To achieve this, the transceiver must switch from receive to transmit and back again, quietly and fast. Because the, transmit to receive (TR) switching is a signal that must be passed from the SDR radio to the PC software and back again, most SDRs have a fairly poor transmit to receive switching time.

A solution to both of these problems has been found and implemented by the 100 Watt SDR transceiver makers and by some of the QRP transceiver manufacturers. The CW latency and QSK TR switching time issues have been fixed by keying the transceiver using embedded firmware code in the FPGA rather than the older method of keying a tone generated in the PC software. This has resulted in very fast CW generation with immediate side-tone and full QSK operation up to at least 60 wpm. These developments are quite new. FPGA CW keying was introduced for the Apache ANAN series of radios in July 2014 and a similar technique has been implemented in the FlexRadio 6000 Signature range transceivers since their introduction in 2013.

Technical TIP: This advancement is a good example of learning that SDR is different. The old method of generating CW was the same as the technique that is used in most modern SSB transceivers. The CW keyer turns on and off an audio frequency tone that is then sent to the SSB modulator and mixed up to RF.

In the new method the FPGA simply generates a digital 'carrier' signal which is turned on and off by the keyer. The data is then sent to the DAC and converted to an RF signal in the usual way. In both cases, the waveform rise and fall times are shaped to avoid harsh sounding key clicks.

DO SDRS HAVE A POOR DYNAMIC RANGE?

No! They actually have very good dynamic range. Some online pundits claim that SDRs have poor dynamic range and that the owners are lying about how good they are. This claim is just plain wrong and it has led to the widespread but mistaken impression that 16 bit SDRs are inherently better than 14 bit SDRs.

In fact, the dynamic range of 14 bit radios is very similar to 16 bit radios. However, I am prepared to admit that 14 and 16 bit radios are generally better than 8 bit models. I cover this in more detail later in the section describing the ADC. But take it from me; SDRs have much better dynamic range than conventional Superheterodyne architecture radios, which need AGC to extend their dynamic range to an acceptable level.

A good quality DDC based software defined receiver will typically have a dynamic range in excess of 120 dB in a 2.4 kHz bandwidth.

The confusion arises from a lack of understanding about the formula for the maximum dynamic range achievable using analog to digital converters, $DR=20*log(2^{\wedge}Nbits-1)\ dB$. What is often overlooked is that the dynamic range as specified in the formula relates to the entire frequency response of the analog to digital converter. As the bandwidth of the signal is reduced using frequency decimation and filtering down to the final receiver bandwidth of around 2.4 kHz for SSB, the dynamic range increases. This effect is called 'process gain'. It is the ratio of the initial and final bandwidth expressed in decibels. It is not really a 'gain,' it is an increase in dynamic range resulting from the exclusion of noise. Think of it as having a sliding door open when your grandchildren are playing outside. If the door is open wide you get a lot of noise and it is hard to hear the TV. If it is only opened to a narrow slot, you get less noise and you are able to hear the TV.

Process gain is the reason that you use a narrow filter for CW. You get less noise so you can hear weaker signals. You can try this at home. Tune your SDR to a part of a band that has no signals, so you are just hearing noise. As you drag the receiver filter to a narrower bandwidth the noise that you hear on the speaker reduces and the signal showing on the S meter reduces. Note that the spectrum display is not affected by your changes to the receiver bandwidth, because it is created separately.

Technical TIP: Process gain is a fundamental part of the panadapter display. The data used to plot the panadapter spectrum display is derived from measuring the levels of thousands of narrow bandwidth frequency samples, known as 'bins.' The bins are obtained from the ADC data output using the FFT process. The amplitude of the signal in each of the bins is used to plot the points along the spectrum display. Because each bin represents a very narrow bandwidth, each bin has a low noise floor and the panadapter can display a large dynamic range. In fact, it can display signals below the noise floor of the 2.4 kHz receiver slice. So the panadapter will display any signal that is strong enough to hear from the receiver.

DO SDRS HAVE A POOR SIGNAL TO NOISE RATIO?

No! They have very good signal to noise ratio as well. This is actually the same question as the one about dynamic range since the maximum receiver level is limited by the clipping level of the ADC and the difference between that level and the noise floor of the receiver is the maximum possible signal to noise ratio.

Some mathematical wizardry produces the formula for the maximum possible signal to noise ratio for an ADC, $SNR = 6.02*Nbits+1.76\ dB$. Like the dynamic range, the maximum possible signal to noise ratio is related to the number of bits used to describe each sampled input voltage level. This is the formula that causes all the aggravation in online forums because on first glance it indicates that the maximum achievable signal to noise ratio (SNR) is not very good and nowhere near the figures quoted in SDR product documentation and reviews.

The formula indicates significant differences between the performance of the 8 bit, 14 bit, and 16 bit ADCs used in various SDR models, which is much less apparent in real world tests. Actually, the typical signal to noise ratio of most ADCs is a little worse than the maximum that is predicted by the formula. But, as the bandwidth is reduced from the ADC sampling bandwidth down to the receiver bandwidth, the dynamic range, and the signal to noise ratio improves due to process gain.

Actually, the number of bits is not a very reliable indicator of the receiver's signal to noise performance. This is because an ADC can't sample very weak signals accurately. So even though a device may have a 16 bit output signal the effective number of bits 'ENOB' that actually carry valid information is always less than 16 bits.

DO I HAVE TO USE A MOUSE? – I LIKE KNOBS AND BUTTONS

Yes, you will have to use a mouse. But, you soon get used to using a mouse instead of traditional controls. Using the radio becomes the same as using any other program on your PC. You don't expect knobs on your Internet web browser or email client.

If you really need a tuning knob, there are options available. FlexRadio and Woodbox Radio both offer remote VFO knobs. They have two or three buttons that you can dedicate to other transceiver functions. Some people use a 'Hercules' Midi music 'DJ console' to provide a suite of slide controls, and buttons. I have tried some of these options, but I find mouse control easier and faster. FlexRadio offers a console called Maestro for the Signature range.

When you get used to the different way of operating your radio, I think you will find that the mouse works very well, especially if it has a mouse wheel between the buttons for fine tuning the receiver frequency. I am not the only person to believe that mouse control is better. The latest top end conventional radios like the Icom IC-7850 have mouse controlled band scopes, to make operating them more like using a software defined radio.

ARE SDRS ARE TOO TECHNICAL AND EXPERIMENTAL?

Playing around with software defined radio can be as technical and experimental as you want it to be. You have the option of buying a software defined radio and just using it in the same way as any other radio. Or you can get involved with high specification wideband boards, building your own SDR, or writing your own software.

In the case of most commercially available SDR receivers and transceivers, the experience is pretty similar to setting up and using any new radio. It might even be easier. Most of the small receivers and dongles use a USB connection. Simply plug the USB cable or dongle into your computer. Load a SDR program, connect an antenna and you are ready to play!

Most of the 100 W SDR transceivers need an external 25 Amp 13.8V power supply, the same as many regular transceivers. There will also be an Ethernet cable, which in the case of an ANAN radio is best connected to the PC via a 1 Gb Ethernet switch (not a hub). Connect another port on the Ethernet switch to your broadband Internet router and a third to the PC. Load the SDR program, connect an antenna and you are almost done. You will need a second set of amplified PC speakers and a microphone wired for the socket on the radio as well. Then you are ready to go.

I guess if you want to use cutting edge technology with continuing development, you must expect things to be somewhat fluid and experimental. This is especially true with open source software defined radio because we are relying on the enthusiasm of amateur software and hardware developers who are collaborating together. It does help if you have some computer skills, for example the ability to install new programs and understand directory folders. To keep up to date, you might have to install a new software revision, or download a firmware file and use a utility program to send it to the radio.

If you want to run digital modes with a conventional radio, you would need to install a computer program, connect up a radio to a power supply and antenna, then connect up a CAT cable and audio leads to the PC. To do the same on an SDR, it is essentially the same. Install a couple of computer programs for the audio and com port connections, connect the radio to a power supply and antenna, and plug in an Ethernet or USB cable. It only needs to be configured once. If you are in doubt or you do have problems ask a teenager or raise a question on an online SDR forum.

Building SDR radio kits is fun and much the same technical challenge as building a QRP radio or an electronics kit. In most cases any 'tricky to solder' surface mount chips are supplied already soldered to the board. If you want to throw yourself in the deep end, building a mcHF SDR is a more challenging project. If you are interested in programming, you can give GNU Radio a try, or write an application that takes advantage of the FlexRadio API. There is huge scope for you to become involved in either software or hardware development.

SDR SOFTWARE

On radios that use the PC for the digital signal processing the SDR software makes up at least half of the radio. In the receiver, it usually does the demodulation, filtering and noise reduction. In the transmitter, it does the filtering and the modulation. It also presents the front face of the radio with the controls and the panadapter display. So it is a key part of the software defined radio experience. SDR software offers a user interface that is quite different to a conventional radio and you have to get used to operating in a different way. But essentially this is really no different to learning how to operate any new receiver or transceiver.

There are dozens of different software defined radio receivers available and there are also some software defined radio transceivers. With the exception of the software defined radios 'with knobs', they all need a computer of some kind to provide a way to control the radio. The computer screen or 'window' that displays the radio controls and panadapter display is known as a graphical user interface (GUI) or sometimes a 'console'. Basically, the computer software application provides the knobs and controls that are missing from the front panel of the radio. It also displays the panadapter spectrum and waterfall displays. The other part of most SDR software, provides the digital signal processing (DSP) functions such as noise and notch filters, modulation and demodulation.

Most ham radio, transceivers produced over the last 20 years or so can be controlled using PC software. Computer control is handy for things like operating digital modes, logging, and CW keyers. If you use CAT (Icom CI-V) or digital mode software you should have no trouble adjusting to using a SDR. But the PC software for an SDR is much more than just an interface to the radio. Other computer programs may be able to remote control a conventional radio and your digital mode program may include a spectrum or a waterfall display, but only SDR software includes the DSP functions.

One of the big advantages of using an SDR is the ability to try different software with the same radio. New software can completely change the way the radio looks and operates, with new modes and features. Trying a new SDR application is like getting a whole new radio and it helps to keep your radio completely up to date.

SOFTWARE TYPES

There are also dozens of excellent SDR programs available. A lot of it is free-ware, usually developed under the open source software rules. Other programs are commercial products or are intended specifically for a particular software defined radio. Some software defined radios will only work with software developed by the manufacturer; other radios may work with a variety of different applications.

Depending on what radio you purchase it can be a real challenge working out what software is compatible with it. Luckily, help is never far away, with a multitude of online forums on the Internet.

Open source software code is available for anyone to modify, update, and reissue as long as the open source rules are followed. Some open source SDR software has variants, known as 'forks', which have been developed for different generations of SDR hardware. This is particularly apparent with the many flavors of PowerSDR, which was initially developed for the FlexRadio Systems 'Flex' series of radios. There are versions of PowerSDR that support:

- The FlexRadio Systems SDR-1000, FLEX-3000 and FLEX-5000 radios which use a FireWire interface

- The FlexRadio Systems FLEX-1500 which uses a USB interface

- The I.F. output from a conventional receiver

- Genesis, SoftRock and other 'sound card' based SDRs

- Home brew SDRs (often use PowerSDR IQ)

- Interfacing with an external 'DJ console' (PowerSDR UI and others)

- The OpenHPSDR Mercury receiver board – USB interface

- The OpenHPSDR Hermes transceiver board – Ethernet interface

- The Apache ANAN range of transceivers – Ethernet interface

- Adaptions for radio astronomy, receiver diversity, beam steering, and transmitter adaptive pre-distortion

SDR software whether commercial or open source is usually developed for a particular model or type of software defined radio. Broadly, these align with the generations of SDR. There are applications aimed at Generation 1 'sound card' software defined radios where the PC sound card performs the analog to digital and possibly digital to analog conversion. Other applications are configured for the 'dongle' and other small box radios using a USB interface. Some versions of PowerSDR are configured for the FireWire interface that is used on the FlexRadio FLEX-3000 and FLEX-5000 models. Finally, there is software for radios, which use an Ethernet interface. Another consideration is the operating system that the personal computer employs. There are applications for Microsoft Windows, Apple Mac, and Linux. There are even applications for single board computers and Android smart phones.

For some reason, there is a wealth of online information about how the SDR hardware works. But there is relatively little information about how the PC software works, even at a block level. I find it fascinating how simple some of the software code for filters, modulation, and demodulation is.

TABLE 3: SDR SOFTWARE AND HARDWARE COMPATIBILITY					
Software	*System*	*Hardware*	*TX/RX*	*Interface*	*SDR type*
cuSDR	Win	Hermes, Apache	Receivers	Ethernet	DDC
CuteSDR	Mac	RFSpace, Afedri	Receivers	USB	DDC
DL2SDR	Mac	SR, SC, Fifi, Lima, FA-SDR	Receivers	USB SC	QSD
GQRX	Mac Linux FreeBSD	FCD, USRP, Osmo, HackRF, RFSpace Red Pitaya	Receivers	USB Ethernet	DDC
GSDR	Win	Genesis, SR,SC, Fifi	Receivers	USB SC	QSD
HDSDR (WinradHD)	Win	FCD, RTL, FDM-S1, SC, FDM-S2, SR, Fifi, Hermes, Apache, Perseus, Afedri, BladeRF, HackRF, Andrus	Receivers	USB SC Ethernet	QSD and DDC
Hetrodyne	Mac	Hermes, Apache	Transceivers	Ethernet	DDC/DUC
Kiss Konsole	Win	Hermes, Apache	Transceivers	Ethernet	DDC/DUC
Linrad	Win Mac Linux	RTL, RFSpace, Perseus	Receivers	USB	DDC
Multimode	GNU Linux	RTL	Receivers	USB	DDC
PeddleSDR	Win	SR, SC, FCD, Elektor, RFSpace, HPSDR Mercury	Receivers	USB SC	QSD and DDC

TABLE 3: SDR SOFTWARE AND HARDWARE COMPATIBILITY					
Software	*System*	*Hardware*	*TX/RX*	*Interface*	*SDR type*
PowerSDR	Win	FlexRadio 1000, 1500, 3000, 5000	Transceivers	FireWire USB	QSD/QSE
PowerSDR IQ	Win	SR, SC, RTL	Transceivers	SC USB	QSD and DDC
PowerSDR mRX PS	Win	Hermes, Apache	Transceivers	Ethernet	DDC/DUC
PowerSDR UI	Win	FlexRadio 1000, 1500, 3000, 5000	Transceivers	FireWire USB	QSD/QSE
QtRadio (Ghpsdr3)	Win Linux	RTL, Hermes, Apache, SR, SC, Perseus, RFSpace, HiQSDR, USRP	Receivers	USB SC Ethernet	QSD and DDC
Quisk	Linux	Fifi, Afedri, SR, SC	Receivers	USB SC Ethernet	QSD and DDC
Rocky	Win	SR, SC	Receivers	SC	Gen 1 QSD
SDR Touch	Android	RTL	Receivers	USB	DDC
SDR#	Win Mac	FCD, RTL, SR, SC, Fifi, RFSpace, HackRF	Receivers	USB SC Ethernet	QSD and DDC
Sdrangleove	Linux	FCD, RTL, Osmo, BladeRF, HackRF, USRP, RFSpace	Receivers	USB	DDC
SDR-RADIO V2	Win	RTL, Fifi, RFSpace, FDM-1, USRP, FCD, SR, SC	Receivers	USB SC	QSD and DDC

TABLE 3: SDR SOFTWARE AND HARDWARE COMPATIBILITY					
Software	*System*	*Hardware*	*TX/RX*	*Interface*	*SDR type*
SeeDeR	Win	RTL, FCD, BladeRF	Receivers	USB	DDC
SmartSDR (not open source).	Win	FlexRadio Signature 6000 series	Transceivers	Ethernet	DDC/DUC
SoDiRa	Win	RTL, SC,SR, Elektor, Fifi, RFSpace, FCD, Pappradio, Afedri	Receivers	USB	QSD and DDC
Studio 1 (not open source).	Win	Perseus, RFSpace, RTL, SR, SC, FCD, FDM-S1, Apache, QS1R, USRP, PMSDR	Receivers	USB SC Ethernet	DDC
Wavesink +	Android	RTL	Receivers	USB	DDC
Winrad	Win	SR, SC, LD, RFSpace, Elektor	Receivers	USB SC	QSD

This list is not exhaustive and some software may work with SDR hardware that is not listed. It is as accurate as possible as at the time of writing. My apologies to any I inadvertently miss out. Inclusion or exclusion from this list does not imply any endorsement or criticism of any particular hardware or software.

Apache = ANAN-10, 10E, 100, 100D, 200D   FCD = FUNcube Dongle (all versions)

FDM-S1 by ELAD may include FDM-S2 and others

FlexRadio Signature 6000 series, FLEX-6300, 6400, 6500, 6600, 6700

Hermes = OpenHPSDR, may include Mercury boards

LD = Lazy Dog SDR   RFSpace may include SDR-14, SDR-IQ, SDR-IP

RTL = RTL Dongles   USRP = Ettus Research radios

SC = Sound card, may include PC sound cards and USB sound card devices

SR = Softrock and most other generation one sound cardSDRs

Win = Microsoft Windows operating system

Mac = Apple Macintosh operating system

Linux = Linux operating system

GNU = GNU Radio design (usually Linux based)

Android = Android smart phone software

THE GRAPHICAL USER INTERFACE

The graphical user interface (GUI) "Goo E" is the on screen representation of the knobs, buttons, and displays that you use to control the functions of your software defined radio. Many radios have hidden menus for setting lesser used options. Most software defined radio programs do as well.

Older software tends to have a user interface designed to look like a hardware radio. Settings that are adjusted often usually appear on the main screen or the 'face of the radio'. Slider controls replace the volume control and other knobs because they are easier to use with a mouse. As well as a panadapter, all of the usual controls, a frequency indication, and an S meter are displayed. Newer software has a less cluttered look with a larger panadapter and waterfall displays. The user controls pop-up when you move the computer mouse to control areas on the computer screen. A quick Internet search for images of SmartSDR or cuSDR, illustrates the new approach while PowerSDR or SdrDX shows the more traditional approach.

TIP: PowerSDR has two or three ways to adjust many of the settings. Some settings in the Setup menu may change if you make adjustments on the main screen (and vice versa). This is normal, but you might wonder why a setup item has changed status.

The on screen controls will be familiar to users of digital mode software, but for computer 'Newbies' here is a quick guide on how to set the main kinds of control. If you are left handed the mouse buttons may be reversed.

- 'Click' means to move the mouse over the control that you want to change then press and release the left mouse button

- 'Click and hold' means to move the mouse over the control then press and hold down the left mouse button. You will be able to adjust the control by moving the mouse sideways and/or vertically.

- 'Right click' means to move the mouse over the control then click the right mouse button. As with your word processor and most other programs, the right click is used to display additional menu items. A pop-up window will list the options that you can select with a left click. If the list of available options is longer than the display size of the pop-up window, moving the mouse vertically will scroll through the list.

- 'Mouse wheel' is the wheel located between the two mouse buttons. It might not be an option on Mac computers. Click on a control then use the mouse wheel to change the value. In most SDR software, clicking on the panadapter will allow the mouse wheel to fine tune the frequency. Clicking the mouse wheel may create a scrolling action where moving the mouse vertically has the same effect as rolling the wheel. I don't like using that mode of operation.

Slider – click and hold to adjust. Or click to the right or left of the knob for a coarse adjustment.

Text box – click inside the box and type in a new value. Often the mouse wheel and up and down keys may be used to change numeric values.

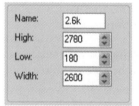

Right click – may display a list of options. Then left click on an option to make a selection. Sometimes a new window will open to display choices that are more complex.

List Box – click the up or down arrows to adjust the value, or click in the text box to type in a new value. New entries may be restricted to pre-set values.

Drop down box – click on the down arrow to open a list of options. Sometimes the list has scroll bars on the right to show more choices. Then click on an option to change the selection. Normally an unopened dropdown box shows the last chosen option.

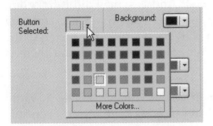

Check Boxes – click in the square to place a check mark 'tick' beside options that you want to activate. Click again to unset. Multiple options can be selected.

Radio Buttons – click in the circle to activate an option. Like an old fashioned car radio, you can select any one of the available choices.

Color chooser – a drop down box that lets you set the color of an item on the main display for example the text in the frequency read out.

Button – just click on it. They usually latch. Click the button to turn a function on, click again to turn it off. The graphic will change to show when the button is active or depressed.

Hover –holding or moving the mouse over items and controls on the screen, may cause pop-up windows to appear. These may display 'tool tips' of information relating to the function of the control, or they may show a list of hidden setup options.

Figure 12: common SDR program controls

PANADAPTERS AND WATERFALLS

In software defined radio applications, the band scope is called a panadapter. It shows the signals being received across all or a part of the band that the radio is tuned to. Unlike the band scopes on conventional radios, many software defined radios can display multiple panadapters at the same time. This means that you can monitor several bands or band segments at once. The ability to display signals on a panadapter display is definitely one of the major advancements offered by software defined radios and usually the panadapter display dominates the computer screen.

A waterfall display shows the history of the spectrum display. Stronger signals, which show as peaks on the spectrum display, are indicated as brighter colors on the waterfall display. You can see signals that are not on the spectrum anymore such as a station, which has just finished calling CQ.

Yes, some conventional transceivers offer a band scope display and they are beginning to offer a waterfall display as well. And yes, they did it first. But, the band scopes on conventional radios are usually small and the functionality is usually not as good as an SDR panadapter. For instance, the band scope may freeze while you are tuning across the band and there is usually no mouse control of tuning.

With the release of each new radio from the major amateur radio manufacturers, we are seeing larger band scopes, with more versatile features, such as the ability to display the panadapter on an external monitor. This is an indication of just how useful the panadapter is. New radios without a built in panadapter sometimes have an I.F. output, which can be used to drive an external SDR receiver or a band scope display.

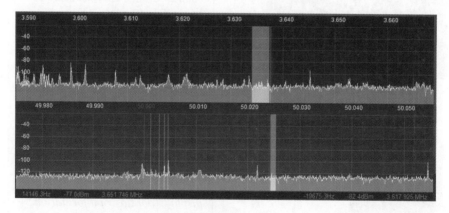

Figure 13: panadapters on the 80m and 6m bands.

The upper panadapter is showing some of the 80m band and a lower sideband receiver. The lower panadapter is on the 6m band with an upper sideband receiver. The five vertical lines are tracking notch filters.

Normally the frequency that the radio is tuned to is at the center of the panadapter display. Signals above the tuned frequency are shown on the right side and signals that are below the tuned frequency are shown on the left. The panadapter is often referred to as a 'spectrum display.' It looks like the display you would see on a spectrum analyzer, test instrument.

One or more 'receivers' will be shown superimposed on the spectrum display. They represent the part of the band that you are listening to, as opposed to the part of the band you are looking at. The receivers are normally depicted as a vertical line indicating the receiver center or 'carrier' frequency, next to a shaded area, which represents the receiver's bandwidth. An upper sideband receiver will be shown as a vertical line with a 2.5 to 3 kHz wide shaded area on the right side. Lower sideband shows the shaded area on the left side of the carrier. On AM or FM mode, the shaded area will be displayed on both sides of the center frequency, indicating a double sideband signal. CW is the same as SSB but with a narrower bandwidth.

TIP: You have to get used to the idea that the frequency of the receiver that you are listening to is not be the same as the center frequency that the radio is tuned to. The radio has a wide bandwidth and the receiver has a narrow bandwidth.

A 'receiver' on a software defined radio is like a VFO on a conventional radio. Most HF amateur radio transceivers have two VFOs to facilitate 'split' operation, or a quick jump to another frequency on the same band. Most SDR software will support two (or more) receivers on the same band, so you can run 'split' mode. Unlike the conventional radios, you may have the option of hearing both receivers at the same time, often one on the left speaker and the other on the right speaker. This is great for listening to a DX station as well as the pile-up. Unlike most conventional HF transceivers, software defined radios can often support receivers on multiple bands at the same time. Dual band FM radios often have this feature, so that you can monitor or scan VHF and UHF channels at the same time.

One of the real joys of operating a software defined radio is the ability to adjust the receiver bandwidth very precisely, in order to eliminate unwanted noise or interference. For example when you are listening to an SSB signal there is no point in having the receiver bandwidth set any wider than the signal that is being transmitted by the other station. Too much receiver bandwidth just makes the signal sound noisy. Too little cuts the audio frequency response. You can see exactly how wide the transmitted signal is by looking at the spectrum or waterfall display. You simply drag the shaded receiver bandwidth to be the same width as the waterfall image.

On most SDR transceivers, the panadapter is capable of displaying a representation of your transmitted signal while you are in transmitting mode. This can be helpful to ensure that your transmitted signal is not distorted.

Next, we need to define some terms for the panadapter display.

PANADAPTER BANDWIDTH

The panadapter bandwidth is the maximum frequency range that the panadapter can display on the computer screen. It is determined by the sampling rate of the digital signal. In 'generation three' and 'generation four' direct sampling radios, the panadapter bandwidth is usually an integer division of the sampling rate of the analog to digital converter. Depending on the radio model, these radios can display multiple panadapters from 384 kHz to more than 14 MHz wide. Most 'generation one' and 'two' designs can only display a single 48 kHz or 96 kHz wide panadapter. In this case, the displayed bandwidth is determined by the maximum sampling rate of your PC sound card, because it is working as the analog to digital converter. Choosing a different sampling rate changes the maximum panadapter bandwidth. Some software automatically adjusts the sampling rate as you zoom in to view narrower sections of the band of interest.

The Nyquist theorem states that as long as the sample rate is at least twice the rate of the highest frequency in the analog signal then the original analog signal can be recreated accurately from the digital data. Most PC sound cards can do a stereo analog to digital conversion at 48 ksps (48,000 samples per second), or 96 ksps (96,000 samples per second). Some elite sound cards can manage 192 ksps. To keep Mr. Nyquist happy, this means the maximum bandwidth that can be sampled with a sound card is 24 kHz, 48 kHz or maybe 96 kHz. But because the QSD Tayloe detector is acting as a mixer, both of the audio output streams contain signals from above the local oscillator frequency and signals from below the local oscillator frequency. Once these are separated and the image signals are cancelled, by using the 'phasing method,' our SDR receiver can display a spectrum 48 kHz, 96 kHz or 192 kHz wide.

Technical TIP: In a QSD type of SDR the maximum panadapter display bandwidth is equal to the sampling rate. This is often misunderstood because the formula for sampling 'Nyquist' bandwidth is BW=Fs/2, i.e. the maximum bandwidth is equal to the sample rate divided by two. The wider bandwidth is achievable because the QSD Tayloe detector is a single conversion receiver. Frequencies from above and below are mixed together in the detectors output. By using both the I and the Q signals, we can eliminate the image signals and show signals from both sides of the center frequency. In a QSD SDR, the maximum bandwidth is BW = Fs/2 + Fs/2, or simply BW=Fs.

In direct sampling software defined radios for the HF bands there is no mixer before the ADC, so the maximum bandwidth is Fs/2, i.e. half the sample rate of the ADC. The maximum panadapter bandwidth is usually a lot less than the receiver bandwidth due to limitations of the data path between the radio and the DSP.

Some direct sampling radios such as VHF and UHF transceiver boards have a mixer or a tuner before the ADC, so they are able to achieve the full Fs/2 + Fs/2 bandwidth. However, unless the DSP is being performed on the radio board, the final bandwidth that can be sent to the DSP software is limited by the data capacity of the Ethernet or USB interface.

PANADAPTER SPAN

You usually don't want to display the whole panadapter bandwidth on your PC screen. When you display the full bandwidth, the signals look too narrow and close together to easily select them individually.

You will probably want to zoom in, so that you limit the panadapter to display the wanted shortwave band, SSB band segment, digital mode, or CW part of the band. The part of the panadapter that you choose to show on the screen is known as the 'Span' of the display. It is usually fully adjustable from around 1 kHz displayed across the screen up to having the full panadapter bandwidth displayed.

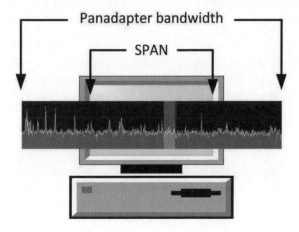

Figure 14: span is the part of the panadapter that is displayed

TIP: If you change the panadapter zoom level, it may be possible to have a receiver active on the panadapter that is not visible on the span that you are displaying. It can be confusing to hear a signal from a receiver that is no longer being displayed on the panadapter.

PANADAPTER RESOLUTION

How far you can zoom in before the display becomes degraded, is limited by the FFT (fast Fourier transformation) process that converts the signal from the time domain to the frequency domain. The bandwidth of each FFT output bin is dependent on the sample rate of the data being presented to the FFT stage and the number of bins that the FFT calculates. (For more on fast Fourier transformation, see the FFT magic chapter later).

A typical example would be a panadapter with a sample rate of 192,000 samples per second and an FFT of 2048 bins. This results in a bin width of around 93 Hz, so the panadapter or 'display' resolution is 93 Hz, $[F_R=F_S/N]$. If you are receiving two signals that are further apart than 93 Hz, you should be able to see or 'resolve' them both on the panadapter display. But, if the signals are closer than 93 Hz apart, you may not be able to separately identify them. One may be missed or the two may merge together on the display. Zooming in does not improve the situation; it just makes it look wider. The only way to improve the panadapter resolution is either to increase the panadapter sampling rate, or to increase the number of FFT bins.

If we have a 1024 pixel display screen and the span is set to the full 192 kHz panadapter bandwidth, the display will plot the level of every second FFT bin on the panadapter display. That is one dot per 187.5 Hz of input spectrum.

If you zoom inwards to a span of 96 kHz, the display plots 1024 FFT bins and the remaining 1024 bins are not displayed. At this 50% zoom level, the display is at the panadapter resolution. One dot per of 93 Hz of input spectrum. Of course, in this zoomed in condition you can only see half of the maximum panadapter bandwidth.

As you zoom in even further, the picture begins to become grainy and signals become less well defined. This is because some of the bins are being plotted more than once. By the time, you reach a span of 48 kHz, every displayed bin is being plotted twice. The display is showing two identical dots for every 93 Hz of input spectrum.

At very high zoom levels, i.e. very narrow spans, the signals on the panadapter look blocky. To improve the image quality at narrow spans you can either increase the sample rate or increase the number of FFT bins. Doubling either the bins or the sample rate halves the bin width and doubles the resolution. Unfortunately, this comes with a penalty. Increasing the FFT to 4096 bins or the sample rate to 384 kHz increases the time that it takes to calculate and display the panadapter. This increases the computer cpu loading and the time it takes to display the spectrum (signal latency).

PANADAPTER FREQUENCY

The panadapter frequency is the frequency that is at the center of the currently displayed Span. For a QSD receiver the panadapter frequency is usually the same as the frequency of the hardware oscillator, although some QSD radios use an offset of around 6 to 11 kHz to eliminate the DC spike on the display. For direct digital down conversion receivers, the panadapter center frequency is the same as the frequency the local oscillator. In this case, the local oscillator is a digital data stream created by a computer program running on the firmware inside the FPGA, tuner chip, or DSP section of the radio.

Some SDR programs display an indication of both the panadapter and the receiver frequency and others only display the panadapter frequency. The receiver frequency can and usually will be different from the panadapter frequency. This is different to what you would expect from a conventional radio, where the center of the band-scope is almost always at the radios frequency that the receiver is tuned to. It is more like digital mode operation where your received and transmitted signal is at an offset from the radio frequency.

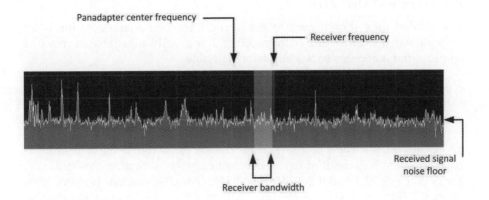

Panadapter center frequency

Receiver frequency

Received signal noise floor

Receiver bandwidth

Figure 15: more panadapter features

RECEIVER FREQUENCY

The panadapter shows many signals across the band, but you only want to listen to one or maybe two of them at a time. The receiver graphic is an indication of the part of the spectrum that is being passed to the demodulator software and associated filters. It shows the frequency and the bandwidth of the signal that you are listening to, as opposed to the panadapter center frequency.

The receiver frequency is depicted as a vertical line on the panadapter spectrum display. The position of the line on the panadapter is equivalent to the frequency that would be displayed on the frequency indicator of a conventional receiver. Usually a shaded area is displayed next to or on both sides of the receiver frequency. It indicates the receiver's bandwidth.

You can click the mouse on the screen to move between the signals that are displayed on the panadapter. Sometimes this moves the panadapter so that the receiver stays in the center of the display and sometimes the panadapter stays fixed and the receiver moves. With PowerSDR, you have the choice of either option. You may be more comfortable with one mode or the other, or you might use different settings for different situations.

You may be able to have two or more receivers active on the same panadapter. With headphones or stereo speakers, you can listen to the DX or contest station in one ear and the pileup in the other. This is actually surprisingly useful. Some software offers stereo effects such as CW signals that move from left to right as you tune up the band. This can give you a sense of spatial awareness about where the signals are in a CW pileup.

Some SDR software allows multiple receivers on the same panadapter.

RECEIVER BANDWIDTH

The shaded area shown next to the vertical receiver frequency line is an indication of the bandwidth of the receiver. It is usually adjustable in very fine steps so that it appears to be completely variable.

Normally you can adjust both the low and high frequency cut and can also shift the pass band. This is equivalent to adjusting the I.F. high and low cut, or the I.F. width and I.F. shift controls, on a conventional receiver.

Technical TIP: You would normally set the receiver bandwidth to the same width as the other station's transmitted signal, as indicated by the width of the waterfall trace. For SSB it will be between 2.4 kHz and 3 kHz. For CW, you will probably set it between 200 Hz and 500 Hz. Setting the SSB receiver bandwidth any wider than the transmitted signal unnecessarily increases the noise level on the signal you are listening to. Keep the bandwidth tight to maximize the signal to noise ratio.

Reducing the bandwidth so that it is narrower than the transmitted signal reduces the fidelity (quality) of the received signal, generally the high frequency audio response. This can be used as a technique to reduce splatter and interference from an overlapping QSO (signal).

Often there is more than one way to adjust the receiver bandwidth settings. Typically you can drag the edges of the shaded image with your computer mouse, adjust slider controls, or simply press an on-screen 'bandwidth' button.

By the way, many hams don't realize that you can change the pre-set bandwidth buttons for every mode on PowerSDR. Just right click any bandwidth button to change the preset high cut and low cut frequencies on any of the twelve buttons. You can also customize the button names to suit your needs. I configured my SSB bandwidth control buttons so that I have 2.4, 2.5, 2.6, 2.8 and 3 kHz pre-sets. I also set the low cut to 180 Hz on all of the SSB filters because it suits my sound system better than the default of 150 Hz. I renamed the DIGU filters to 'wide', 'medium', and 'narrow' since the actual bandwidth is not critical.

PANADAPTER NOISE FLOOR

The wiggly line at the bottom of the panadapter spectrum display represents the noise level that you are receiving with your particular antenna system. Its average level is commonly referred to as the 'noise floor'

Due to the magic of FFT (fast Fourier transformation), the noise floor displayed on the spectrum display should be well below the noise within the receiver pass-band, as indicated in dBm on the S meter (with no other signals present). This means that the panadapter will be able to display any signal that you can hear on the receiver.

If you disconnect the antenna, the displayed noise at the bottom of the panadapter should drop by around 10 to 20 dB. You will see the noise floor of the actual SDR receiver without any received noise. Ideally, the spectrum should be flat right across the panadapter with no spikes or signals.

The noise level that is displayed when the antenna is disconnected is mostly dependent on:

- The signal to noise ratio of the analog to digital converter. (This is related to the ENOB, not the number of bits that the ADC uses to describe the sampled voltage levels).

- The sampling rate of the analog to digital converter. (Unless frequency shifting or under-sampling is in use, this also determines the maximum frequency of the receiver).

- The decimation ratio from the ADC sampling rate down to the sample rate of the displayed panadapter.

- The FFT bin width and windowing filter shape factor.

When you connect the antenna, the noise level rises because you are receiving atmospheric and electrical noise and interference on top of the noise being generated inside the radio. Generally, the noise level will be higher in urban areas and lower in rural areas. If the level of the noise displayed at the bottom of the panadapter does not rise when you connect the antenna, the receiver is not good enough to display very weak signals that are just above the ambient noise level at your location.

A typical noise level for urban areas is -103 dBm. The typical noise level for rural areas is -109 dBm. The actual noise level you see at your house, with your antenna connected, is dependent on the effectiveness of your antenna system and the level of electrical noise at your location.

Exceptionally large incoming signals appearing at the input of the analog to digital converter can cause ADC gain compression, which results in a higher noise level being displayed right across the panadapter. The noise floor may jump erratically. This happens even if the offending signals are outside of the bandwidth currently being displayed by the panadapter, so you probably will not be able to see the interference signals on the display. Receivers that do not have band-pass filters before the analog to digital converter and radios using 8 bit ADCs, which have much less dynamic range to begin with are more likely to suffer from this effect.

A high noise floor limits the dynamic range of the receiver. The dynamic range is the difference in dB between the clipping level, which is the maximum level that the receiver can handle without severe distortion and the noise floor, which is the minimum signal that you can hear on the receiver.

WIDEBAND DISPLAY

A wideband panadapter will typically show the entire frequency range of the receiver on a single panadapter. The displayed resolution is much lower than the standard panadapter display. The wideband display is used to provide an indication of band activity rather than to display individual narrowband signals. Say for example the wideband display covers up to 61.44 MHz and the display window is 1024 pixels across. That would mean that each dot on the panadapter display is at a spacing of one dot per 60 kHz. Normally there are more FFT bins than dots on the display, so each displayed dot represents the peak level of a group of several bins. This gives the wideband spectrum display a 'peak hold' effect.

In comparison, a typical 192 kHz wide standard panadapter, created from the IQ data streams, can display signals that are spaced at 187.5 Hz apart. On the standard panadapter, you will be able to see individual AM or SSB signals. You may need to zoom in a bit further to ensure that you can see every individual CW signal. As you zoom in you can see more detail, but there is a limit.

In the Hermes and Apache Labs ANAN radios, the data that is sent to the PC for the wideband display is not the same as the IQ signal that is used for the standard panadapter, DSP, and demodulation. The data for the wideband display is sent as 'EP4' data frames, which contain a 1024 byte data payload direct from the ADC. Each frame carries 512, sixteen bit, ADC samples.

The data is held in a buffer until either 4096 or 16,384 samples have been received. There are two options for the display of the wideband spectrum. The larger buffer uses a bigger FFT and this puts a higher loading on the computer. For this example, we will consider the version using the smaller buffer. After being converted to a spectrum using the FFT process, each frame represents the signals across the whole HF spectrum, $Fs/2 = 61.44$ MHz.

The EP4 frames are not sent to the PC very often, so the required data capacity is small. The wideband display is refreshed at the same rate as the main spectrum and waterfall displays, (approx. 1 to 50 times per second). If the 4096 word buffer is selected, the EP4 frames are received from the radio at eight times the display refresh rate and if the 16,384 word buffer is selected, the EP4 frames are received from the radio at 32 times the display refresh rate.

The data rate from the receiver for a wideband display, refresh rate of 1 to 50 frames per second with a 4096 sample buffer is only 65.536 kbits to 3.277 Mbits.

The data rate from the receiver for a wideband display, refresh rate of 1 to 50 frames per second with a 16,384 sample buffer is only 262.144 kbits to 13.107 Mbits.

In this example, the FFT for the wideband display uses 4096 bins. This is twice the number of bins used for the main panadapter, because in that case the FFT has to manage both the, I stream and the Q stream. The wideband display is created from a single data stream. At the output of the FFT, there are 4096 frequency bins, one for every 15 kHz of received spectrum. The display is 1024 pixels wide, so the maximum level of each group of four samples is converted to a logarithmic (dB) scale and plotted on the display. The display resolution is one dot for every 60 kHz of received spectrum (4 x 15 kHz).

If we had selected the 16,384 samples buffer, the bins would have been spaced at 3.75 kHz. The maximum level of each group of 16 samples is plotted on the display. The display resolution is still one dot for every 60 kHz of received spectrum (16 x 3.75 kHz). The displayed level of some of the 1024 displayed dots (pixels) might be a tiny fraction different as the 'peak hold' is over more, closer spaced, bins.

Note that PowerSDR mRX cannot display a wideband spectrum display. However, other SDR software for ANAN / Hermes including Kiss Konsole and cuSDR can.

PANADAPTER DISPLAY

On most SDR receivers, the main panadapter is built from the same IQ data that is used for the DSP and demodulation. The display resolution changes if you change the sample rate. The FlexRadio 6000 series of radios do their DSP and demodulation inside the radio so the data that is sent to the PC is just graphics information used for the panadapter display.

In the Hermes and Apache Labs ANAN radios, the FFT for the panadapter produces 2048 bins. The number of bin levels that are displayed as pixels on the screen depends on the span (zoom level). The panadapter display resolution depends on the panadapter sample rate. Either data stream can be used to create the panadapter. Generally the I stream is used.

INFORMATION DISPLAYED ON THE PANADAPTER

The spectrum display shows frequencies across the screen and the levels of received signals on the vertical axis. The waterfall display shows frequencies across the screen, with the levels depicted as brighter colors. The vertical axis of the waterfall shows the signals at earlier times. It depicts a history of the received signals.

Have a look at the panadapter image on page 71. At the top there are numbers indicating the range of frequencies being displayed. You can zoom in to show a narrower range in more detail, or out to the maximum panadapter bandwidth to show a wider range of frequencies. The maximum bandwidth of the panadapter is determined by the IQ sample rate, which is always an integer division of the ADC sampling frequency.

The numbers at the left side of the spectrum display indicate the received signal level in dBm. You can adjust the maximum and minimum levels shown on the display by changing setup settings or in some SDR software by dragging the spectrum display axis with your computer mouse.

Note that the levels indicted on the spectrum display are the levels within the FFT bin bandwidth, not the levels inside the receiver bandwidth. The noise floor in the receiver pass-band should be higher than the noise floor displayed on the panadapter. This means that if you can hear a signal on the receiver you will also be able to see it on the panadapter display.

MAKING THE MOST OF THE PANADAPTER AND WATERFALL

You can choose to display either the spectrum or the waterfall, but most hams prefer to display both at the same time because they tell you different things. The panadapter spectrum display shows you the amplitude of signals across the band of interest. You can see how wide each signal is and on SSB or AM, you get an indication of how flat the transmitted audio is. If you zoom in so that the signal is a couple of cm wide on the screen, you can see high or low frequency roll off in the modulated signal. You can see the effect of splatter caused by a poor linearity transmitter or linear amplifier as a wider than normal transmission. More importantly, you can see interference signals from other stations, carriers, Ionosondes, over the horizon radar, pirates, and in my case spikes from my ADSL router. When you can see these interfering signals, you have a good start on adjusting your receiver bandwidth and other settings to minimize the problem. For example, you can precisely locate a manual notch filter, adjust the receiver bandwidth, or set a noise filter.

Technical TIP: The spectrum display is very fast. I find it less irritating to leave the averaging function turned on. It slows down the flicker from the noise displayed on the spectrum display. If it still bugs you, adjust the display so that the noise floor is not showing on the screen.

The waterfall adds the dimension of time. It shows a history of the signals that have been on the panadapter. Strong signals are shown as bright colors and weaker signals as weaker colors. The background noise level should be very dark or black. One or two models allow you to scroll the waterfall image even further back in time, to show signals that are no longer being displayed.

You can display the waterfall with a range of different color palettes including grey scale. Everyone has their favorite, so try them out. Changing the waterfall levels alters the color range and the contrast between weak and strong signals. Especially on CW, it can show very weak signals that are so far down in the noise you can't see them on the spectrum display. FlexRadio Systems has a video online that shows how effective the waterfall display can be for weak signal work.

You can tell a lot from the waterfall display. Bursts of color indicate short transmissions such as a CQ call. CW signals can almost be read off the screen and you can definitely see a 'clicky' signal as small horizontal streaks at the start and end of the 'dits' and 'dahs'. Stronger signals are represented by brighter colors like orange or yellow and weaker levels are more subdued. With SSB signals, you can sometimes tell if the operator is a woman because their signal has more power (brighter colors) in the higher frequencies and less in the lower audio range close to the carrier frequency.

It is easy to differentiate between PSK and RTTY transmissions by looking at the shape and width of the waterfall tracks. You can see the exact width of a transmitted signal and if two signals are overlapping. Signals that are changing frequency show as diagonal streaks of color and lightning or noise bursts show as bright horizontal bands across the display.

Noise on a frequency will show as a fuzzy brighter region down the screen and stray carriers as a bright vertical line.

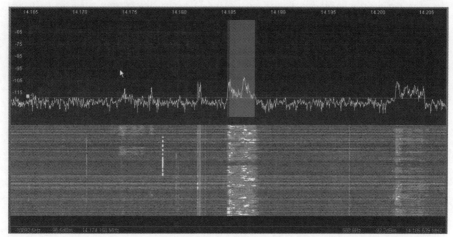

Figure 16: a spectrum & waterfall panadapter can show many interesting things

The spectrum is drawn like the trace on an oscilloscope from left to right across the display. A complete waterfall line is normally added to the waterfall image immediately after each spectrum line has been displayed. You can usually adjust the number of times per second that the spectrum and waterfall is redrawn on the panadapter. This is called the 'frame' rate.

The panadapter image shows three upper sideband SSB signals with differing signal strengths. You can see from the shaded part of the panadapter that the operator is listening to the strongest signal. The waterfall indicates that there was a CW signal at about 14.178 MHZ. The lack of a corresponding signal on the panadapter spectrum indicates that it has stopped transmitting. It was probably someone setting up a linear amplifier prior to calling CQ. You can see two weak fixed carriers and an interference signal just to the left of the receiver slice probably from my ADSL router.

The receiver bandwidth as indicated by the shaded section on the spectrum display has been adjusted to almost the same bandwidth as the transmitted signal, which is clearly shown on the waterfall display. Note the small 150 Hz gap between the lower cut off, of the receiver bandwidth and the receiver frequency indicated by the vertical line. At the top of the panadapter are the frequencies included in the displayed span. You can zoom in for more detail or out to show more of the band. The numbers on the left of the spectrum display indicate the scale of displayed levels in dBm.

The 'banding' across the waterfall is caused by variations in the amount of the received wideband background noise. Ignition noise from nearby cars tends to look like repetitive bright dashes across the waterfall. Lightening crashes look like wider bright bar and are often accompanied by a jump in the panadapter spectrum display, caused by ADC gain compression.

USING A PANADAPTER TO SHOW INTERFERENCE AND DISTORTION

The spectrum display on a software defined radio is basically the same as the display on a spectrum analyzer, so your SDR can double as a radio test set. Spectrum analyzers display the signal amplitude on the Y-axis and frequency on the X-axis, the same as the SDR panadapter does. With software like PowerSDR, the panadapter vertical axis is marked in dBm and it is pretty accurate, so you can make the same sort of comparison measurements as you would with a spectrum analyzer. Some useful features are missing such as the ability to add marker frequencies and have the test set measure the difference in frequency and amplitude between them. Nevertheless, it is still a very useful tool for looking at interference signals. You can also monitor the quality of your own transmitter signal. Unlike most spectrum analyzers, you also get a waterfall display, which can show interference in the time and frequency domain at the same time.

SDRs are great for helping to identify the type of modulation being used by intruders on the bands. Digital modes all have their own individual 'look' on the spectrum and waterfall displays. The bandwidth and pulse duration can be read from the waterfall axis.

A waterfall can indicate what type of digital mode is being transmitted. PSK looks like a railway track. Wider PSK indicates that a faster baud rate is being used (PSK63 or PSK128). RTTY also shows as two lines but the spacing is wider due to the 170 Hz tone offset. Modes like JT65 and Domino use tones sent in sequence so they look like little dots climbing stairs. Radio Fax, digital transmissions, SSTV and phase shift modes all have distinctive images on the waterfall. With CW, you can see the individual dits and dahs as short and longer lines. You may even be able to read the Morse code off the screen.

The spectrum display can show wideband noise from devices like LED lighting, plasma TVs, or other interference signals. You can see if a ham has a badly adjusted transmitter causing splatter across the band. In fact, you can see exactly how wide each SSB transmission is, or if a transmitter is off frequency. If you are in a contest, you can see fixed carriers or stations transmitting on top of other stations. Stations that are 'tuning up' show clearly on the spectrum and the waterfall as a fixed carrier or CW signal.

Signals that are being swept across a band of frequencies show as a diagonal line on the waterfall and as a 'bunny' that hops across the spectrum display. You can also tell what the normal received noise level is at your location. This is handy to know if you ever experience wide band noise problems.

As a PSK operator, I often see over modulated PSK signals on the waterfall display. They look like a wider than normal PSK signal with horizontal streaks flecking away from the sides. A clean PSK signal looks like a fuzzy railway track. You can see the same signal on the waterfall display of your digital mode software, but filtering in the software may hide the distortion caused by over modulation. CW key clicks look interesting. They appear on the waterfall as horizontal streaks at the top or bottom of each dit or dah.

SOFTWARE DISTRIBUTION METHODS

Commercial – you pay for the software when you order it. Normally the source code is proprietary and is not available to the 'general public.' The companion commercial software for particular radio models may be shipped with the radio or made available as a free download from the vendor when you purchase a radio.

Shareware – you can download (or order) the software and pay for it after you have tried it out. Usually there is an incentive to register the software and send the author or distributor a payment. Either the full functionality is not available in the unregistered version, or the software will stop working after a period of time. Normally the source code is proprietary and not available to the 'general public.' But software can be both open source and shareware.

Freeware - you can download (or order) the software and use it for free. But the source code may not be available to the public.

Open source – software developed and distributed under the open source rules. Very often you can download (or order) the software and use it for free, but charges can apply. Not all open source software is freeware. Even if the product is available free of charge there may be a charge for the CD and postage. The source code must be available to other developers.

OPEN SOURCE SDR SOFTWARE

A lot of the software that is available for use with your SDR hardware has been produced under the 'open source' rules. Even when the software is a commercial proprietary product, external open source .dll files or APIs may allow you to use your SDR with their product. Firstly, I had better explain what 'open source' means.

"Open source software is software that can be freely used, changed, and shared (in modified or unmodified form) by anyone. Open source software is made by many people and distributed under licenses that comply with the open source Definition." http://opensource.org/.

The open sources rules allow software developers to use software code developed by others in their own software programs. This is tremendously beneficial as it saves everyone from having to 'reinvent the wheel.' The programmer can choose to give away the resulting software application or they can sell it, but the rules state that they must make their source code available to others under the same terms as the license of the original software. There are other rules mostly relating to fairness and non-discrimination. See http://opensource.org/definition for the full definition.

Open source software is terrific because, depending on the SDR that you are using, you may be able to try several different programs with your radio. It also means that the software evolves and extends as other developers contribute new ideas or upgrades to the software code. You may be able to suggest improvements or cool new ideas, which might eventually be incorporated into new revisions. The radio astronomy and PureSignal transmit pre-distortion upgrades to power SDR mRX PS are very good examples of this type of collaboration. Hermann von Hasseln DL3HVH updated his cuSDR program to incorporate the new WDSP library written by Warren Pratt, NR0V. WDSP is already used in the latest versions of PowerSDR. This spirit of sharing makes SDR development much faster and much cheaper. The developers can concentrate on interesting new stuff and everybody wins.

"A report by the Standish Group (from 2008) states that adoption of open-source software models has resulted in savings of about $60 billion per year to consumers." *http://en.wikipedia.org/wiki/Open-source_software*.

Most open source software is developed by amateur developers for free and there is no guarantee of any future support or bug fixes. Surprisingly, given the challenges for developers who have only their leisure time for programming, open source software programs such as PowerSDR mRX, cuSDR, SDR#, HDSDR and many, many, others is extremely well written and performs very well indeed. In most cases the developers seem to be very approachable, interested in extending the software and responsive to constructive criticism and requests.

"Open-source software (OSS) is computer software with its source code made available with a license in which the copyright holder provides the rights to study change and distribute the software to anyone and for any purpose. Open-source software is very often developed in a public, collaborative manner." *http://en.wikipedia.org/wiki/Open-source_software*.

In many SDR software applications the developers have reused open source DSP code, which is responsible for the filtering, modulation and demodulation functions. The spectrum display and some filters rely on very complex mathematical fast Fourier transformations (FFT). Luckily, the software for performing FFT calculations is provided free of charge, as open source .dll files. Many SDR computer programs use the FFTW .dll file.

"The Fastest Fourier Transform in the West (FFTW) is a software library for computing discrete Fourier transforms (DFTs) developed by Matteo Frigo and Steven G. Johnson at the Massachusetts Institute of Technology.

FFTW is known as the fastest free software implementation of the Fast Fourier transform (FFT) algorithm (upheld by regular benchmarks). It can compute transforms of real and complex-valued arrays of arbitrary size and dimension..." *http://en.wikipedia.org/wiki/FFTW*

One down side of using open source software is that because you didn't pay for the software, you can't expect individual support, or any guarantee that it will even work on your particular computer and radio setup. However, all of the widely used packages have online forums where you can ask for help.

The open source developers are enthusiastic about adding new features and extending the ways that SDR technology can be used. Sometimes they are less enthusiastic about the mundane things like providing a user manual. I find it rather frustrating when new revisions of the software introduce new features and setup options which I don't understand or know how to use. This is less of a problem with simple SDR programs as they don't have a lot of setup options. Pretty much all SDR programs do have a 'Help' menu covering at least the major functions.

OPEN SOURCE .DLL FILES

One of the 'spin offs' of the open software approach is the ability to add 'patches' or 'add-ons' to existing software. An example of this is the various flavors of *extio.dll*, which allow various software defined radios to work with already existing SDR applications. For example, the installation of the correct extio.dll into the program directory of many SDR programs will allow you to use them with the RTL dongles. The *extio.dll* provides an interface between the data that the radio is sending out of the USB port and the type of data structure that the software is expecting to see.

This patch approach only works if the original SDR program developer has incorporated the possibility of it being present, into their code.

The program must do something like; "*go and look in the program directory for a file called extio.dll. If it exists, run the code inside it. If it does not exist, carry on without it.*" This is why there are several versions of extio.dll with the same file name but intended for use with different radios. You have to download the one that is intended for your radio.

A .dll is a 'dynamic link library' file. It is used on computers, which are running a Windows operating system. It contains one or more software programs or subroutines, which can be accessed or 'called' from another piece of software. They can also contain data files or other resources like constants. The intention is to avoid re-work. Rather than 'cut-n-pasting' the same pieces of software code into every application that a developer writes, they can put a lot of useful code blocks into a .dll file. The routines inside the .dll file can be called from the main software program. Also, the .dll file can be made available to other software developers.

SharpDSP by Phil Covington, WDSP by Warren Pratt, and FFTW by Matteo Frigo and Steven G. Johnson are all examples of open source software that is made available to developers in the form of .dll files.

The .dll file needs to be in a location where the calling program can find it. Traditionally they are placed in one of the Windows System directories where any program can find them, but they might be in the same directory as the SDR program or other application. In that case, only the calling program will be able to find the .dll file. The *extio.dll* file usually resides in the program directory because there may be several different versions of it on your PC.

API (APPLICATION PROGRAMMING INTERFACE)

An API is a set of rules, published as a standard or document that are intended to formalize a method of interfacing with a software application.

A modern SDR has several layers of computing, which means that there may be more than one level at which a software developer can interface with the radio hardware.

The radio hardware normally uses a USB or Ethernet interface to connect to the PC, so that is often the first point that a PC software developer can access the data and control signals. They can write a completely new software application that reads the data from the Ethernet or USB port and writes back control information. If the radio is a transceiver, the audio for transmission can also be sent to the radio hardware. The new application could interface with the 'native' SDR program or completely replace it. But first, the software guru needs to understand the way that the data is being carried over the USB or Ethernet cable, which is known as the 'protocol.' They also need to know the format of the data, which is known as the frame structure. The protocol usually follows a known data standard, for example, UDP or TCP-IP, but the data format may be unique to any particular type of radio. At this basic hardware level an API would consist of tables describing the data frame structures and the control information. As well as information about how the radio will respond to commands.

In addition or alternatively, there may be a higher level of interface, where the developer can query and receive data or control information from the SDR software application.

I guess you could say that the CAT (computer aided transceiver) commands that are sent from digital mode and logging programs to the radio are a kind of high level API. A CAT implementation uses a table of commands that can be sent to the SDR program and a list of responses and data that will be returned. If you know the CAT command structure you can write your own program to control the SDR program and hence the radio. The difference is that a real API allows you to control the radio in the same way as the client program. You get full access to the radio rather than the restricted commands that CAT offers. API access would usually be much faster because CAT is done over a slow serial connection and is a low priority for the microcomputer in the radio, or the SDR program.

You might use the API interface to replace the existing GUI so that your new program changes the way that the SDR looks and operates. Or you might just add a new filter or mode. In the future, the most common use of the API will be to add an interface into logging or digital mode applications. In other words replacing the CAT interface with a more integrated and faster way of getting status and control information to and from the radio. One developer is using the FlexRadio API to add the FreeDV (Codec II) digital voice mode written by David Rowe, to the Signature series radios. Another possibility would be to add a built in CW, PSK or RTTY decoder and memory keyer.

LATEST TRENDS

The latest trend is to write 'client / server' SDR programs. The traditional SDR program is split into two new programs with different functions.

The server program resides on a PC that is physically connected via USB or Ethernet to the radio hardware. Alternatively, it might be running on a computer board or a microprocessor housed inside or near the radio. The sever program usually has no direct user access. Its job is to act as a channel between the radio and the client software.

The SDR client software may be running on the same computer as the server, or on another computer connected to the same computer network via an Ethernet cable or Wi-Fi. It might even be on a remote computer connected via the Internet. The SDR client does all of the display and control 'GUI' functions. The server typically does the DSP and signal routing. An API will be written to describe the data requirements and controls between the client and the server.

In the future, it will be possible to have more than one client application connected to a server at the same time. An API would be written to describe the data requirements and control instructions for communication between the client and the server. Different developers may write specialist client software for the same radio server software and the server may work with a range of different radio hardware. For example, you might use PowerSDR and cuSDR at the same time, to monitor different bands on different computer devices.

You might be able to listen for 6m band openings on your phone, while talking to a station on 20m SSB in your shack, while the XYL is listening to the BBC on a notebook PC in the lounge.

Maybe you don't want to do all of that, but the client / server architecture does have several advantages. Firstly, the server can do much of the DSP work. There will be a large continuous amount of data flowing between the radio hardware and the server program. But data between the server application and the client can be much reduced. It only needs to carry the graphics for the actual panadapters being displayed, audio in both directions, information data like the S meter and frequency readouts, and the control commands (like volume, filter width etc.). Less data allows you to use less powerful computers like phones, Netbooks, or tablets and Wi-Fi connected or Internet connected devices.

A range of developers could provide client software designed to work with the server. This would mean faster development time, as they only need to create a GUI. The difficult DSP and FFT code will be in the server program. You could have a choice of user interface styles based around the same server program and radio. Your favorite digital mode program could talk directly to the server, without having to work through SDR software.

FlexRadio Systems have already followed this route for their Signature 6000 range of transceivers and the 6700R receiver. Their developers wanted to create a radio that was capable of being operated by any computer connected to a computer network. They were aware that the huge amount of data required would be a severe limitation especially for wireless and Internet networking so they moved to a server / client design. The FlexRadio has a powerful ARM processor and DSP chips inside the radio. These act as the server. The SmartSDR software running on the PC acts as the client. You can run SmartSDR on several devices and they will all be able to control the radio.

Although the SmartSDR is a proprietary application (not open source) and the source code is closed to the public, FlexRadio have generously allowed for three levels of API access. This is interesting because it will allow software developers to write open source software applications that will work seamlessly with the closed source FlexRadio SmartSDR software. In this way, the wider SDR community will be able to develop new capabilities for the new FlexRadios. The ability to add customization will keep the radio fresh and stimulate innovation without pushing up the price. I am sure that Flex users will welcome the ability to add to what is already a first class package.

Very soon DX cluster, logging, skimmer, and digital mode programs will be able to interface directly with your software defined radio without using CAT control. The result will be fully integrated programs where the radio can be operated quickly and smoothly from your other applications.

The PureSignal transmitter pre-distortion system dramatically improves the transmitter intermodulation performance of SDR transmitters, so I am sure that it will be incorporated into other HF SDR transceivers from now on. PureSignal relies on the software defined radio being full duplex (able to receive and transmit simultaneously) and having a wide (48 kHz) transmit baseband.

CESSB (controlled envelope SSB modulation) is another enhancement that is available on the latest HF SDR transceivers. CESSB is a way of maximizing the talk power of your SSB signal. It works like a commander but it is impossible to overdrive the modulator. There is no clipping and overshoot is controlled. Your average transmitted power is almost double. That is like adding another Yagi on top of your existing antenna. Both of these advancements are possible due to the fact that the signals to be transmitted are digital signals, which can be manipulated by software before being converted to analog and transmitted. The computing power that is available is another factor. CESSB could be implemented in conventional radios with DSP, provided there is sufficient number crunching capability in the radio.

DFC (direct Fourier conversion) is not a "latest trend" yet, in fact, it is still very much at an embryonic experimental stage. Only a handful of people know anything about it. But I think that DFC will be a 'game changer,' in the same way that the move from QSD architecture to DDC direct sampling was.

AUDIO CONNECTIONS FOR DIGITAL MODES

It is very common to connect the auxiliary audio input and output from your transceiver to your PC sound card, so that you can use digital mode software to send and receive RTTY, PSK, JT65, SSTV, Packet, CW, FreeDV and many other formats. This usually involves the installation a cable between the radio and the PC sound card, or perhaps plugging in a USB sound card interface.

With software defined radios, the audio section of your receiver or transceiver is being implemented in the PC software. This presents a problem when we want to interface the radio for digital mode operation. Yes, you can send the audio from the radio out of the sound card to speakers and you can input audio into the transmitter via the sound card as well. But using that method, you would need another sound card to get the audio signal back into the PC for the digital modes program. It is better to connect the audio signals directly between the SDR software and the digital mode software without having to use any cables. FlexRadio includes an integrated utility for managing the audio interconnect. But strangely, this functionality is not usually built directly into open source SDR software. A separate utility program to provide interconnection of the audio signals is needed.

VIRTUAL AUDIO CABLES

VAC (virtual audio cable) is commercial software provided by Eugene Muzychenko. http://software.muzychenko.net/eng/vac.htm. VAC works like an additional sound card on your PC. It does not use the physical sound card at all. It remains available for other programs.

Using VAC is like having cables between the radio (SDR software) and the digital mode software. You have to set up two 'audio cables,' using the VAC setup software. This only has to be done once. After that, you set the SDR software to output audio on VAC cable 1 and the Digital mode software to receive the audio on VAC cable 1. Likewise, you set the SDR software to receive audio on VAC cable 2 and the Digital mode software to send the audio to the radio on VAC cable 2.

You are encouraged to download the free trial version before paying to register the program. There are three options at differing prices; no support, basic support, and full support. I went for the cheaper 'no support' option and have had no problems. Note that the trial version has an annoying embedded voice message, so you really do have to register the software before you can use VAC for transmitting digital mode signals.

VAC can also be used to connect other programs. For example, you can use it to record Skype conversations by sending the audio to a sound recording program.

VB-Audio offers an alternative to VAC. There are two options; VB-Cable and HiFi-Cable See http://vb-audio.pagesperso-orange.fr/Cable/index.htm. VB-Audio is 'donation ware'. If you use the software, please make a donation to the developer so that he is encouraged to write more great programs. You get one 'cable' for free and additional 'cables' are available for a small donation. HiFi Audio is similar except that it is more configurable and can support higher sampling rates. VB-Cable it is easy to get working. After the initial installation, apart from pointing the applications at the new virtual sound card, there is no setup required.

IQ OUTPUT FROM POWERSDR AND OTHER PROGRAMS

Some SDR software can send IQ data to other programs. PowerSDR can output two IQ signals to other software via VAC (or similar). FlexRadio SmartSDR can send up to four IQ data streams via the DAX interface. The ExpertSDR2 software can also send two channels of IQ data to another application. Other programs may have similar ability. These IQ audio signals can be used by other SDR software applications, perhaps to decode specialist modes like DRM short-wave broadcasts or for CW Skimmer.

DAX - DIGITAL AUDIO EXCHANGE

DAX is the audio interconnection manager provided with SmartSDR for the new FlexRadio 6000 radios. It is much more powerful than the audio interconnection programs currently used with other radios.

DAX provides eight virtual audio output cables for the FLEX-6700 and FLEX-6700R, The FLEX-6500 and FLEX-6600 have four virtual audio cables to match its four available receiver slices. The FLEX-6400 and the FLEX-6300 have two virtual audio cables. DAX can route audio to and from programs on any computer device connected to your local network. This allows you to listen to audio from receiver slice one on one PC, while another device decodes RTTY at a different location. Depending on the radio, you can have up to eight receiver slices connected to eight different digital mode programs at the same time.

DAX also provides up to four audio IQ channels. The IQ channels are output only and they provide up to 384 ksps of data. This could be used as a single 384 kHz wide spectrum, two 192 kHz spectrums, or four 96 kHz spectrums. Note that the FLEX-6300 only has two DAX IQ channels up to 96 kHz wide. The IQ outputs can be used to display panadapters on different computers, or to run CW Skimmer and other SDR software.

Technical TIP: Windows defaults to an audio sample rate of 44.1 kHz, which is the standard for CD audio. The connection works best when set to a multiple of the 24 kHz sample rate used by SmartSDR. It is suggested that you change the sample rate on all DAX audio RX, DAX audio TX, DAX reserved audio RX, and DAX reserved audio TX channels to a 48 kHz sample rate.

SDR FOR SHORT WAVE LISTENING

A lot of software defined radios are used for listening to the shortwave bands and for listening to other interesting signals like the aircraft band or the marine band. You can also listen to commercial traffic and unencrypted military communications. There is also a wealth of other special interest transmissions, which are of interest to some people. Aircraft ADS-B positioning information can be presented on maps showing commercial flights. ACARS text data has information sent from air crew to the ground stations. Maritime VHF AIS beacons indicate ship name, cargo, and position information.

Software defined radios are great for short wave listening. You get great performance and often a much wider frequency range. Most SDR software has good noise suppression filters, which are important when you want to listen to broadcast quality audio like music and news. Another big advantage is that you can set the bandwidth to match the signal that you are listening to. The AM filters in older receivers designed for SSB may be too narrow and not adjustable. Being able to adjust the receiver's bandwidth precisely means that you don't have to listen to noise from outside of the transmitted signal. Being able to increase the bandwidth past 3 kHz means that you can listen to the full fidelity of the AM signal. The audio sounds much nicer. Also, software defined radios have a better ability to drag out weak signals that are near large signals they are less prone to intermodulation distortion.

AM, SAM, DRM, DAB

There are a dwindling number of commercial AM broadcast stations on the HF short wave bands. Many of the remaining ones are religious stations and some countries still broadcast general music, news, weather, and current affairs. The BBC, Radio Australia, and Radio New Zealand International are some of the broadcasters still broadcasting 24 hours a day on several frequencies. The frequencies are changed during the period to maximize the reach into various regions as daily propagation changes. You can check out http://shortwaveschedule.com/ for shortwave schedules. The main reference book for SWLs (short wave listeners) is, 'The World Radio and TV Handbook.'

SAM is an acronym for synchronous amplitude modulation. The SAM mode is useful when the received signal is fading because the resultant audio doesn't suffer from the loss of intelligibility during fading that the audio from a normal AM envelope detector does. The SAM detector in your SDR software uses a different algorithm to demodulate the AM broadcast signal. Rather than using a simple 'envelope detector' the SAM detector phase-locks to the transmitted AM carrier and then uses a beat frequency oscillator with product detection.

DRM stands for Digital Radio Mondiale (French and Italian for World). It is a method of sending MPEG-4 coded digital audio signals over HF or VHF radios. DRM is widely used in Europe and it has replaced many of the old AM shortwave broadcast stations. DRM can deliver FM-comparable sound quality on frequencies below 30 MHz and there is a different DRM+ variant for VHF frequencies. It is rapidly becoming the standard for digital broadcast radio, competing with DAB and satellite bases systems. DRM is more spectrally efficient than AM or FM and this allows more stations to share the band. Most DRM stations are in band I (47 to 68 MHz), band II (87.5 to 108 MHz) and band III (174 to 240 MHz). Most people use the Dream program to decode DRM with their software defined radio. Winrad, SoDiRa, Fraunhofer DRM, and DRM Discoverer are other options.

The DRM coding is quite complex and most SDR software does not support the DRM mode directly. Even when it has been demodulated, the audio is still in an MPEG format. However, you can connect the audio from your SDR to a specialist DRM decoder in the same way as connecting to a digital mode program. The Elad FDM-S1 model has DRM integrated into the receiver.

DAB+ is Digital Audio Broadcast. It is another digital format for radio broadcasting. It is not used below 30 MHz and is typically allocated to channels between 174–240 MHz and between 1.452 – 1.492 MHz. SDR-J seems to be the only open source SDR software for DAB.

FAX AND WEATHER FAX

You can decode unencrypted commercial radio fax and weather fax pictures. Some of these are on the HF bands and some use satellite downlinks. Software defined radios are excellent for receiving the 137 MHz NOAA weather satellites because you need a wide band FM receiver. Unlike software defined radios, most VHF communications receivers and amateur band transceivers capable of receiving 137 MHz only have narrow band FM.

There are weather fax transmissions on many HF frequencies. Radiofax is also known as HF FAX, or WEFAX, although WEFAX is also used to describe satellite downlink based systems. Reception of WEFAX requires an SSB receiver. Note that the published frequencies for weather fax refer to the frequencies marked on dedicated weather receivers. An SSB radio should be tuned for upper sideband at 1.9 kHz below the nominated frequency.

APRS

APRS is the amateur radio positioning system. It includes position and other data relating to; ham radio operators, experimental balloon and rocket flights, vessels using inland waterways and seaports, and even satellites. APRS is also used by amateur weather station operators, so you can use it to check the real time weather conditions at various locations around your city or elsewhere.

SDR FOR CW

There has been a lot of criticism of the CW performance of software defined radios. This is partly due to the way that CW used to be created by the SDR software and partly due to a reluctance to adapt to new technology. Most of the early problems have been eliminated. These days CW operators can expect excellent performance from SDR transceivers.

The historical problems were caused by latency, which in this case is the delay between the time the Morse key is pressed and the time that the computer takes to process and send the CW signal.

The issues were:

- Delay between CW 'key down' and the time that the 'side-tone' is heard. This really upsets your ability to send CW while listening to the 'side-tone.'

- Delay between CW 'key down' and the time that the signal is transmitted. This is annoying and it could cost you contacts in a pressure situation like trying to work a rare DX station in a pile up.

- Slow change over from transmit to receive and receive to transmit. This limits the speed of QSK operation and it could potentially cause stations to 'double.'

It is a pity that these historical problems have limited the acceptance of software defined radios by CW operators, because they are mostly fixed now and there are significant advantages in using an SDR for CW operation. Using the waterfall and panadapter spectrum displays you can see the strength and quality of each CW signal on the band. This allows you to easily, skip from station to station across the band. Tuning each signal is a breeze. Just click on each station on the waterfall. The very narrow filters allow you to listen to only a single CW signal without hearing other QSOs. At the same time, you can run CW Skimmer or other software like MRP40 and see all of the activity on the band, or on several bands.

Technical TIP: These CW issues have been fixed in the latest firmware and software releases for the main 100 W transceivers, (SmartSDR for FlexRadios, PowerSDR mRX for the ANAN radios, and ExpertSD2 for the Expert Electronics MB1).

The old problem was that the CW signal was generated by SSB modulating an audio tone created by the SDR software running on the PC. This meant that the radio had to detect the Morse key operation, run the raw CW signal through the keyer software on the radio to trim the dit or dah length and spacing and then send it over the Ethernet or USB interface to the PC.

The PC software had to detect the information and create bursts of tone, suitably tailored to eliminate key clicks. This was then sent back to the radio to be transmitted. All of this takes time and the speed is limited by the capacity of the data path between the radio and the PC and by the processing power of the PC.

The solution was to eliminate the traditional method of generating CW as an audio tone and instead to generate it directly at the transmit frequency within the radio. Recent firmware updates and releases of PowerSDR cure the problem for the ANAN and OpenHPSDR radios. The FlexRadio 6000 series also use direct CW generation inside the radio.

Because the CW is now generated within the radio, the side-tone is not delayed and the radio can work at QSK rates up to at least 60 wpm.

CW SKIMMER

CW Skimmer by Afreet Software (Alex Shovkoplyas, VE3NEA), has been developed with wide band receivers like software defined radios in mind. When used with a conventional radio, Skimmer is restricted to decoding CW signals within the radio's 2.5 kHz pass band. But when using the IQ signal from a software defined radio, Skimmer can decode up to 700 signals in parallel. You can download CW Skimmer for free for a 30 day trial but after that, the program must be registered.

CW Skimmer is widely used by CW enthusiasts, DXpeditions and contest stations. It decodes many CW signals simultaneously allowing the operator to quickly identify stations without having to listen to them. You can easily move up the band working each station in turn, without duplicating contacts or wasting contest time listening for call signs.

MRP40 SDR

There is a new version of the MRP40 Morse decoder, which has the ability to send or receive over an IQ signal rather than standard audio. With this version, you get the ability to control the radio frequency and filter bandwidth, plus a waterfall display. It can demodulate SSB voice as well.

The sampling rates are for audio IQ signals at 48, 96, or 192 kHz, with either 16 or 32 Bit conversion.

BUILT IN CW

Some software defined radios and some + SDR radios include a CW decoder as well as the more normal CW keyer. The Elecraft KX3 (SDR) and K3S (+ SDR) radios can decode and display CW, RTTY, and PSK. If you are proficient with a bug, the KX3 can also convert the CW that you send via the 'key' into RTTY or PSK transmissions.

SDR FOR DIGITAL MODES

The main advantages of using an SDR for digital modes are the ability to adjust the filter bandwidth so that you can see and decode the whole of each digital mode band segment, the ability to operate on several bands at the same time, and the ability to operate several digital modes at the same time. You also get the same advantages as when you use your SDR for SSB operation such as a range of noise reduction filters and blankers.

Using software defined radios for digital modes is not much different to using a conventional radio. You do get the advantage that you don't need to connect an audio cable between the radio and the PC for digital mode operation. The audio signal between the SDR software and the digital mode software is carried by a 'virtual audio cable,' which is a software utility program. If you have a Signature range transceiver, you will use the built in DAX (digital audio exchange). To connect most other SDR transceivers you will need to download and install 'virtual audio cable' software and a 'com port manager.' There are free options for both of these. Many people use Virtual Audio Cable 'VAC' for the audio connection. See the section about 'audio connections for digital modes'. Rig control is performed using CAT commands sent to the SDR software over a virtual com port. You can use com0com or Virtual Serial Port 'VSP' to connect the digital mode software Com port to the SDR software Com port.

In the near future, we will see digital mode software that supports IQ input signals, or which includes a virtual audio cable and a com port manager.

SmartSDR is able to send audio or IQ audio signals from individual receiver slices to different digital mode programs. This means that you can decode PSK, RTTY, and CW from the same or different bands all at the same time. In a contest situation you could watch RTTY signals on three bands and then 'search and pounce' at will across the three bands. The same would apply if you were looking for unusual DX. PowerSDR, ExpertSDR2, and probably others can send the output of receiver 1 to one audio cable and the output of receiver 2 to a second audio cable. ExpertSDR2 also supports separate CAT control for each receiver.

One difference when you are using an SDR is that the bandwidth of the signals sent to the digital mode software can be changed. For example, you can view much more than the normal 2.4 kHz of PSK signals. When you have decided to concentrate on one signal, you can narrow the receive filter down so that only one signal can be heard (or seen) and decoded. This may make copying the signal easier, although the DSP in the digital mode software is so effective that there may be no advantage. It certainly means that you are saved the irritation of having to listen to other RTTY or PSK signals while you are working a station.

DOLLY FILTERS

PowerSDR mRX has 'Dolly' double lobe filters especially for receiving RTTY signals. They are very good. If you use PowerSDR for RTTY, you really should try them out. They will allow you to copy with 100% accuracy signals that are just random strings of letters without the filter. This type of filter is not available on most non-SDR transceivers.

JT65 OPERATION

The WSJT digital mode software is open source software initially developed by Joe Taylor, K1JT for very weak signal work. WSJT includes digital modes designed for ionospheric scatter, meteor scatter, EME, and QRP operation. The JT65 mode, initially used for EME operation is becoming popular on the HF bands, especially for low power QRP stations and stations with rudimentary antenna systems. JT65 can successfully transfer short messages when the received signal is at or even below the ambient noise floor. It relies on slow transmissions. One station transmits for about 48 seconds and then receives while the other station transmits. Using the unique full duplex capability of some SDR radios it is possible to hold two JT65 QSOs at the same time, transmitting to one station while receiving another and then transmitting to the second station while receiving from the first.

SMARTSDR API

The SmartSDR API will allow the developers of digital mode software to write applications that interface directly with the FlexRadios. There is scope for specialized, mode specific, DSP filters and for transmitter management. Transmit filters and pre-distortion could be modified to maximize transmit power on digital modes. It should be possible to decode and send common digital modes from within SmartSDR. Perhaps a spectrum plus waterfall plus decoded text or pictures display. CWX already contains macros for use in CW mode and this function could be used for digital modes as well.

FUTURE POSSIBILITIES

There is significant scope for improvement in the way that SDR software interfaces with digital mode software. FlexRadio Systems are leading the way and I am confident that others will follow. PowerSDR mRX could be modified to interface with an external .dll file in the same way that many programs use ExtIO.dll to interface differing hardware with programs like SDR#. A defined API would allow digital mode software to become an extension of the SDR software, effectively adding the digital modes as new modes to the SDR software. This integration would remove the need for virtual com ports and audio cables because the audio and control signals would be directly connected. Different programs could add specific individual modes using the same .dll interface. In addition to the current and future digital modes we could have, digital voice modes, DRM or other decoders for shortwave, and modes for sending data files, pictures, or video.

SDR FOR CONTESTING

I love using my software defined radio in contests. It is one of the areas of the hobby where using a software defined radio really helps a lot. In an SSB contest, most stations are spaced at 1 kHz or possibly 500 Hz apart. If you set the mouse wheel tuning for a 500 Hz step, you can click directly onto any station in the panadapter and jump to the exact frequency. This is great for 'search and pounce' contest operation. You simply click on each signal in turn and work up and down the band. You will quickly know where the 'big gun' stations are operating, because you can see them on the panadapter. You get to recognize the "look" of each station, so you won't waste time carefully tuning them in over and over again, through the night.

If you are in 'run mode,' you will be able to see if your frequency is being squashed by big stations nearby. You can check the status of other bands by opening a second panadapter. No more wasting time and possibly losing your run frequency to end up tuning around a dead band.

In a busy contest, it is inevitable that there will be stations overlapping. You will be able to see this on the waterfall and panadapter displays. With careful filtering, you can usually eliminate enough of the interference to work both stations. Conventional receivers without I.F. DSP don't have that advantage. Being able to see exactly where the two signals are really helps you to set the filters in a way that accentuates the wanted signal and masks the unwanted one. You can watch the relative levels of each station as you turn the beam as well.

The receiver filters are sharper than non-digital filters and they can be adjusted to exactly the right place. On a FlexRadio, you can also see exactly where to place a tracking notch filter. Other radios may have good filters and they may be adjustable, but they lack the ability to place them exactly where you need them. The FlexRadio tracking notch filters stay in place, so you won't have to set them every time you tune across the band.

There is no point in having a receiver passband that is any wider that the transmitted signal. All that you get outside that bandwidth is unwanted noise. The waterfall display will show you exactly how wide each transmitter is operating and you can adjust the receive filter width for the best signal to noise.

The AGC action in conventional receivers will reduce the receiver gain if there are strong signals within the I.F. passband. This desensitizing makes it hard to work weak stations that are near strong signals. Another really big advantage in using a software defined radio for contesting is that this desensitizing does not occur in software defined radios. So, it is much easier to work weak stations.

Technical TIP: Usually the blocking dynamic range of a software defined radio is equal to the clipping level of the radio. SDRs do not exhibit any loss of sensitivity when there are big signals within the receiver pass band or displayed on the panadapter.

During a contest, the band is packed with many signals operating very close together. Receiving a lot of signals in the receiver pass-band at the same time is a problem for conventional radios. The signals mix together and mix with the local oscillators inside the receiver causing intermodulation products, which can be heard. This distortion adds to the cacophony of noise that is so typical in a contest situation. A lot of old timers who complain that they "can't hear anything" during contests are experiencing this kind of intermodulation distortion. They believe that it is poor transmitters causing splatter, when in fact it is intermodulation distortion occurring within their own receiver. This intermodulation problem is why we prize receivers with very good 'close in' (2 kHz spacing) IMD performance.

Technical TIP: You will note that the Sherwood Engineering list which ranks the best amateur radios, is sorted on the results of the, 'narrow spaced two tone IMD' performance test. Software defined receivers have very good narrow spaced two tone IMD. Unlike conventional receivers, the receive IMD performance is the same at any spacing from the nominal receiver frequency. Not only that, software defined radios actually get better when the band is busy! It is a peculiarity of SDR designs that when the ADC samples a mixture of signals at varying levels, the IMD performance improves.

Most SDR software has a selection of different noise reduction filters and noise blankers. You should be able to find one to combat any kind of noise interference. In some SDR software, you can change the mathematical parameters of these filters, but you wouldn't want to do that while actually competing in a contest.

Another advantage of using a software defined radio for contesting is that, you will probably be using a contest logging program and you might be using digital mode software or an application like CW skimmer as well. It is convenient to be operating the radio on the same computer. The best way is to have the SDR displayed on a second computer monitor. PowerSDR mRX has just introduced a function that will return active control to the N1MM logging program or other nominated software as soon as you have finished making any adjustment on the radio. This is specifically intended for use during contest operation. It gives the logging program priority over the radio to stop you inadvertently entering keystrokes into the SDR program when you want them in the logger or CW keyer.

With the latency and delayed side tone problems now fixed, SDRs are great for CW contesting. The same advantages mentioned above also apply to CW contesting. You can click directly on each CW signal and net automatically to the transmitter offset tone.

You can actually see the Morse code on the waterfall display, including any key clicks on the transmission. The software for the 100W HF transceivers includes configurable keyers with keyboard macros. You can use the same keyboard to send the CQ and other calls as you do for the logging. With an SDR, you can use super narrow 'brick wall' filters, which can isolate one CW signal even when the band is frantic. With careful filtering, you can make a signal sound as clean as a code practice oscillator in the shack.

PowerSDR mRX and SmartSDR both can use enhanced SSB which can compress your transmit audio without any risk of clipping or distortion. This means that you get a higher average 'talk power.' In a busy contest, more talk power usually equals more contacts and more points.

Finally, although it may not be a significant advantage to you, using PureSignal or another form of adaptive transmitter pre-distortion, makes your transmitted signal cleaner. You will be able to operate closer to another station without causing interference on their spot. Actually having a transmit signal with better transmit intermodulation performance, may give you some advantages. If you are transmitting slightly off the frequency that the other station is listening on, your signal will sound much nicer. That may make it easier for them to copy your call sign and signal report. If you are a 'run' station, your signal should be cleaner and easier to tune in to. Plus, if you are not transmitting intermodulation products, the additional power will add to your wanted transmission. This extra amount is probably insignificant, but hey, everything counts in a contest!

So in summary;

- You can see where the signals are and click right onto them

- You can see if other bands are open without actually switching over to them

- The receiver filters are sharper and they can be adjusted to exactly the right frequency and width

- CW filters are very narrow and very sharp

- You can adjust your receiver bandwidth to exactly the width of the received signal, thus avoiding unwanted noise

- The SDR has excellent noise reduction, blockers and notch filters

- SDRs have better receive intermodulation performance on busy bands and no desensitizing due to strong signals near the weak signal that you want

- SDR software offers integration of the radio with logging and digital mode software

SDR FOR INTERFERENCE MONITORING

Some people like to monitor the bands for interesting signals and intruders on the amateur radio bands. Software defined radios offer many advantages for this type of activity. For a start, a software defined radio is effectively a spectrum analyzer, so fairly accurate measurements of the signal level and frequency can be made. You can monitor a wide range of frequencies on the panadapter and waterfall display so you will see bursts of illegal transmission that might be missed if you were just tuning around with a conventional receiver.

IONOSONDES AND SIGNALS THAT CHANGE FREQUENCY

'Whistlers,' Ionosondes, and other signals that are swept across a frequency range may only show up as a blip on a conventional radio, but they are displayed as a diagonal line on a waterfall display. Since you know the rate that the waterfall is updating in frames per second and its width, you can calculate how fast the signal is changing frequency. Fast sweeps cause a flat diagonal line on the waterfall and slow sweeps cause a steeper diagonal line.

An Ionosonde is a Radar that examines the Ionosphere by sweeping the HF band and receiving the echos. Ionosondes sweep from 1-40Mhz. They send a line of very short pulses up the band. It looks like a slanted line when observed on a waterfall display. http://www.sigidwiki.com/wiki/Ionosonde.

RECORDING

Many SDR programs include the ability to record signals or even the whole panadapter. If you have recorded the whole panadapter IQ stream, you can listen to signals that you were not tuned to when the recording was made. This means that you can leave the receiver recording a band overnight, then observe, and listen to any of the signals at a later time. This is a really neat feature if you are watching a band for intruders or waiting for a signal. You could use this feature to find out when a band is open to a DXpedition, to watch the downlink from a satellite that is passing over at an inconvenient time, or to catch a pirate who is operating intermittently.

IDENTIFICATION

The waterfall and spectrum displays can help you to identify what mode is being transmitted. Digital modes and signals like fax and packet have distinctive patterns, which can be observed on the screen. You can see and hear what some modes sound like at:

http://www.astrosurf.com/luxorion/qsl-ham-history15.htm (Picture below)

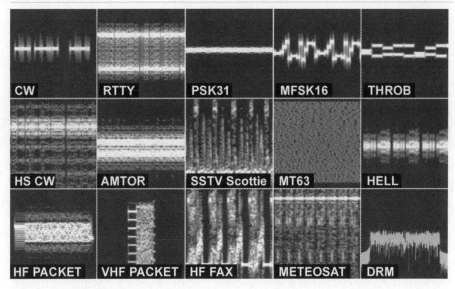

Figure 17: digital modes have distinctive patterns

INTERFERENCE

You can use the panadapter to see what kind of interference you are experiencing. Wide band noise, wobbly frequency variations, and multiple interfering signals show up very well. Combs of signals and swept signals are also easy to spot. Some signals carry an identifier that is readable on a waterfall display. Sometimes you can see interference that is generated inside your building. Likely culprits are plasma TVs, switch mode power supplies (especially cheap ones powering computers and other portable devices), and low voltage lighting systems. I have found that some computer monitors cause very localized wideband noise. I had one that wiped out the 40m amateur band when I used it in the shack, but it was OK when relocated to another room in the house. ADSL routers used for Internet connections are another source of local interference. They typically radiate a collection of closely spaced carriers at intervals right across the HF spectrum.

Figure 18: embedded text at the end of a digital mode transmission

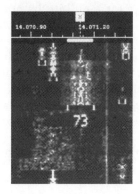

DIVERSITY RECEPTION

Software defined radios which have two phase coherent receivers can be used in some very interesting ways. 'Phase coherent' just means that both receivers are clocked from the same source. This means that if both receivers are connected to the same antenna and are tuned to the same frequency the receiver outputs will be at the same level and exactly in phase. If you use two antennas, the phase difference that results can be used to enhance a wanted signal or reject an unwanted one. The SDR software can delay the signal from one receiver with relation to the other and alter the gain of each receiver.

You can use the diversity mode to make the signals from two antennas add together. For example, on the low bands, you might have a Beverage receive antenna and a long wire or V beam transmit antenna. If you are receiving two stations and you only want one of them, you can change the phase relationship to null out the unwanted signal. Say for example you want to hear a signal from New Zealand, but there is a European station on or near the same frequency. The phase relationship of the ZL station will be different from the EU station. So you can manipulate the diversity mode phase and level to pull the ZL out. Then if you want to work the other person, just change the phasing to emphasize the European station. This technique is called 'beam steering' because you are emphasizing signals from a particular direction. Beam steering can also be used to find the direction that a signal is from without having steerable antennas. This is useful when you are trying to identify and track down the location of intruders and pirates on the lower part of the HF spectrum.

If you are suffering from received noise or interference, you can use diversity reception as a noise filter. It works best if the second antenna is picking up signals at around the same level as your wanted signal. But a wire dipole or a long wire 'noise antenna' can be surprisingly effective. Nige Coleman G7CNF has posted a very good video demonstrating diversity noise suppression at www.youtube.com/watch?v=qdQm17udCSo. The idea is to use the phase cancellation mode to null out the high noise level.

To reduce the noise, you tune the diversity phase and level control on the SDR software for a null in the noise level rather than for a peak in the wanted signal. Diversity noise suppression can be very effective and make the difference between barely hearing a signal and an easily heard station. Up to 40dB of noise suppression should be achievable. For this application your secondary noise antenna should be placed not too close to your transmit antenna. You don't want to couple too much energy back into your sensitive receiver. Avoid purposely placing the noise antenna near a noise source as that would just make the situation worse by coupling more noise into the system. The idea is for the noise antenna to be receiving the same noise level but with a different phase relationship to the wanted signal.

SDR FOR EME, MICROWAVE AND SATELLITES

Software defined radios are becoming popular for VHF, UHF and microwave operation. Many software defined radios can be locked to a GPS disciplined or other very stable clock source, which makes them good platforms for use with receive converters or transverters. Many of the new SDR boards work well up into the microwave region so you can work microwave frequencies directly, without a transverter. Previously a LNB (low noise block) would be connected at the feed point of a microwave dish to convert the signal down to a lower frequency. Now you can use a LNA (low noise amplifier) and a SDR directly at the wanted receive frequency.

Receivers like the RTL and FUNcube dongles and transceivers like the HackRF and the Ettus USRP, are much cheaper than conventional radios covering the same range of frequency bands.

Technical TIP: Very stable oscillators are important when you are using a converter or transverter. Any frequency error becomes multiplied. For example a good HF radio may have an oscillator with a 0.5 ppm (parts per million) frequency stability. At a frequency of 30 MHz, this is a respectable frequency error of plus or minus 15 Hz. At 6 GHz the same oscillator has a frequency error of plus or minus 3000 Hz. Frequency stability is normally measured after the radio has been operating for at least an hour because oscillators are often very sensitive to temperature variations.

The panadapter is great for weak signal work such as EME (Earth – Moon – Earth) operation or VHF DX. You can see signals that are outside of the passband of a conventional receiver. For example if you were working 2m EME with a conventional receiver you might easily miss a station transmitting a few kilohertz up or down the band. As well as displaying a wider bandwidth, the waterfall can show signals that are very weak or on a different frequency to what you expect.

The SpectraVue program is popular for weak signal work. With careful adjustment, it can display signals, which are very difficult or impossible to see on the waterfall displays of other SDR programs.

The same is true when working amateur radio satellites with linear transponders. You can display the entire transponder width and see any downlink signals. You can see the relative strength of the downlink signals and compare them to the level from the beacon if there is one. Sometimes working out if a signal is actually from the satellite is confusing. You can get spoofed by local signals. The waterfall display from a software defined radio will show a slanted signal from a satellite because the frequency of the signal will be moving due to Doppler shift. A signal from a terrestrial source will not show any slant. You will even be able to tell if the satellite is coming towards your location or heading away. *(If you were correcting the receiver frequency for Doppler shift, it would be the terrestrial signals that show as slanted).*

Cross polarization loss is a big problem, particularly for EME operations. Big EME stations often have both horizontal and vertical polarized antenna arrays, but they don't usually use both at the same time.

Combining the antennas into a circular polarized array creates a 3 dB penalty in received signals strength, which EME operators can't afford.

Software defined radios, which have two front ends can combine signals from the vertical and horizontal polarized arrays and adjust the phase relationship to enhance the received signal. This will make use of both antenna arrays at the same time providing gain and eliminating the deep nulls that often result from cross polarization.

The height that your antenna is above the ground can also cause nulls in the received signal strength as the Moon rises. This is called ground gain (or loss). It happens when the signal coming direct from the Moon is enhanced or partially cancelled by a signal reflected from the foreground surface. If you have antennas at different heights, a software defined radio with two receiver front ends can be used to combine them in order to maximize the received signal. The advantage over having a fixed antenna 'stack' connected together with coax cable matching sections, is that the phase relationship between the signals is not fixed.

SDR FOR RADIO ASTRONOMY

Some people are using software defined radio receivers for other weak signal work including radio astronomy and propagation studies. One project is Sudden Ionospheric Disturbances (SID monitoring). There is special software for astronomy use at www.radio-astronomy.org/rasdr.

This topic is way out of my area of expertise, but there is plenty of information available online for those that are interested in using a software defined radio for this kind of activity.

If you are interested in using a SDR for radio astronomy there is an interesting paper by Dr David Morgan www.dmrdas.co.uk on the topic, at; http://www.britastro.org/radio/projects/An_SDR_Radio_Telescope.pdf.

'A 21cm Radio Telescope for the Cost-Conscious' by Marcus Leech, of Science Radio Laboratories, Inc. is another interesting article on using software defined radio for radio astronomy. The pdf is available online at; http://www.sbrac.org/files/budget_radio_telescope.pdf.

There is an article by Pieter-Tjerk de Boer, PA3FWM on using the WebSDR at Twente University to create 'Ionograms' from data obtained by tracking the ionospheric reflections of signals generated by 'Chirp' transmitters. http://websdr.ewi.utwente.nl:8901/chirps/article/ .

SOFTROCK RADIOS

The SoftRock SDR receivers and transceiver are all simple circuit boards available either as a kit or built up. They have been massively popular because they provide experimenters with a cheap introduction to software defined radio. SoftRock boards are generation one SDRs and to a large extent they have been overshadowed by newer designs with better performance, albeit at higher prices.

"The SoftRock SDR kits came into being in 2005 based on Tony Parks KB9YIG's experience with an SDR 1000 Software Defined Radio and the series of seminal articles in QEX by Gerald Youngblood K5SDR.

The kits were introduced as a low cost technology sampler for Software Defined Radio and Tony continues to offer the kits as such. Many people have contributed to the design and testing of the various kits to lower the cost of the kits and to improve performance and functionality. It is estimated that, since the SoftRock's inception in 2005, over 15,000 kits have been shipped to builders in about 60 different countries. http://www.wb5rvz.com/sdr/."

All SoftRock models use the Tayloe QSD detector patented by Dan Tayloe N7VE in 2001. The transmitter section of the TXRX model uses the same circuit in reverse as a QSE (quadrature sampling exciter).

"Tony Parks (KB9YIG) and Bill Tracey (KD5TFD) designed the original SoftRock-40 kit." http://softrocksdr.wikispaces.com. There have been many models since that first release.

These little boards have been the first introduction to software defined radio for thousands of hams and experimenters, including me. My first SDR was a fixed tuned SoftRock on 9 MHz connected to the IF output of my old Yaesu FT-301. They are fantastic value for money and they are still a great low cost option, especially for use as a band scope on the I.F of a conventional receiver.

I recommend building your own SoftRock kit. Give it a go. It is fun. But please note that the kits do have very small surface mounted integrated circuits and chip capacitors so you need good lighting, and good eyes or a forehead magnifier. You can solder surface mounted devices (smd) with a temperature controlled soldering iron with a fine tip, or you can use solder paste and an oven or hot plate. I use a soldering iron, but these days I find that I can only solder surface mount chips during the daytime because I need bright light. You also need a very clean anti-static work surface, because if you drop a smd capacitor on the carpet you may never find it again. I lost one for three days and was very lucky to find it at all. If soldering the components onto the board is too much of a challenge but you are happy to pop the board into a case and connect up some cables, you can buy the boards pre-assembled.

If you don't want to build your own or you don't want to bother with an un-mounted circuit board, I would suggest buying a FUNcube Dongle Pro Plus or a small box DDC based receiver like the Perseus or QS1R. I am not endorsing those particular radios. They are just examples of receivers that have a good reputation. There are dozens of good small box receivers of all descriptions to choose from. Personally, I am not a fan of the RTL dongles although a lot of people love them. The FCD pro+ has outstanding frequency coverage, from LF to SHF and a lot of other great features such as being a plug-n-play USB device. Read the chapter on the FCD for more details.

SOFTROCK PERFORMANCE

It is amazing how well these tiny, super cheap radios work. The audio quality is often excellent compared to conventional radios. The reason is mostly due to the SoftRock receiver not having several oscillators and mixers contributing phase noise and intermodulation.

The main limitations are imperfect image signal suppression and only being able to support a single narrow panadapter. The panadapter bandwidth is limited by the performance of the analog to digital converter in the PC sound card. Most sound cards can sample at up to 96 ksps (96,000 samples per second), which means that the radio will be able to display the center frequency, plus and minus 48 kHz. This results in a 96 kHz wide spectrum and waterfall display on the panadapter. Some sound cards and purpose built analog to digital converters can manage a sample rate of 192 ksps, which provides a 192 kHz panadapter bandwidth. PC sound cards do not work well at very low frequencies and the direct conversion process contributes noise near the local oscillator frequency. This combines to produce a spike of noise at the center of the panadapter. Very good sound cards will have a reduced noise peak and some SDR programs can filter it out. Isolating the audio lines between the radio and the PC with audio transformers or isolators can help to kill mains hum, which is often a big part of the problem. If you see a noise peak in the middle of the panadapter you can be sure that the radio is a QSD based SDR. The noise spike is not a problem when you are listening to signals away from the center frequency, but it is rather annoying when you are using the SDR as a band scope.

The main competitor to the SoftRock series is the RTL dongles, which are sometimes cheaper and they are direct digital down conversion receivers. The dongles come fully assembled in a package like a flash drive 'memory stick'. They have a much wider frequency range, but they don't cover the whole HF band unless you add an additional mixer and oscillator up-converter board.

TECHNICAL DESCRIPTION

SoftRocks are the archetypical 'generation 1' SDRs. Minimal hardware with the analog to digital conversion being done using the stereo PC sound card and all of the DSP processing being performed by the PC software. They work with a very wide selection of SDR programs.

One of the first SoftRock compatible programs was Rocky written by Alex Shovkoplyas, VE3NEA. Alex also invented the adaptive image cancelling algorithm, used in Rocky, and subsequently widely used in other SDR software for QSD based receivers. At the time, those few lines of software code were a major advancement.

QSD receivers are single conversion receivers, a process that results in signals from above and below the local oscillator becoming mixed together in the audio output. On the right side of the SDR panadapter, we want to see signals from above the local oscillator frequency without image signals from below. On the left side of the SDR panadapter, we want to see signals from below the local oscillator frequency without image signals from above. The, I and Q signals are used to cancel out the image signals, but the cancellation is never perfect across the receivers pass-band. Alex's algorithm learns the characteristic of the receiver by comparing on air signals and continuously adapting the phase and amplitude compensation to reduce the corresponding image signals. This technique vastly improves the image cancellation and it revolutionized SDR software. This is another example of the way that open source software benefits everybody. Without the open source movement, his clever technique might not have been available to other programmers.

The heart of the SoftRock is the Tayloe detector, which converts the incoming RF from the antenna into two audio signals. One of the audio signals is delayed with a 90 degree phase lag to create the I and Q streams that are fundamental to software defined radio. The PC sound card creates two digital streams and the PC software does the DSP and the graphical user interface. Newer SoftRock models use an ATTiny 8bit microcontroller to process control information from the PC via a USB cable. You can control the frequency of the Si570 oscillator chip so that a much wider band of frequencies can be covered. One SoftRock model covers the entire HF band from 1.8 MHz to 30MHz. On some models, the microcontroller also switches band pass filters and on the TXRX version, it also manages the PTT.

CURRENTLY AVAILABLE SOFTROCK MODELS

SoftRock kits and assembled boards are available from http://fivedash.com/. Prices for the various models range from around $21 to $89. I don't know how they can be offered at such cheap prices. They are excellent value for money.

The models that are currently available are:

- The Lite II combined receiver kit, is a single band fixed tuned radio. Using a Lite II an SDR program will be able to display a 96 kHz wide panadapter centered on the oscillator frequency, which can be on any HF frequency. It is a QSD design using a Tayloe detector. It uses a fixed tuned crystal oscillator instead of the Si570 used in the other models. You order the kit for a particular HF band, or you can pick from a range of crystals for common I.F. frequencies between 455 kHz to 10.7 MHz, so it is a good choice if you are building a band scope.

- The 6m/4m/or 2m Ensemble receiver. The kit has components for all three bands. You choose which one of the three bands your receiver will cover. The board has a USB port for frequency control of the Si570 oscillator. Following a preamplifier, the RF is mixed down to an I.F. frequency in the HF band. The Tayloe detector is tuned to the I.F. frequency.

- The Rx Ensemble II HF Receiver, covers 1.8 to 30 MHz, it has four band pass filters, which can be switched via commands sent over the USB port. It uses a wider bandwidth double balanced Tayloe detector, and it features USB frequency control of the Si570 oscillator.

- The Rx Ensemble II LF Receiver is the same basic design as the HF version, but it covers 180 kHz to 3 MHz. It has four band pass filters, which can be switched, via commands over the USB port, a wider bandwidth double balanced Tayloe detector, a Si570 oscillator and USB frequency control.

- The Rx Ensemble II Receiver kit has the components to build either the LF or HF version

- The RXTX Ensemble Transceiver works on 160m, or 80m & 40m, or 40 & 30m & 20m, or 30m & 20m & 17m, or 15m & 12m & 10m. The kit contains components for all band options and you choose which one at build time. It has a Si570 oscillator and USB control of frequency and PTT. The RXTX Ensemble is a standard QSD and QSE Tayloe design.

- The RX Ensemble III HF Receiver covers 1.8 MHz to 30 MHz. It features a 9.5 dB Preamp for use above 16 MHz and a Si570 for frequency control. The USB port provides frequency control and band pass filter switching. There are four band pass filters. It is a standard Tayloe QSD design.

- Small cases are also available which you can use to house your SoftRock.

GENESIS RADIOS

The Genesis SDR range of QRP transceivers are kits manufactured by Genesis Radio in Australia. They can be ordered online of via a Yahoo group. They are also marketed in the USA by Green Mountain Radio & Electronics (Bruce Greenleaf KF1Z), http://kf1z.com/genesis/order.html.

The main Genesis Radio website is at http://www.genesisradio.com.au/.

There are two models of transceiver the G11 and the G59 plus a 10W power amplifier kit, the GPA10. The G11 is configured for two HF bands, although an add-on, band pass filter board can be added. The G59 covers all of the amateur radio bands from 160m to 6m.

These radios are only sold in kit form. You can buy a case to hold both the SDR and the 10 W power amplifier. There are a few smds but most of the components are easy to solder through hole devices. I have never seen one of these radios, but I am a keen kit builder so I am inclined to buy one. If you want to order one, you may have to wait a while because the kits are manufactured in batches of 50 units.

The G59 is a QSD / QSE based generation 1 transceiver, but it is a big step up from the basic SoftRock TXRX model. The design is a bit dated, but the G59 might appeal to those who want to build a kit. At present the kit, the amp and a box will set you back around $613, which is comparable with the price for a FLEX-1500 at $699. The FLEX-1500 is not a kit and only has 5 Watts of output power, but overall the performance should be pretty similar.

GENESIS G59 TECHNICAL SPECIFICATIONS
- Generation 1 QSD / QSE transceiver card
- Frequency control of the Si570 local oscillator over USB
- Uses the PC sound card for analog to digital conversion
- It will work with a range of software. There is a 'fork' of PowerSDR called 'GSDR' which was written especially for the Genesis SDR
- Excellent build notes and a full assembly manual available online
- The receiver covers 1.5 MHz to 75 MHz (160m to 6m) with seven optional band pass filters, a pre amp, and a front end attenuator.
- The transmitter covers the ham bands from 160m to 6m
- Build time around 100 hours
- Transmitter power 10 mW, or 10 W with GPA-10 power amplifier

RTL DONGLE

I am by no means an authority on the RTL dongle type of SDR, but there is a huge amount of information available online. They are extremely popular probably because they are very cheap. I will say right up front that I am not a fan! These radios have quite limited performance. They are not designed for general amateur radio and short wave listening, although some dongles did ship with closed source software to allow the reception of digital audio and FM broadcast stations.

Online sources credit; Eric Fry, Antti Palosaari, and a company called Osmocom, with working out how these devices work and how they can be used as general purpose SDR receivers.

The RTL dongles are designed as a cheap way to receive DVB-T digital television stations on your notebook or tablet PC. You can buy them online for less than $20, but you must make sure to buy one with the right chipset. Not all models are compatible with the 'Zadig' driver and the ones that are not compatible won't work as a general SDR receiver. The dongles that use the Realtek RTL2382U chip will work and some others might work. I bought a dongle with the wrong chip and it definitely did not work with the Zadig driver, although it did work with the bundled TV software. I also bought one that failed to work in any capacity. After that, I gave up.

"DVB-T dongles based on the Realtek RTL2832U can be used as a cheap SDR, since the chip allows transferring the raw I/Q samples to the host, which is officially used for DAB/DAB+/FM demodulation." http://sdr.osmocom.org/trac/wiki/rtl-sdr.

TECHNICAL INFORMATION

The RTL2832U has an 8 bit analog to digital converter and outputs an 8 bit IQ stream over the USB port to the PC. The Zadig driver converts the data into a format that can be used by the SDR software. The maximum sampling rate is 3.2 Msps but the USB interface can't support data transfer at that rate so the actual sampling rate is lower. Apparently, it is possible to display a bandwidth of around 2.5 MHz. that's a lot more than the FUNcube dongle pro+, which only has a display bandwidth of 192 kHz.

The frequency range varies depending which manufacturer made the dongle. The best is the Elconics E4000, which works from 52 to 2200 MHz with a gap from about 1100 MHz to 1250 MHz. Others cover 24 to 1766 MHz and one version works from 146 to 924 MHz with a gap between 308 MHz and 438 MHz. Check http://sdr.osmocom.org/trac/wiki/rtl-sdr.

They are generally very sensitive receivers with typical MDS figures around -139 dBm. Clipping occurs at around -60 dBm.

The RTL dongles work well at VHF and above, but they do not cover the MF and HF bands. NooElec makes a USB powered up-converter with a local oscillator on 125 MHz to allow you to receive the HF spectrum. The up-converter costs about twice as much as the RTL dongle but the whole package is still very cheap. See http://www.nooelec.com/store/ham-it-up.html. DX Patrol also sells an up-converter for RTL dongles and a receiver, which comprises of an RTL dongle and the up-converter mounted in a small plastic case.

RTL dongles have a filter in front of the preamplifier but they do not have separate band pass filters for particular bands, so they are prone to overload and ADC gain compression. The 8 bit ADC means that they don't have a particularly large dynamic range to begin with. ADC gain compression is the effect where large signals reduce the receiver's dynamic range. The large signals do not have to be visible on the panadapter. Any signal present at the input of the analog to digital converter can contribute to the problem. ADC gain compression will cause the noise floor on the panadapter to rise or jump erratically. The RTL dongle might be affected by big signals from TV or FM broadcast signals if you live close to a broadcasting tower. If you are using an HF up-converter with no front-end filtering, high power AM broadcast stations could cause overloading or ADC gain compression.

Note that the connectors on RTL dongles are 75 Ohm TV connectors. There will be a small mismatch loss if you connect a dongle to a 50 Ohm antenna, but it is not a problem. Many small 'rubber duck' type antennas are not 50 Ohms anyway and random bits of wire could be any impedance.

Walter Schellenberg HB9AJG published a very comprehensive performance report on two of the most commonly used RTL dongles. It is available at http://www.rtl-sdr.com/wp-content/uploads/2013/08/Some-Measurements-on-E4000-and-R820-Tuners.pdf.

He points out that some of the dongles are direct conversion receivers, which are prone to image signals and are likely to show a noise spike or hump in the center of the panadapter. Other RTL dongles use an I.F. frequency so they are less prone to these issues. The data shows excellent sensitivity but the direct conversion model has a fairly poor image response. The Intermodulation performance is generally poor and there are several unwanted signals, mostly harmonics of the clock signal. Given the very small size of these receivers, it is extremely difficult to shield the sensitive input to the pre-amplifier and ADC from the digital signals in the receiver. Apparently, the usable dynamic range is only around 60 dB above the noise floor.

"Of course these neat, little toys are no match for 'real' software defined receivers. They do have some limitations, but you get a LOT of radio for almost no money! They are fun to experiment with, and to learn more about SDR technologies." Walter Schellenberg HB9AJG.

FUNCUBE DONGLE

Unlike the RTL dongle, which has a similar USB stick layout and case, the FUNcube dongle (FCD) was designed to be a radio receiver. These radios are a bit more expensive than the RTL dongles, but they have major technical advantages. They are very easy to setup because the computer reads them as a USB HID (human interface device), essentially the same as a computer mouse. Just plug the FCD into a USB port and it will work. You don't need to install any driver software, just the SDR program. The FCD will work with any operating system that can recognize a USB device.

The FCD was designed in 2010 by Howard Long, G6LVB, as the ground station companion to the FUNcube satellite being built by AMSAT-UK. The satellite was finally launched on November 21st 2013. After the successful launch, the satellite was awarded an OSCAR 'Orbital Satellite Carrying Amateur Radio' number of AO-73. Since then, FUNcube-2 was launched as a piggy back on the UKube satellite on the 8th of July 2014 and FUNcube -3 was launched on 19th June 2014. FUNcube-3 was given the OSCAR designation of European OSCAR 79 (EO-79). There is a fourth FUNcube satellite planned.

These satellites have a dual role as amateur radio transponders during night time and weekend passes over the UK and as educational outreach satellites for school programs during daylight passes. The satellites have uplinks on the 2m band and downlinks on the 70cm band. The Educational telemetry transponder runs higher power during the day when the amateur radio transponder is turned off. *Information from http://funcube.org.uk/.*

The idea behind the FUNcube dongle receiver was to create a cheap, high performance receiver that schools could use as a part of the educational goals for the FUNcube satellite program. Initially there was to be a version specifically for the 2m and 70cm bands that the satellite is using and a wide coverage version at a slightly higher cost. But I believe that only the wide coverage version was produced. Around June 2012, Howard experienced problems sourcing the Elconics tuner chip and the manufacturer eventually went into liquidation. So he designed an improved FCD version called the FUNcube Dongle Pro+, released in September 2012. The pro plus is the one to buy. It is far superior to the original version.

The original FCD had a typical frequency range of 51.5 MHz to 2000 MHz with a gap between about 1100 MHz and 1270 MHz.

The new FCD Pro+ has a typical frequency range of 150 kHz to 260 MHz and 410 MHz to 2.05 GHz. This means that it covers every ham band from the 1800m band to the 23cm band. In New Zealand, that is L.F to L Band. Seventeen amateur radio bands, from a receiver you can carry in your pocket!

TIP: Don't try to use a random piece of wire as an antenna. Initially I didn't have the right adapter and tried using a piece of hook-up wire poked (carefully) into the RF input of the FCD receiver. If you do this, you will be disappointed to see spikes all across the panadapter display. I believe that the radio picks up its own clock signal. This does not happen if no antenna is connected, or if a good antenna is used. For HF reception the FCD works best with a proper antenna located at a distance from the USB dongle.

FCD PRO+ TECHNICAL INFORMATION

Front end filters are important in any SDR to avoid ADC gain compression and overloading of the low noise pre-amplifier. The FCD pro+ has 11 automatically selected filters before the tuner chip, including very narrow SAW filters on the amateur 2m and 70cm bands. Remember that the receiver was initially designed for receiving a satellite, which uses those two amateur bands. The filters are important to stop overload especially at VHF. For frequencies above the HF band, there is a low noise amplifier to provide additional sensitivity. Preamplifier and I.F. stage gain are adjustable.

TIP: A SAW filter is a surface acoustic wave filter. It is a ceramic or crystal filter in a small sealed package. They are commonly used in cell phones and can be ordered on common frequencies from electronic suppliers. A typical size for a UHF one is 3mm x 3mm. The cellular band ones can be as small as 1.1mm x 0.9mm.

TECHNICAL COMPARISON FCD VS FCD PRO+

The new FCD pro+ is much better than the original FCD. It has;

- A better LNA (low noise amplifier) than the original FCD model

- A better TXCO local oscillator (typically 1.5 ppm): The original FCD used a crystal oscillator with a stability of around 20 ppm.

- Better frequency range: The new model includes the LF, MF, and HF bands and the high frequency range has been extended to include the 23cm band.

- The sample rate was increased from 96 kHz to 192 kHz, which means a 192 kHz panadapter display. This is still a lot less panadapter bandwidth than some of the new experimenter's boards.

- A 32 bit ADC with 16 bits of resolution to the SDR software.

- Better local oscillator phase noise, excellent sensitivity (0.15uV on 2m and 70cm)

Both models have an internal 5V 'bias T' that can be used to send volts up the coax feeder cable to power a mast head preamplifier.

Data sourced from the FUNcube website at http://funcube.org.uk/.

USB CONNECTED RECEIVERS

Small SDR receivers and in some cases small SDR QRP transceivers that are fitted inside a small case and connected to the PC over a USB cable are the most common form of commercially available SDR. There are dozens of models available. Because there is so much choice, this type of radio is the most difficult to evaluate. Some are old QSD designs, some are hybrids, and some use direct digital synthesis. Price is not necessarily a good indicator of quality or their technical performance. To make things worse some of them work with a wide range of SDR software and others will only work with specific software supplied by the radio manufacturer. It is a bit of a mine field! The table on page 54 shows a list of SDR software and compatible radios. It is best to buy a model with direct digital synthesis, even if it has a 14 bit ADC.

USB Technical Information: There are basically three classes of USB interface, plus a few revisions and subclasses. The initial USB 1.0 standard only allowed a data rate of 1.5 Mbits (1,500,000 bits per second) but later versions manage up to 12 Mbits. The USB 2.0 standard works up to a maximum of 480 Mbits per second and the USB 3.0 standard ranges from 2.5 Gbits to 4.8 Gbits per second (i.e. up to 10 times faster than USB 2.0. The new USB 3.1 standard can work up to 10 Gbits per second.

The USB 1.0 and 2.0 interface has a four wire connector. It uses three wires for data transfer and outputs +5V at up to around 300mA on the fourth connector pin. The USB 3.0 interface uses nine pins and can support asynchronous full duplex (i.e. it can receive and transmit data at the same time). It's +5V output can support loads up to 900mA. The USB 2.0 interface is half duplex meaning that it can send or receive data but not both at the same time.

USB devices are backwards compatible, so you can plug a USB 2.0 device into a USB 1.0 port, but the data rate will be reduced to the USB 1.0 speed. Similarly, you can plug a USB 1.0 device into a USB 2.0 port and it will work fine. But, some users experience driver problems when trying to use USB 2.0 SDR devices on USB 3.0 ports. Most USB connected software defined radios are made for connection to USB 2.0 ports. The USB driver software included with your SDR software may not be compatible with the USB 3.0 port(s) on your computer. USB 3.0 devices and ports can be identified by the 9 pin connector which often has a blue plastic inner. There is a second row of 5 pins in addition to the 4 pins used by the earlier standard. USB 2.0 and USB 1.0 connectors have black or grey plastic inside.

If the radio supports the USB 3.0 standard, (USRP, HackRF, BladeRF etc.), you should use a USB 3.0 port on your computer. Some models will work with a USB 2.0 port but the bandwidth available would be significantly reduced. This would limit the width of the panadapters and / or the number of panadapters that can be displayed.

USRP, NOCTAR, HACKRF AND BLADE RF BOARDS

These boards are designed for experimenters, recently known as 'hackers.' They are not primarily aimed at radio amateurs, but of course radio hams are 'hackers' too. We have been experimenting with new radio technologies for many years.

The Ettus Research USRP (universal software radio peripheral) boards are bare board versions of their more expensive commercial products. The other boards and boxed radios are for industrial research and for integration into commercial applications. The B200 and B210 boards are the most accessible to hams and hackers on a budget.

The Ettus, Noctar, Blade RF, and HackRF radios all have amazing frequency coverage from HF or VHF right up into the GHz microwave frequencies and they all have, very low power, transmitting capability.

These boards and radios may be of interest to radio amateurs building microwave frequency DX or EME stations. You can operate directly on the bands of interest without transverters or converters. Of course you would still need a low noise amplifier mounted at the receive antenna and a UHF or microwave power amplifier. Ultimately, these radios may also be of interest to amateur radio satellite operators and maybe satellite makers. But currently there are no Hamsats using microwave frequencies.

The ability to observe received signals on a wide panadapter is a real plus of this kind of radio compared with older technologies. Small frequency errors or drift in the oscillators of frequency transverters, exciters, or receivers can lead to large errors when mixed or multiplied up to microwave frequencies. This can be very frustrating. Most of these boards can be locked to accurate frequency standards and the panadapter can show received signals that are off frequency and possibly outside of the pass band of conventional converters.

Some of the boards have dual coherent receivers and even transmitters, which allows the use of techniques such as beam steering of signals, diversity reception, and diversity noise reduction.

Some of the radios are full duplex, which is great for satellite operation where being able to hear your downlink signal while transmitting on the uplink frequency is virtually mandatory. The wide panadapter can help with Doppler control, as you will be able to see the received signal changing frequency.

There are online communities of interested people who can assist you with your projects. Most of these boards already have established GNU Radio software and a range of open source, software code sources.

SDRS WITH KNOBS

SDRs with knobs are radios, which use a typical SDR architecture like direct digital synthesis or a quadrature sampling detector or exciter. They are not to be confused with the + SDR or 'hybrid' radios which use a conventional Superheterodyne arrangement with an IQ output from their I.F. DSP. Some people do not consider SDRs with knobs to be "real" software defined radios because not everything is software defined. This class of software defined radio usually uses dedicated DSP chips and the control functions are managed by a microprocessor or microcomputer inside the radio.

Some conventional transceivers offer an I.F. output on the rear panel, so that you can connect an SDR receiver for a band scope. I am sure that the next evolution will be conventional transceivers, which include an internal SDR receiver connected either to the I.F. stage or after the front end filters and RF preamplifier. This addition will be introduced specifically to provide a band-scope with better performance than the current + SDR models. A band scope on the I.F. output can offer a much wider panadapter than the audio IQ signals from the DSP stage. A software defined radio connected near the antenna input can offer a wide panadapter and other SDR features.

Here are some examples of the various types of software defined radios 'with knobs.' A brief summary of each radio's technical specifications such as frequency coverage, ADC sampling rate and transmit power is included in the 'glossary of software defined radios' near the end of the book.

ELECRAFT KX3

The Elecraft KX3 is usually classed as a software defined radio. It is a QRP transceiver, with a maximum transmit power of around 10 Watts and it has exceptionally good receiver performance. The radio was designed for field and portable use, but many people are using it as their primary base station because it has such a good receiver. Note that the Elecraft K3 and K3S transceivers use conventional Superheterodyne architecture. They are classed as + SDR radios.

The radio is essentially a generation three SDR design. Its receiver uses a single conversion to generate audio frequency I and Q streams, which are sampled with an on-board ADC chip. Dedicated DSP chips process the audio and an MCU (microcontroller) manages the inputs from knobs and buttons, as well as the display, memories, and CAT commands. The audio frequency IQ streams coming out of the quadrature detector (QSD stage) are available on a jack at the side of the radio for use with sound card type, SDR software. The radio is excellent but the external SDR functionality provided by the audio IQ output is disappointing. It suffers from the limitations inherent in any sound-card based software defined radio.

Depending on the sampling rate of your sound card, you usually only get a 48 kHz or 96 kHz panadapter bandwidth and you are likely to experience ground loop hum and a DC noise spike in the center of the panadapter display. The IQ output has a roll off at high audio frequencies so the resultant panadapter shows significant droop at the edges, especially when displaying a 96 kHz panadapter. The KX3 supports CAT commands over a USB to serial adapter, so your SDR software should be able to display and change the radio frequency. Unless you have a very good PC sound card, the effectiveness of using the KX3's IQ output as a band scope is limited by the noise spike, which appears on the panadapter right at the frequency that you are listening to. Some SDR software is able to eliminate the 'DC' noise spike and having a top quality sound card really helps as well.

Elecraft does offer a companion band scope which has a maximum panadapter span of 200 kHz and which doesn't display a noise spike. I understand that the radio was designed for portable operation and not as a base station, but it is a pity that the IQ and control signals were not integrated into a mini USB port instead of separate serial and audio signals.

ALINCO DX-SR9T

The Alinco DX-SR9T has a conventional double conversion Superheterodyne receiver with intermediate frequencies of 71.75 MHz and 455 kHz. The SDR capability consists of audio IQ signals from a mixer stage, probably a QSD detector on the I.F. So the radio is a + SDR or 'hybrid' radio. The freely available SDR software from Alinco allows for a 48 kHz panadapter. The DX-SRT is a good radio at a reasonable price. But, in my opinion, having a pretty limited audio IQ output does not make it a software defined radio. Apart from the ability to apply firmware updates there is nothing software defined about the radio. It uses conventional Superheterodyne receiver architecture. However, with connection to a PC and the free software you do get a panadapter display at a much lower cost than buying a transceiver with a built-in band scope. The free software allows for transmit operation from the PC and you can use it to receive signals from anywhere on the 48 kHz panadapter, so it offers a bit more than just a simple band scope.

ADAT ADT-200A

The Swiss made ADAT ADT-200A is an example of a direct digital synthesis HF SDR transceiver with a built-in computer to manage the controls and display. It had many groundbreaking design features, but unfortunately, it is no longer being produced.

"The receiving portion uses a 14bit A/D converter which offers a S/N ratio of 74 dB over the half Nyquist bandwidth of 36.86 MHz. After the subsequent decimation, a blocking dynamic range of 120 dB will be achieved.

The ADT-200A uses the latest generation of high performance DSP manufactured by Analog Devices Inc. capable of up to 2 billion instructions per second leaving room for future options. The power amplifier is equipped with high voltage MOSFET's capable of producing 50 Watts within the range of 1.8 MHz to 30 MHz with an efficiency of up to 70%. Adaptive pre-distortion delivers an undistorted transmission signal, which is a first in an amateur radio application."

http://www.eham.net/reviews/detail/7037.

The ADT-200A was the first commercially available software defined amateur radio transceiver to include adaptive transmit pre-distortion, which dramatically improves the transmitter intermodulation performance. I believe that it was also the first direct sampling, stand alone, 50 Watt HF SDR for the amateur radio market.

EXPERT ELECTRONICS MB1

The MB1 is a full digital sampling HF SDR transceiver with an Intel Core i5 based PC inside the radio box. The computer runs on either Linux or Windows. The radio has an impressive list of quoted specifications. It even covers the 2m VHF band. As at January 2016, you can place a pre-order, but so far, the radio has not been released for general sale.

MIDNIGHT DESIGN SOLUTIONS SDR CUBE

The SDR Cube is a QRP radio, which has on-board DSP and a microcomputer to manage the controls and display. It was designed to be a DSP / standalone add-on for a SoftRock QSD / QSE transceiver that you purchase and build separately, but now there is an RF board available, which will cover the complete HF band. The radio can be provided either, assembled and tested, or in kit form.

ELAD FDM-DUO

The FDM-Duo is a direct sampling QRP transceiver, which can be connected to a PC for spectrum display and operation as an SDR. It has a fast LTC2165 ADC with a 122.88 Msps sample rate, so it should have good performance figures. Transmit power is 5W to 8W. It can be used standalone or with a PC running the Elad FDM-SW2 software.

ICOM IC-7300

The IC-7300 is the first software defined radio to be released by one of the 'big three' amateur radio manufacturers. It is a true DDS SDR with on board DSP.

SUMMARY

Some of these radios use quadrature sampling and some use direct digital synthesis. The Alinco is a + SDR radio with a conventional Superheterodyne architecture and I.F. DSP. The KX3, SDR Cube, and FDM-Duo are all QRP transceivers and the others are 100 Watt HF transceivers. All of them offer at least a taste of the software defined radio experience, while also offering the ability to be used without connection to an external PC. If you want to, you can forget the internal technology and use the radio the in same way as the radios that you are familiar with. An SDR with knobs may be just what you are looking for. But... do you get the 'best of both worlds?'

ON-BOARD OR EXTERNAL DSP?

The digital signal processing functions like filtering, demodulation, modulation, and audio signal processing are software functions performed on the digital signals after the ADC sampling process. The DSP software can be implemented in several ways:

- Dedicated DSP chips inside the radio: These are the same specialized DSP chips as the ones used in many conventional amateur radio transceivers and receivers. These chips are specialized 'microprocessor like' devices, which can be updated periodically by uploading new firmware to the radio. Examples of radios that use dedicated DSP chips include the FlexRadio Systems Signature 6000 series, the Elecraft KX3, and most of the 'SDR with knobs' radios.

- Software running on a computer chip inside the radio: This could be a 'soft core' microprocessor emulation or Verilog code running on an FPGA. Or it can be software running on a microcontroller, an ARM (Advanced RISC Machine) chip, or a microprocessor. The difference is that this approach uses a computer or FPGA rather than 'commercial off the shelf' (COTS) DSP chips. This type of DSP is also updated by uploading a firmware file to the radio. This technique is used by some of the software defined radios with knobs.

- SDR 'server' software running on a single board computer external to the radio: The server box could be updated via a direct network connection, or updates might be 'pushed' down over your local network from a client application running on your PC.

- Software running on a PC mounted inside the same box as the radio. The internal PC might run the Windows or MAC operating system, Linux is the most common. The PC in the box works just like your desktop or notebook PC. The SDR software would be updated from the Internet. The Expert Electronics MB1 transceiver is an example of this approach.

- Software running on your PC, as a part of your favorite SDR program: The SDR software would be updated from the Internet. With some radios, you can choose from a selection of SDR applications. This is the traditional 'thick client' approach used by most SDR equipment manufacturers. The radio hardware acts as a front end and the DSP is done by SDR software running on your PC. Examples include everything from the SoftRock kits to the Apache Labs ANAN radios.

If the radio is to be used as a stand-alone device without the need to connect it to a PC, the DSP has be done inside the radio. But even in the, 'no knobs' radios which do need a PC there is a strong trend towards moving the DSP functions away from the PC and into the radio. This idea of splitting the DSP 'server' activities from the control and display 'client' activities has many advantages. The most important being the dramatic reduction in the amount of wasted data being sent from the radio to the PC over the Ethernet connection. With the 'thin client' on-board DSP radios, only the wanted data like the panadapters that you want to display and the receivers that you want to hear is sent to the PC.

Some direct sampling SDRs with knobs, like the Expert Electronics MB1 and ADT-200A, which can be used without connection to a PC, use a built-in computer. This internal PC is setup to run PC based SDR software usually specifically designed for the radio. This architecture is convenient but expensive, because you have to pay for a computer as well as the radio. It is a good idea if you want a high performance SDR all in one box without the need for network connections or USB interconnection cables. The internal PC can run other programs at the same time as the radio; like your station log, contesting software, or digital modes.

Stand-alone generation three SDRs, like the Elecraft KX3, usually use dedicated DSP chips similar to those used in conventional architecture radios. Unfortunately, you don't get the advantage of the internal DSP processing when you operate the KX3 using PC based SDR software. You only get an audio frequency IQ stream for use with 'sound card' SDR software.

There are some good arguments for performing the DSP processes inside the PC software. The best one is that it makes the radio hardware cheaper. But overall, I think that the benefits of the thin client, DSP inside the radio, method are becoming obvious. Unless there is a step change in the amount of data that can be routed to the PC over Ethernet or USB, the thin client mode is going to win. It is not such an important issue for small box receivers and dongles because they generally do not support more than one panadapter. The software supporting those types will probably continue to be based on the cheaper DSP in the PC software approach. After all, low cost is one of the big advantages of those radios.

High performance HF transceivers and the wideband VHF/UHF/SHF radios will probably end up with DSP on-board. With the high frequency radios, you want very wide panadapters because the bands are bigger and signals are further apart. For the HF transceivers, you want to display lots of panadapters on different bands. Either option requires huge amounts of data to be passed from the radio to the PC. Sending all of the IQ data for frequencies outside of the wanted bands or panadapters just overloads the data path. With DSP in the radio, you only send the graphics for the panadapters, and the demodulated audio, not all of the underlying IQ data.

The new DFC (direct Fourier conversion) method may eventually replace the DDC direct synthesis method. This approach needs massive computing power because the FFT is done on a very wide received bandwidth. Whether the FFT is performed by a single board computer, or by PC software, the DSP will probably be done by software running on the same computer.

USING ANAN / OPENHPSDR WITH A SINGLE BOARD COMPUTER

Not having DSP on board, is a significant handicap for the Apache Labs ANAN radios because it limits the panadapter bandwidth and the number of panadapters that can be displayed. Unlike the thin client system used by FlexRadio, the ANAN radio sends all of the 24 bit IQ data for each displayed panadapter over the Ethernet connection to the PC. The DSP software running on the PC derives the receiver (audio) signals from the same data as the panadapters. This 'thick client' approach is wasteful of Ethernet bandwidth. It is used because it makes the radio easier to produce. Adding on-board DSP and computer chips would significantly increase the complexity and the cost of the radios.

Members of the OpenHPSDR group are experimenting with a reasonably low cost, 'work around' for this problem. Their proposed solution is to place a very powerful single board computer between the radio hardware and the PC. Currently they are experimenting with the NVIDIA Jetson TK1 computer board. They are adopting a client / server approach similar to that used by FlexRadio Systems. Digital signal processing including the creation of the panadapters will be performed on the Jetson TK1 server and a new client program called 'Thetis' is being developed as a replacement for PowerSDR.

The interface between the radio and the single board computer will run at full 1 GbE (Gigabit Ethernet) capacity allowing the DSP software running on the single board computer access to a slice of a bit over 30 MHz of the HF spectrum. This is compared to around 6.14 MHz of bandwidth available from the transceiver at present. A 16 bit, 61.44 Msps data stream is sent over the Gb Ethernet to the Jetson board. This requires a continuous data rate of 983 Mbits, pushing the limits of the Ethernet connection. USB 3.0 and PCI are other candidates for the interface.

The group is experimenting with using the TK1 computer board to implement direct Fourier conversion (DFC) rather than using digital down conversion performed by the FPGA. The radio plus external computer combination, while a little more expensive, will allow you to display more and wider panadapters and give you the ability to have panadapters of differing sizes. For example, you could set a wide panadapter on 40m and a narrow one on 20m. This project is a great example of the continual development and innovation being applied to ham radio SDR.

Using an external single board computer is an experimental short term solution. I expect that future direct sampling HF SDR transceiver designs will perform the DSP functions inside the radio by using either DSP chips or DSP firmware code running on a built in computer board. The DFC approach is a great idea. If it works as well as expected, it could replace the digital down conversion arrangement. Or perhaps there will be three types of SDR receiver commonly available, QSD, DDC, and DFC. A big advantage of DFC is that the DSP is only being presented with the wanted range of signals. It will be interesting to compare the performance of DFC vs DDC receivers.

THE FLEXRADIO SYSTEMS TRANSCEIVERS

I think that it is fair to say that the FlexRadio FLEX-6700 transceiver and the bundled SmartSDR software is the current leader in the category of 100 Watt software defined HF amateur radio transceivers. It has great technical performance and SmartSDR has some excellent features that are not available on any other amateur radio SDR. Users are kept in touch with developments via 'The Flex Insider' email newsletter and there is a thriving user forum on the company website.

The 6700R is a receiver only version of the FLEX-6700 transceiver. It has the same receiver specifications as the transceiver. The FLEX-6600 is the mid-range transceiver and the FLEX-6400 is the entry level model. Models with an M suffix include the Maestro front panel controls and display. Older models currently still available include the FLEX-6500 and FLEX-6300.

These radios have superb technical performance. The FLEX-6700 is currently at the top of the renowned Sherwood Engineering list. It also rated very well in ARRL testing as reported in the QST review of April 2105.

The 'Signature 6000 series' radios work on the 'thin client' model where the DSP functions are performed by DSP chips inside the radio. A PC is required, to display the panadapters and for control functions. Thin client connections allow the use of less powerful client computers, including Netbooks, tablets, and phones. It will ultimately make remote operation over the Internet easier to achieve. However, this has not been implemented yet because firewall and security issues are yet to be addressed.

MAESTRO

Maestro is a portable user device, or console, for the FlexRadio 6000 series of radios. It is much more than a box supplying the controls that are missing from the front panel of the radio. It is a completely standalone client which can operate the radio without another version of SmartSDR running on your PC. The device has three options for connection to the radio via your home LAN: Wi-Fi, Bluetooth, and Ethernet. As well as control knobs and some buttons, it features an 8 inch touch screen, so you can control the radio with your fingertips. The display can support two panadapters, which is really all you could expect to use on an 8 inch monitor. You can run truly portable, as there is an internal battery pack. The radio has jacks for electret or dynamic microphones, Morse key or bug, PTT, speakers and headphones. There is a mono speaker inside as well.

With Maestro you really can operate your FlexRadio from anywhere in the house. I expect that the long term intention will be that Maestro will become the client terminal when you operate your FlexRadio remotely over the Internet. Future options might include running SmartSDR on the PC and Maestro at the same time.

SMARTSDR

SmartSDR is the software package that is provided with the FlexRadio Systems Signature 6000 series. I have no firsthand experience with it since I don't own one of those radios yet. I admit that I am very keen to try out SmartSDR, as it looks very impressive. I have gathered some information from online videos and the brochures published by FlexRadio Systems.

Unlike the other software I have discussed, SmartSDR does not include the DSP processing. This is done inside the radio. The GUI display is very modern with most of the screen dedicated to the spectrum panadapter and waterfall displays. Many of the controls are hidden until needed. The most used controls and indicators are displayed in a little box, which attaches to the normal receiver indication. This information stays with the receiver when you move it across the panadapter. The receiver is shown as a vertical line indicating the nominal carrier frequency and a shaded zone indicating the receiver bandwidth. FlexRadio call this a 'slice receiver.' The new GUI has some very advanced and clever features, which make it very user friendly.

SPECTRUM PANADAPTER

Each SmartSDR panadapter can be extended out to a massive 14 MHz of bandwidth. Normally you would operate with the panadapter set to cover a band of interest, for example the 350 kHz wide 20m band, or perhaps just the CW segment. If you have a FLEX-6700, SmartSDR can support up to eight panadapters and eight slice receivers, using up to two different antennas. You can have more than two slice receivers on a panadapter. For example, you could have a receiver on CW, one on PSK, and also monitor both sides of a split SSB operation. Then you still have four spare panadapters to watch signals on four other bands!

The FLEX-6600 has two receiver ADCs (called Spectral Capture Units) so it can receive signals from two antennas at the same time.

The FLEX-6600 and FLEX-6500 support up to four 14 MHz panadapters and four slice receivers. The FLEX-6300 and FLEX-6400 support up to two 7 MHz panadapters and two slice receivers.

A neat feature is that you can change scale of the display in either direction by simply dragging the axis with the computer mouse. To make the panadapter wider just drag the display to the right. To change the level of the displayed signals just drag the vertical axis. This sounds very logical but most SDR software can't do it. You can change the receiver slice frequency by dragging it left or right and you can move the whole panadapter higher or lower in frequency by dragging that. Finally, you can move the divider between the spectrum and the waterfall to make a big waterfall and a narrow spectrum or the other way around.

THE WATERFALL DISPLAY

Experienced SDR users and digital mode operators are used to using a waterfall display. Most people prefer to run both the spectrum and the waterfall at the same time because they both contribute useful information. The waterfall shows the history of what has been happening on the spectrum display. This mode is called 'Panafall.' Each SmartSDR panadapter can simultaneously display a waterfall display.

The SmartSDR waterfall display adds some new features that are not included on the majority of SDR software packages.

Older programs like PowerSDR store the waterfall information as a graphics image, like a photo, that is built up line by line. As each line is added to the top, the oldest line disappears from the bottom of the picture. If you change the panadapter frequency, the colored vertical lines showing active signals, curve to the new frequency. If you reduce the panadapter bandwidth, the waterfall lines will suddenly transition to a wider trace. In other words, the waterfall shows the history of the spectrum exactly as it was when it was captured.

Unlike most SDR programs, if you change the panadapter width on SmartSDR the waterfall display adjusts to compensate. It recalculates the entire displayed waterfall at any time that you change the frequency or bandwidth. This may not sound like a big deal, but it is a very nice feature. When the panadapter is dragged wider, the whole waterfall adjusts to a wider or narrower trace, not just the top line. This can create black voids where the spectrum information had not been captured, but overall I think it looks better. If the panadapter frequency is changed, the whole waterfall moves with it, so you don't get curved traces.

The other innovation is that you can stop the waterfall and look back into the history. Depending on the update speed that you are using, you can scroll back and see waterfall images that occurred up to 10 minutes earlier. While you are doing this, the waterfall is still being recorded, so you don't miss anything when you return to the normal mode. This feature is available on at least one other SDR application. With that program, you can actually listen to signals back in time as well.

In common with most other SDR software, you can change the colors and brightness of the waterfall display. Or you can select an automatic mode, which adjusts to different band noise and signal levels. Most users will leave the radio on this automatic setting. There is quite a nice grey scale option and a sort of inverted mode where signals show up dark on a bright background. This last mode can show very weak signals, so it would be good when using transverters or for other weak signal work.

Technical TIP: When you drag the panadapter wide, the radio switches to a wideband mode by switching out the front end receiver pre-selector filters.

TRACKING NOTCH FILTER

The tracking notch filter is a useful feature that SmartSDR inherited from its older cousin PowerSDR. It is good to see it back.

Most notch filters are implemented on the audio signal after the demodulator. You use a notch filter to eliminate interference carriers and 'birdies' within the passband of the receiver. They eliminate signals that are static or that change much more slowly than the wanted speech signal. Often you can adjust the depth of the notch, its bandwidth, and the audio center frequency. An automatic notch filter can find the interfering carrier and move the notch onto it. Sometimes the interference is a bunch of carriers or a modulated signal. If you set the notch fairly wide, it should be able to eliminate any 'long term' signal.

The trick with the FlexRadio tracking notch filter is that it remembers the RF frequency that the radio is on as well as the audio offset. In effect, it remembers the frequency of the interfering signal. So when you change frequency the notch moves as well. It stays on top of the interfering signal. A standard notch filter would continue to filter the same audio frequency even when the radio was moved to a new frequency. If you go away to a different part of the band or even another band and then return later, the notch will still be in place, filtering out the interference signal.

CWX (CW EXCHANGE)

CWX is similar to the CWX Morse keyer included with PowerSDR. You can send as you type, or type ahead and then send. It has text macros that are easy to change. They are mapped to the keyboard function controls so they can be sent either by clicking the mouse or by pressing a function key. The radio can do full break-in 'QSK' up to very high speeds. It supplies everything you need from an auto-keyer. But it is not a full digital mode option, as it does not include a CW decoder for reading Morse code.

API (APPLICATION PROGRAMMING INTERFACE)

The SmartSDR API is a novel feature of SmartSDR. Even though the SmartSDR application is not 'open source,' the API allows software developers to contribute functions and extensions. In fact, the hardware level API could allow you to write a complete replacement for SmartSDR. This gives the radio a link into the Open Source development resource and I am sure some great features will result from this collaboration. There is already a FreeDV digital Voice implementation available for use with SmartSDR, which uses the Waveform API.

LAN REMOTE

The LAN remote function is one of the cool new functions of SmartSDR. It allows you to operate the radio remotely from any computer connected to your private LAN. You can use a notebook PC connected by Wi-Fi, a desktop

PC, or even some mobile devices. Eventually it will probably be extended to allow operation of the radio over the Internet.

Using LAN remote, the radio supports devices connected by Wi-Fi although the signal needs to be good. The 'widget' on SmartSDR displays a signal strength indication, which actually shows signal quality and latency rather than Wi-Fi signal strength. The indicator looks like the signal indicator on your mobile phone. A right mouse click brings up a small popup window with more information about the remote data connection and quality.

LAN Remote allows you to use your FlexRadio away from the radio hardware. You can sit in the lounge or the kitchen rather than going out to a cold shack in the winter. Or maybe just leave the radio running while you are waiting for a friend to call. The audio from the receiver comes out of the PC speakers on the remote computer and if there is a microphone it will be live for transmit. If the MOX (microphone operated switch) button has been selected, you can use the keyboard space bar as a PTT control. To reduce the pickup of background noise like the PC fan, it is recommended that you use a USB headset if you intend to operate using a remote setup.

DAX (DIGITAL AUDIO EXCHANGE)

DAX is used to connect audio signals to other applications, mostly digital mode software. You can also send IQ signals to an external program so that you can run external SDR software, for example a DRM receiver. For each of the DAX audio output channels a sound card is created on your PC, which provides receive audio to your digital mode software. All of the DAX outputs can work at the same time. A single DAX sound card is created for routing audio from digital mode programs to SmartSDR. Only one transmit audio channel is required since the radio can only transmit one signal at a time.

If you have a FLEX-6700, there are DAX audio channels for each of the eight slice receivers, (four in the 6500 and two in the 6300). There are also four IQ output channels. You can connect each receiver slice to a DAX audio channel. Then you can configure your digital mode program to work with the DAX channel. The DAX channels are included in the list of available Windows sound cards, so they can be selected in the setup tabs of the digital mode applications.

SmartSDR can send audio or IQ data to multiple digital mode programs at the same time. You can receive digital modes simultaneously on different bands with automatic transmit switching as required. This can be used to operate modes such as PSK on 20m while working JT65 on 40m, or to operate the same mode across several bands at the same time. You can even run full duplex, receiving on one band while transmitting on another. For example, you can hold two JT65 conversations at the same time, transmitting JT65 on even minutes on one band and odd minutes on another band. How cool is that? The DAX IQ channels can be used in any combination, which does not exceed a total of 384 ksps. The options are; 1x 384 ksps, 2 x 192 ksps, 1 x 192 ksps plus 2 x 96 ksps, or 4 x 96 ksps.

Technical TIP: Windows defaults to an audio sample rate of 44.1 kHz, the standard data rate for CD audio. But the connection works best when set to a multiple of the 24 kHz sample rate used by SmartSDR. It is suggested that you change the sample rate on all of the DAX audio 'sound cards' to the 48 kHz sample rate.

FLEXRADIO SYSTEMS, SMARTSDR API – TECHNICAL DESCRIPTION

The FlexRadio Systems 'SmartSDR' program is a client / server application. In this case, the server is running as a Linux application on the ARM processor in the radio. The client is a Windows application running on your PC. The client has distinct layers. At the bottom there is a data handling section, which manages the interface with the server software in the radio. The communication is UDP and TCP-IP packets carried over the Ethernet interface. The UDP packets carry all of the panadapters, waterfalls, IQ streams, audio from the PC to the radio, and the audio streams from each active Slice Receiver. The TCP-IP packets carry control and status information. TCP-IP uses a standard socket connection to port 4992. The data is not encrypted and currently no authorization is required. An authorization requirement will be incorporated before the ability to control the radio over the Internet is included into SmartSDR. At the moment, the radio can only be used by devices running on the same subnet as the radio, (i.e. your home network). The data format of the UDP packets follows the ANSI VITA49 extended standard. Control over the TCP-IP is in the form of easy to read text strings, so it is easy to develop applications to remote control or read information from the radio. You can ask the radio to send you application an IQ stream or audio from a receiver via the UDP packets.

The next layer is a dynamic link library called FlexLib. It converts the VITA49 data into complex and real streams, which can be used by high-level software.

The top layer is a Windows based .NET graphical user interface application.

SmartSDR offers three levels of API. That means that if you are writing a program that will talk to a FlexRadio there are three ways you can arrange for your program to interface with the radio. They are called the 'Waveform API' the 'Ethernet (or Network) API' and the 'Flexlib API'. The API that you choose to interface with depends on what you are trying to achieve.

THE FLEXLIB API

The FlexLib software library provides access to SmartSDR commands, control signals, radio status, panadapter, waterfall, panel meter, and data samples. If you are writing an application that will run on a Windows based PC and you like using a high-level .NET based programming language like C or C# then you would interface to SmartSDR using FlexLib. This will be the best option for people who want to link data from the radio with the logging or digital mode program that they have written for Windows. It is effectively the same level of access as the SmartSDR GUI client has.

The FlexLib library provides a way to create much faster and more closely integrated connections between the radio software and digital mode programs than using traditional CAT control does. I expect that the developers of software such as Fldigi, MixW, and HRD will be interested in using the FlexLib API to add direct FlexRadio support to their digital mode applications.

THE ETHERNET, (NETWORK) API

You could use the Ethernet API if you were writing a completely new client program designed to connect with the server software running inside the radio. This level of API concentrates on receiving and sending UDP and TCP-IP data to and from the radio. It can operate without SmartSDR, but that means that you would have to duplicate a lot of the functionality of SmartSDR in your new program. This added complexity makes writing code that uses the Ethernet API level of access to the FlexRadio a much more challenging programming task. The most logical use of the Ethernet API would be to create a SDR client application, which would run on the Linux or Mac platforms.

The interface between your software and the radio will be faster since your application is directly connected to the server inside the radio. Commands and data streams sent over the Ethernet do not have to be passed through SmartSDR.

Since the Net FlexLib library will only work on a Windows platform, you can't use the FlexLib access to interface a FlexRadio with an application designed to run on a Linux, Mac, or an Android based computing device. So if you want to interface a FlexRadio with a program running on a 'non Windows' device, you have to use the Ethernet API.

THE WAVEFORM API

The third type of API is different because the code does not run on the client PC. You can download your firmware code into the radio and run it on the ARM processor. The SmartSDR client is set up to access Waveform API functions. If you add a new operating mode, SmartSDR will automatically create a button on the GUI for it. This is very cool indeed. Your open source software can add functions to the FlexRadio server software. Wow!

The Waveform API it is primarily intended for new modes. For example, you could add; digital voice, JT65, WSPR, or DRM as a standard mode. Or perhaps a new noise filter, CW keyer, or a PSK decoder. The possibilities are endless. These new functions could be added by interfacing with the high level APIs on the PC, but this way, the new function is actually in the radio. The advantage of this becomes apparent when you operate the radio using different computers. You would not need special software patches or additional software. Also, it means that there is no additional Ethernet bandwidth required to implement the new mode.

THE APACHE LABS ANAN TRANSCEIVERS

Apache Labs has replaced its old line up with two new transceivers, the 100W 7000DLE and the 200W 8000DLE. Both cover the HF bands and 6m. The 7000DLE comes in the familiar aluminum extrusion case while the 8000DLE comes in a completely new case design.

There are five older models, two 10W QRP models, the ANAN-10 and the ANAN-10E. The ANAN-10E was cheaper with a correspondingly lower specification. There were three 100W models. The ANAN-100 uses the Hermes transceiver board, the ANAN-100D has the Angelia board with dual ADCs, and the ANAN-200D has the Orion board with dual ADCs and a bigger, faster FPGA. More specifications are included in the glossary of software defined radios.

Technical TIP: Confusingly the 'European' versions of these transceivers, sold in England, had an E added to the model name. This means that the ANAN-10 became the ANAN-10E and the ANAN-10E was the ANAN-10EE. Not great thinking in the naming department! This means that an English ANAN-10E has a higher specification than an ANAN-10E purchased in or from any other country. In Europe, the 100 Watt models were known as the ANAN-100E, the ANAN-100DE, and the ANAN-200DE.

The Apache Labs ANAN series of radios are all direct digital synthesis, (DDC / DUC) radios for the HF bands. They have excellent overall performance figures. Using the PureSignal transmit pre-distortion these radio achieve 'best in class' results for transmitter IMD performance and the receiver performance is excellent as well. This chapter covers some technical information about these radios and some tips on using the Alex filters.

PANADAPTERS

PowerSDR mRX is able to display up to three receivers on two different bands, two on the top panadapter and one on the lower panadapter. Depending on the PC performance, cuSDR can display up to seven panadapters with one receiver active at a time. It can also display a full HF spectrum using the 'wideband' function. Note that Apache Labs specifies a maximum of four panadapters for the ANAN-100, but using cuSDR, I can display five panadapters plus the wideband display. Other software may also support multiple panadapters and receivers.

Technical TIP: The current FPGA firmware and communications frame structure from the radio to the PC supports up to seven panadapters. A revised communications frame structure designed for Gigabit Ethernet is under development. This will increase the data throughput making the display of multiple and wider panadapters possible. At present, all panadapters have the same maximum bandwidth. Future options may allow panadapters to have different sample rates, which would result in them having different maximum bandwidths.

THE ALEX FILTERS

The high pass pre-selector filters and the low pass filters used for both transmit and receive are known as the Alex filters because 'Alexiares' was the project name for the original OpenHPSDR design. The name was quickly abbreviated to Alex. The PowerSDR mRX and cuSDR programs both refer to the filters as 'Alex Filters'.

Many of the OpenHPSDR boards are named after Greek, Roman and even Norse mythological entities. Alexiares was a son of Hercules who along with his twin brother Anicetus helped his father act as the gatekeeper of Olympus. A gatekeeper is a fitting description of the role of these filters in the software defined radio design. The Alex filters were designed by Graham Haddock, KE9H with drawing and other technical support from Phil Harman, VK6PH.

The SDR software automatically switches the front end 'Alex' high pass and low pass filters inside the ANAN radio. The low pass filters are used on transmit to limit harmonics and they are used on receive to provide additional protection from aliased signals from the VHF spectrum above the wanted band. The high pass filters protect the dynamic range of the receiver by cutting out signals below the wanted band, particularly AM broadcast signals. In manual mode, you can bypass any, or all, of the high pass filters. If none of the bypass options are selected the radio acts the same as it does in automatic mode.

After passing through the low pass filters, the received signal is routed via the TR switch to the high pass filter section, which contains five software selectable high pass filters that can be bypassed using software commands.

The five high pass filters are not ham band specific. They break the spectrum into zones so that the receiver retains general coverage receive capability. The sixth filter selection is a band pass filter for the 6m band. It includes a low noise amplifier. The Alex board also includes software selectable 10 dB and 20 dB attenuators before the high pass filters.

The ANAN-7000DLE and 8000DLE models have receiver filter banks for both ADCs, all of the other models only have receiver filter banks for ADC1, except for the ANAN-10 transceivers which do not have any at all.

TWIN ANALOG TO DIGITAL CONVERTERS

The ANAN-100D, 200D, 7000DLE and 8000DLE models have two ADCs. This provides two coherent receiver front-ends. The two receiver outputs are in phase because both ADCs share the same clock signal. These models are capable of diversity reception, which can be used for beam steering, diversity noise reduction using a 'noise antenna' or simply using a specialized receiving antenna such as a Beverage at the same time as your main antenna.

The RX2 BNC connector on the back of the ANAN-100D and 200D radios is always connected to the second ADC and the received signal is not routed through any of the high pass or low pass filters apart from the fixed 55 MHz 'anti-alias' low pass filter on the Angelia or Orion board. This means that the input to ADC2 is always wideband. If you did happen to experience overload on RX2 you could add an external filter.

Technical TIP: Don't confuse the RX2 BNC input port on the radio, which is always connected to ADC2, with the RX2 receiver in PowerSDR mRX. The RX2 receiver can show signals from either ADC1 or ADC2 depending on a selection made on the ADC setup tab. It would be much easier if the developers referred to the wideband signals being carried from the radio to the PC as panadapters and the narrow bandwidth slices on those panadapters as receivers.

With the newer 7000DLE and 8000DLE models you can select which antenna port is routed to each ADC.

ANAN ANTENNA SWITCHING – 100 W TRANSCEIVERS

The older 100 W ANAN transceivers have eight RF BNC connectors on the rear panel. Each input and output is controlled by software selectable switches. The ANAN-7000DLE has 7 antenna connectors and the 8000DLE has three.

ANAN-100, 100D and 200D rear panel BNC connectors

1. ANT1, ANT2, and ANT3 are the three connectors normally used for connection to transmitting or receiving antennas. The 100W transmitter output must be routed to one of these three ANT ports. Received signals pass through both the selected low pass filter and the selected high pass filter

2. EXT1, EXT2, and XVTR inputs are routed through the high pass filter but not the low pass filter. You can use these ports for connection of a receive only antenna or for the feedback signal from a splitter used for PureSignal transmit pre-distortion

3. BYPASS is an output for the connection of an external splitter, amplifier or filter. After the external device use one of the EXT ports to route the signal back inside the radio

4. On an ANAN-100D or 200D, the RX2 input is always connected to ADC2. The received signals are not routed through the high pass filter or the low pass filter, only the anti-alias 55 MHz low pass filter on the Angelia / Orion board. On an ANAN-100, the RX2 BNC connector is not connected to anything inside the radio.

For the transmitter there are three antenna connectors, which the SDR software can automatically select for different bands. For example you could have your tri-band Yagi on antenna port one, a 6m antenna on port two and a low band antenna on port three.

There are several ways to configure the receive signal path. In normal use, the signal comes from the same antenna port as the transmitter is using. It passes through the low pass filter and then the high pass filter and on to the Hermes, Angelia, or Orion board. If you want to insert an external filter or pre-amplifier, you can route the signal through the 'Bypass' output and back into the radio via either one of the two 'EXT' inputs. An external filter can be useful if you are using the radio in a multi-radio contesting situation or for a DXpedition.

You can use the EXT1, EXT2, or XVTR RX inputs to connect a 'receive only' antenna such as a Beverage for the low bands. The signal will pass through the high pass filters to the transceiver board, but it is not routed through the low pass filters. Either of the EXT input connectors can be used for the input from the coupler used for the PureSignal pre-distortion function. You must make sure that the level is suitably attenuated.

Finally, there is the RX2 input connector. On an ANAN-100 it is not connected to anything. On the ANAN-100D and 200D, the RX2 input is always connected directly to the second ADC. It is not routed through either the low pass or high pass filters, so the RX2 receiver input is always wideband.

Sometimes there is confusion, about which panadapters are allocated to which ADC. This is in large part due to the PowerSDR developer's practice of referring to panadapters as "receivers." Firmware version 3.4 for Angelia introduced the ability to assign any of the seven possible panadapters to either ADC1 or to ADC2. If no alternate selections are made the radio will default to using ADC1 for all seven panadapters.

THE APACHE LABS ANAN PA AND FILTER BOARD

The 100W PA Filter board includes the high power RF amplifier and the Alex filters. The 10 Watt transceivers have a smaller power amplifier board that includes the Alex low pass filters, but no high pass filters.

ANAN ANTENNA SWITCHING – 10 W TRANSCEIVERS

The 10 W ANAN transceivers have three RF software selectable BNC connectors on the rear panel. They are used for both transmit and receive. The software can automatically dedicate antenna ports for different bands. For example you could have a multi band vertical on antenna port one, a 6m antenna on port two and a low band dipole on port three.

WHY DO WE NEED ALL THESE FILTERS?

There seems to be a lot of high pass and low pass filters in the receive path and there is yet another low pass filter just before each ADC input on the Hermes / Angelia / Orion board. Why does the radio need all of these filters? There are two answers, one is much more important than the other. The more important reason is protection from aliased signals outside the receiver passband. The other reason is protection from ADC gain compression caused by strong RF signals being applied to the ADC.

What do the filters do?

- The low pass filters block 'out of band' signals above the wanted receive frequencies. They prevent interference from FM broadcast and TV stations.

- The high pass filters block unwanted signals below the wanted range of frequencies, such as AM broadcast stations.

ADC dynamic range compression: The dynamic range of the ADC is affected by the total power of all the signals presented to it. This includes signals within the Nyquist bandwidth such as AM broadcast stations, and also signals above the HF bands, within multiples of the Nyquist bandwidth. In the case of the LTC2208 ADC in an ANAN receiver, the ADC can sample frequencies as high as 700MHz. The large signals which could affect your receiver's performance could include high power stations in the FM broadcast band or TV transmitters. A reduction of dynamic range shows up on the panadapter as a high or fluctuating noise floor. Note that this only occurs with extremely high level signals near the clipping level of the receiver. Receiving medium level signals will not affect the noise floor very much at all and will act to reduce the effects of intermodulation distortion. So, receiving a normal range of signals will actually enhance your radios performance.

Technical TIP: If you select Alex manual mode and bypass the high pass filters and you do not notice any rise in the noise floor then the radio is not being subjected to extremely high signal strength signals. At most locations this will be the case.

Receiving Nyquist alias signals: The ability to sample frequencies above the Nyquist bandwidth is known as aliasing. It is a technique used in commercial SDR receivers for receiving signals above the ADC sample rate. For example, the ADC used in the ANAN radio can sample frequencies as high as 700MHz. In our receivers and transceivers, we don't want the ADC to sample signals from above the Nyquist bandwidth because once they are sampled they can't be removed. The 55 MHz 'anti alias' low pass filter near the ADC inputs of the ANAN transceiver boards ensure that any aliased signals are attenuated by at least 100 dB and end up below the noise floor.

The FM band extends from about 88 MHz to 108 MHZ, which would appear as signals between 34.88 and 18.88 MHz in the receiver. At my place, I can't see any sign of the local FM stations within that frequency range even when the filters are set to bypass. So the anti-alias filters are working well.

Technical TIP: You can't bypass the 55MHz low pass filter on the Hermes, Angelia, or Orion boards via the PC software. If you want to deliberately receive VHF signals above 61.44MHz you would need to physically remove it or bridge it out.

The front end filters can mess up your ability to take advantage of the capability to display multiple panadapters on different bands or use the wideband spectrum display. You have to bypass them if you want to view signals on multiple bands. In most cases unless you live in Europe where there are often very close FM and TV stations, bypassing the filters will have no effect on the receiver performance. At my QTH on the 20m band, I see no increase in the noise floor and no unwanted new signals at all when the filters are switched to bypass mode. It is difficult to persuade PowerSDR to bypass the low pass filters because they are automatically selected for the transmit frequency in use. You can adjust the frequencies at which the radio changes filters, so that it switches to bypass when the radio is tuned to a frequency outside the ham bands, but the default is for a low pass filter to be always in circuit. If you want full unfiltered receive capability it is probably easier to use the EXT1 or EXT2 antenna connectors. With cuSDR, the low pass filter engages for each ham band and automatically drops to bypass when the radio is tuned to a frequency outside of a ham band.

POWERSDR MRX FILTER SWITCHING

PowerSDR mRX automatically selects the correct high pass and low pass filters to match the band currently displayed on the panadapter, but this presents a problem when you want to monitor two bands at the same time. The filters may block signals being received on the second band. This is overcome by changing the way that the filters are switched, when two bands are being monitored.

If you turn on RX2 (the bottom panadapter), the radio sets the high pass filter to the lowest band in use and the low pass filter to the highest band in use. This might mean that the low pass filter does not match the band that you will transmit on, so when you switch to transmit, the correct low pass filter is switched in. If Alex is switched to manual mode, you can see this working by looking at the 'radio buttons' on the Setup, ANT/Filters, HPF/LPF tab. The switching still works with Alex set to auto, but the radio buttons on the setup tab don't indicate the changes.

The high pass filter protects the dynamic range of the receiver by cutting out signals below the wanted band. In the absence of strong signals from nearby AM broadcast stations etc., you will probably not notice any reduction in dynamic range if you bypass the high pass filters. You can easily tell if there is any dynamic range compression because the noise floor on the panadapter display will rise when the high pass filter is switched to bypass.

If there is no rise in the noise floor, you don't have a problem from this type of interference.

The way PowerSDR mRX switches the filters depends on whether you have the Alex filters set to manual or automatic mode. You can edit the table of frequencies that PowerSDR mRX uses to decide when to switch filters, but the filters themselves have fixed frequency responses.

- You can bypass all of the high pass filters by setting the 'Bypass /55MHz LPF' check box on the ANT/Filters setup tab and then pressing the 'ALEX' switch to select the manual mode.

- You can bypass individual high pass filters by setting the relevant check boxes. Then then pressing the 'ALEX' switch to select the manual mode.

- If the ALEX button is highlighted (automatic mode selected) the high pass filters will be selected according to the frequency table on the setup tab.

- If the ALEX button is not highlighted (manual mode selected) and you have no filters set to bypass, the software acts exactly the same way as when in the automatic mode.

- The high pass filters are not ham band specific they are designed to work when the receiver is used as a general coverage receiver as well. This is different to the settings used by cuSDR, where the radio drops back to bypass mode between ham bands.

Technical TIP: The Bypass /55MHz LPF check box on the ANT/Filters setup tab bypasses the High Pass Filter bank, leaving only the 55MHz Low pass filter on the radio board, and the current low pass filter in circuit.

PowerSDR mRX selects the high pass filter (HPF) according to the table on the ANT/Filters setup tab. You can change the frequencies on the table if you want to. Note that changing the table does not change the filters themselves; it only changes the frequencies where PowerSDR switches between filters.

Power SDR mRX – default high pass filters	
Filter name	**HPF default settings**
1.5 MHz	1.8 MHz – 6.499999 MHz
6.5 MHz	6.5 MHz – 9.499999 MHz
9.5 MHz	9.5 MHz – 12.999999 MHz
13 MHz	13 MHz – 19.999999 MHz
20 MHz	20 MHz – 49.999999 MHz
6m BPF/LNA	50 MHz – 61.440000 MHz

The default is for a high pass filter to be always selected, but you can make the radio switch to bypass mode outside of the ham bands by adjusting the numbers in the table so that there are gaps between bands.

If for example you set the 13 MHz filter to be active between 13.000 MHz and 13.999999 MHz the receiver would drop to bypass mode when the radio was tuned between 14 MHz and 19.999999 MHz.

- Selecting the bypass check box beside any of the HPF filters causes the receiver to switch to bypass, provided;

    a) the receiver is tuned to a frequency within that filter range, and

    b) the Alex switch is set to manual, and

    c) the 'Bypass/55MHz LPF' check box is not selected.

- Selecting the 'Bypass/55MHz LPF' checkbox causes all the high pass filters to be bypassed whenever the Alex switch is set to manual.

- With an ANAN-100 radio, both the RX1 and the RX2 panadapters use the single ADC and are connected to the same antenna. You cannot have RX2 on a different antenna to RX1.

- With the ANAN-100D or ANAN-200D radios, the RX1 and the RX2 panadapters can be connected to either of the ADCs. ADC2 is always connected to the RX2 BNC input connector. ADC1 is normally connected to ANT1 but it can be switched to one of the other BNC connectors.

- In the current release of PowerSDR mRX, the 'radio buttons' indicating the filter selection on the ANT/Filters setup tab do not indicate the current status of the filter selection, when ALEX is in the auto mode.

When one panadapter is in use the low pass filter (LPF) is selected according to the transmit frequency. When two panadapters are in use, the LPF is set to the higher of the two bands while receiving and the correct band for the transmission while transmitting.

- A low pass filter is always selected while the radio is transmitting. It remains in circuit when the radio is receiving if you are using; ANT1, ANT2, or ANT 3 for your receiving antenna.

- Low pass filters are not included in the receive path if you use the RX2 input for ADC2 on an ANAN-100D/200D.

- They are also not included in the receive path if you use the EXT1, EXT2, or XVTR antenna ports for receiving.

- It is not possible to use software switching to bypass the low pass filter. But selecting the 6m low pass filter has the same effect.

- There is no user control of the LPF filter selection, but you can change the frequencies that cause PowerSDR to switch between filters, creating gaps where the radio will select the 6m filter.

Power SDR mRX – default low pass filters	
Filter name	**LPF default settings**
160m	0 MHz – 2.5 MHz
80m	2.500001 – 5 MHz
60/40m	5.000001 – 8 MHz
30/20m	8.000001 – 16.5 MHz
17/15m	16.500001 – 27.8 MHz
12/10m	27.800001 – 35.6 MHz
6m / Bypass	35.600001 – 61.44 MHz

CUSDR FILTER SWITCHING

Filter selection operates differently in cuSDR. This is because the default settings for the high pass filter and low pass filter switching is not contiguous in cuSDR. The switching frequencies are aligned to the ham bands rather than to general coverage. When you tune to frequencies outside of the ham bands, the filters automatically switch out and the radio operates in wideband mode. cuSDR can display up to seven panadapters at the same time, making the filter operation even more of a challenge.

In the default (automatic) situation, the second and subsequent panadapters are likely to display no signals, until you click the mouse on that spectrum display. This shifts the focus and rearranges the filter switches to that band. This is a bit counter-intuitive since you would expect that every time you open another panadapter that it would be working.

- If you have an ANAN-100D, or ANAN-200D the RX2 panadapter will always show the signal from the 2nd ADC which is connected to the RX2 antenna port. If you want to view another panadapter on the main antenna, simply open a 3rd panadapter and then close the RX2 one.

- Unlike PowerSDR mRX, if you click the mouse on a panadapter, the filters will change to the settings for that display. For example if RX1 is on 20m and RX2 is on 10m, clicking on RX1 will cause signals on the 20m band to display, but the signals on RX2 will disappear. Clicking on RX2 will cause the 10m signals on RX2 to appear, but the 20m signals on RX1 will disappear.

It is not very useful to have seven panadapters unless they can all display signals at the same time. To do that you need to bypass the filters.

Technical TIP: This is a problem with all multi-panadapter SDR receivers. You want to have band pass filters to protect the radio from big out of band signals that could cause aliasing or ADC gain compression, but you also want to be able to take advantage of the ability to display two or more bands at the same time. The best option is a receiver with dual ADCs and dual or switched band pass filter, banks.

One very neat feature of cuSDR is that you can see the effect of the filters that you have selected on the wideband display.

As the filters are changed, you can see the spectrum respond. Of course, if your antenna is a mono-bander most of the energy will (hopefully) be in the band that the antenna is on.

CUSDR ALEX AUTO / ALEX MAN FILTER SETTINGS

Automatic mode: If the Alex Auto button is showing as selected (blue border) on the main cuSDR display, the radio is set for automatic filter selection. This does not seem to be connected with the frequencies in the tables on the HPSDR Filter setup tab.

In automatic mode;

- The green filter selection indicators on the setup tab will not indicate the true state of the filter switching.

- ANAN-100: Until you click on the panadapter to shift the focus, the second and any subsequent panadapters will not display any signals unless they are on the same band as the active selected slice.

- ANAN-100D: Until you click on the panadapter to shift the focus, the third and any subsequent panadapters will not display any signals unless they are on the same band as the active selected slice. However, the second receiver panadapter will work because it is connected to the 2nd ADC via the RX2 antenna port, which is not routed through the low pass or the high pass filters.

Manual mode: If the Alex Man button is showing as not selected (no blue border) on the main cuSDR display, the radio is still uses automatic filter selection! But now, the manual selections and the frequencies in the HPF and LPF tables are active.

In manual mode;

- As you change bands, for example by clicking on the wideband display, the green indicators on the Filters setup page will show the current filter selection.

- You can force the HPF to 'bypass' by setting the bypass button to on.
- You can temporarily remove an HPF band from the table by setting an individual band bypass button to on (blue).
- If you don't have any bypass buttons selected, the radio will;
    i.   Operate in **automatic mode** based on the frequencies in the HPF and LPF tables.

    ii. If the radio slice is tuned to a frequency outside of any of the HPF filters, the HPF will switch to bypass.

    iii. If the radio slice is tuned to a frequency outside of any of the LPF filters the LPF will switch to the 6m position (effectively the same as a bypass).

    iv. It is possible for HPF to be bypassed but not LPF and vice versa.

What this means is that even when switched to 'Alex Man' the radio will probably not display signals on all of the active panadapters and the wideband display will be filtered, not fully wideband. The best way to force cuSDR to display all receiver panadapters properly is to select Alex Man on the main cuSDR display and turn on the Bypass button (blue) on the HPSDR filter setup tab.

The panadapter containing the active receiver is the one that sets the filter selection. All of the panadapters can display a receiver slice, but you can only hear the one on the active panadapter. If you click on another panadapter, the filters will change to the settings for that band and you will hear the audio from the displayed receiver. The high pass and low pass filters may be active or bypassed according to the frequency ranges in the tables below.

cuSDR default high pass filter settings (Alex set to manual)		
Filter name	Band	HPF Default settings
1.5 MHz HPF	160m, 80m, 60m	1.500 MHz to 5.500 MHz
6.5 MHz HPF	40m	7.000 MHz to 7.300 MHz
9.5 MHz HPF	30m	10.000 MHz to 10.150 MHz
13 MHz HPF	20m, 17m	14.000 MHz to 18.168 MHz
20 MHz HPF	15m, 12m, 10m	21.000 MHz to 29.700 MHz
50 - 61.66 MHz BPF	6m	50.000 MHz to 54.000 MHz

Note that unlike PowerSDR mRX, the default high pass filter settings have gaps where the radio will default to bypass. In the Auto Alex mode, as you tune across the HF spectrum, the radio will switch in the high pass and low pass filters. Outside of the nominated frequencies, the filters are switched out and the radio input becomes wideband.

cuSDR default low pass filter settings (Alex set to manual)	
Filter name / band	LPF Default settings
160m	1.800 MHz to 2.000 MHz
80m	3.500 MHz to 4.000 MHz
60/40m	5.330 MHz to 7.300 MHz
30/20m	10.100 MHz to 14.35 MHz
17/15m	18.068 MHz to 21.450 MHz
12/10m	24.890 MHz to 29.700 MHz
6m	50.000 MHz to 54.000 MHz

TRANSMIT PRE-DISTORTION

The 'PureSignal' transmitter 'pre-distortion' function in PowerSDR mRX can dramatically reduce the amount of transmitter intermodulation distortion, making the ANAN radios 'best in class.' This is an important development and it is covered in more detail in the next section. Briefly, a sample of the transmitted output power is taken, usually by using a coupler at the antenna port or at the output of a linear amplifier if you have one. The attenuated RF signal is connected back into the radio via one of the EXT input connectors and demodulated by the receiver. The receiver is always running because the radio is full duplex. The demodulated sample signal is compared with the audio input signal being sent to the modulator. Phase and amplitude changes are applied to the modulation signal to dynamically correct linearity in the power amplifier(s) and thereby reduce the IMD products. The ANAN-200D, 7000DLE and 8000DLE transceivers have internal couplers for sampling the transmitted signal. The other ANAN models require an external coupler, although the system will work reasonably well using 'stray' RF coupling within the transceiver.

If you use a suitable coupler at the output of a linear amplifier, PureSignal can correct for non-linearity in both the transceiver's RF power amplifier and the linear amplifier. It can even correct the non-linearity of a VHF linear amplifier if you are using a full duplex transverter, connected to the ANAN radio's transverter output. The very popular LDMOS 1kW VHF amplifiers can really benefit from this improvement.

HEAT DISSIPATION

The ANAN transceivers have a fairly heavy (2.2 kg on the 100W models) extruded aluminum case which is used as a heatsink to dissipate the heat generated by the electronics inside, especially the RF power amplifier. The radio case feels hot during normal operation. This alarms some people.

Some people have modified their ANAN radios to replace the fan or improve the airflow, but I do not believe that this is necessary. The case is supposed to get hot. It means that the heatsink is successfully conducting heat away from the transistors.

POWERSDR

PowerSDR comes in many variants known as 'forks.' It is probably the most widely used software for ham radio SDR transceivers because it has the most features and because it is one of the few free applications that supports the ability to transmit. The program is very sophisticated and there are many user customizable settings. Unfortunately, because it is open source software and because it evolves so fast with features constantly being added or improved, there is no user manual. This section is not a full a manual, but it does explain some of the innovative features in PowerSDR and it provides useful information about some of the neat things that people may not be aware of.

Various people have contributed information online and there are some very good 'how to' videos on YouTube, by Nige Coleman G7CNF, Mark Abraham NI0Z, and Robert Connelly W1AEX. This section draws on some of those excellent resources and on my own experience as a PowerSDR user. It is mostly based around the 'PowerSDR mRX PS' fork because that is the version I am currently familiar with. It is also the version getting the most new development work. But much of the information in this chapter will apply to most variations of PowerSDR. If you don't use PowerSDR at all, feel free to skip ahead to the next section.

Technical TIP: The PowerSDR fork used with OpenHPSDR and Apache Labs ANAN transceivers is called 'PowerSDR mRX PS'. It can be downloaded for free from the OpenHPSDR downloads page or from the Apache Labs downloads page. The 'mRX' stands for multiple receivers and 'PS' means that the software supports the 'PureSignal' mode. This version of PowerSDR also has facility for diversity reception using dual ADCs and a long-term recorder for Radio Astronomy users.

A SHORT HISTORY

PowerSDR was originally called 'SDR Console.' It was first developed in 2002 by Gerald Youngblood, K5SDR, for the FlexRadio Systems Flex-1000 transceiver. SDR Console and the first version of PowerSDR were written using the Visual BASIC computer language, but this proved to be too limited and the software development was moved to the C computer language. According to the FlexRadio website, www.flexradio.com/amateur-products/flex-series/powersdr/ the current version for use with FlexRadios is written in a combination of ANSI C and C#. The current OpenHPSDR version was written and compiled, using Visual Studio 2010 (Visual C++).

PowerSDR has always been open source software and many people have helped to extend the program. It has been extensively modified and improved over the years. As new technology has arrived, PowerSDR has been modified to support it. There are variants for all generations of SDR and for different interfaces with the host computer.

Some of the many variants or 'forks', include versions for connecting to the I.F. output from a receiver and there are Genesis and Softrock versions. There is a version for the FlexRadio Systems FLEX-1500, FLEX-3000, and FLEX-5000 models and there is the PowerSDR mRX version used with the OpenHPSDR boards and the Apache ANAN transceivers.

Most of the current development work for the mRX PS version is being done by Doug Wigley W5WC and Bill Tracey KD5TFD. Recent innovations include a special recording functionality for radio astronomy and the excellent PureSignal adaptive transmitter pre-distortion algorithm, which was developed by Warren Pratt, NR0V. Warren has also developed new noise reduction and noise blanking filters. The software developers work closely with the OpenHPSDR hardware developers including Phil Harman VK6PH and the team at Apache Labs. This is because some software upgrades require firmware updates for the FPGA on the transceiver boards and correspondingly some firmware upgrades require modifications to PowerSDR. [Sincere apologies if I left anyone out!]

Early versions of PowerSDR including, I believe, the I.F. version, the Softrock version, and the FlexRadio version, all use the DttSP DSP library written by Francis Brickle AB2KT and Robert Gwier N4HY. This .dll file is called by the main program to perform the modulation, demodulation, and filtering tasks. The main program takes care of the user interface and display functions.

Recent versions of PowerSDR mRX (after V3.2.7), use a new DSP library called wdsp.dll, developed by Warren Pratt NR0V. WDSP has different code for FM modulation and demodulation, new noise blankers and noise reduction, new equalizers, FM squelch, AM squelch, and metering. Introduction of the new DSP library resulted in some changes to the DSP options on the setup screens.

PowerSDR mRX evolves fast! There were 24 software releases between January 2014 and April 2016. New versions are usually announced by Doug Wigley W5WC on the Apache Labs Yahoo group.

A MILD DISCLAIMER

I have not been involved in the development of PowerSDR and I don't know what a few of the settings are for! I will do my best to explain the major settings and offer some tricks that can make working with PowerSDR easier. Of course, one problem is that the code is under continual development, so the version you have on your PC may be different in some respects. But most functions tend to carry over from version to version. The OpenHPSDR and Apache Labs development teams are working on the integration of a single board computer to perform the DSP functions, rather than using the DSP software on the PC and also a speed upgrade to Gigabit Ethernet. The GbE upgrade and the development of direct Fourier conversion has resulted in initial development of a yet to be released replacement for PowerSDR mRX PS called Thetis.

USING A MOUSE ON THE PANADAPTER

Not all SDR software is the same. On some programs, you can zoom and change the frequency scale of the spectrum display by clicking on the horizontal display axis and dragging the scale. This requires a click and hold of the left or right mouse button. PowerSDR lacks this feature, but you can use the mouse to adjust the dBm vertical scale of the panadapter. The 'zoom' slider control adjusts the span of the spectrum and waterfall display.

Mouse operation of PowerSDR can be a little confusing. I have assumed that you will be using the 'Panafall' display, which has a spectrum display at the top and a waterfall at the bottom. The Panafall display is by far and away the most popular display mode because it provides you with frequency, signal level, bandwidth, and time information all at the same time.

- A click and hold anywhere on the spectrum display except inside the shaded receiver pass-band allows you to drag the panadapter center frequency higher or lower. Move the mouse right or left on the screen. The frequency numbers at the top of the panadapter will change to indicate that you are moving up or down the band. Note that the frequency readout will change as well, because the receiver frequency is moving. The receiver stays in the same position on the screen as the panadapter is moved underneath it.

- There is an exception to this! If the 'CTUN' (center tuning' button has been selected, the receiver will stay on the same frequency and will move left and right with the panadapter.

  TIP: In a recent update to PowerSDR mRX, the CTUN button was moved from the group of buttons under the power switch to the buttons controlling the panadapter functions below the panadapter drop down box. This is a more logical position for this control.

- A click and hold inside the shaded receiver pass-band allows you to drag the receiver pass-band. It is equivalent to an I.F. Shift control. I find this exceptionally annoying. I would prefer it to drag the receiver frequency, while leaving the panadapter static.

- When you hover the mouse over the edge of the shaded receiver pass-band furthest from the center frequency line, the mouse pointer will change to a horizontal arrow. If you then click and hold, you can drag the receiver bandwidth wider or narrower. This is equivalent to an I.F. width or 'hi-cut' control.

- If you hover the mouse pointer over the left edge of the shaded receiver passband the mouse pointer will change to a horizontal arrow. When this is showing, you can click and hold, to drag the receiver bandwidth wider or narrower. This is equivalent to an I.F. 'lo-cut' control.

- You can also set the receiver width and shift using the slider controls or bandwidth buttons on the lower right of the main window. There are two small numeric displays showing the high and low cut frequencies.

- Changing the receiver bandwidth, either by dragging the shaded receiver bandwidth or by using the slider controls will change the selected bandwidth button to 'variable' (VAR 1 or VAR 2). You can click the bandwidth buttons to reset the receiver bandwidth to one of the 10 preset values.

- A click and hold anywhere on the waterfall allows you to drag the panadapter lower or higher in frequency. Move the mouse left or right on the screen. The frequency display numbers on the panadapter will change to indicate that you are moving up or down the band. If the CTUN button is not selected, the frequency readout will change as well, because the receiver stays in the same position on the screen as the panadapter is moved underneath it.

- A right click on the spectrum display will create yellow cross hair lines. On the waterfall, it is will be just a vertical yellow line. While the cross hair is displayed, clicking on the panadapter instantly moves your receiver to the frequency that you clicked. This is excellent when the band is busy as it allows you to jump directly to each station.

  Technical TIP: To minimize the amount of fine tuning required, position the cross hairs just to the left side of an upper sideband SSB signal or waterfall trace. For lower sideband signals click a fraction to the right side. Click directly on the signal for CW, AM or FM. Fine tune with the mouse wheel, I normally have the mouse wheel step size set to 100 Hz for SSB mode and 10 Hz for CW mode.

- When Receiver 2 or split mode operation is in use, a second right click will create red, cross hair lines, allowing you to position the second receiver on the panadapter. Successive right clicks cycle through, yellow lines, red lines, and normal display mode. If only one receiver is in use, a second right click will turn off the cross hairs. The color of the cross hair lines can be changed in the appropriate setup tab.

THE POWERSDR PANADAPTER

At the bottom right of the PowerSDR panadapter, there are three useful numbers. These numbers relate to the largest signal currently within the displayed span. The first number indicates the frequency offset above or below the panadapter center frequency. The second number is the level of the signal in dBm and the third is its actual frequency. Note that the largest signal might not be the one that you are listening to. You can use this feature to find and measure the strongest signal on the band.

At the bottom left of the PowerSDR panadapter there are three very similar numbers, which relate to the current mouse position. If the mouse is over the waterfall image and not the spectrum the dBm figure changes to the time scale of the waterfall. The first number indicates the offset between the frequency that the mouse is on and the panadapter center frequency. The second number is the level of the received signal at that point in dBm and the third is the actual frequency. I use this feature in contests to check the frequency so that I can tell if I have already worked the station. You can also use this feature to measure the frequency and level of any signal on the waterfall by moving the mouse pointer to its peak level.

The horizontal axis of the panadapter display indicates frequency. The displayed span can be zoomed using the slider control below the panadapter. The vertical axis is calibrated in dBm, so it is a logarithmic scale. It is very accurate.

You can change a setup option if you want to indicate a time scale in seconds on the waterfall display.

SETTING THE AGC GAIN CONTROL

It is important to set the front panel, AGC gain control correctly. You should adjust this control every time you change bands because the noise floor will be different on each band. The AGC Gain control works like the RF Gain control on a conventional non SDR receiver. If it is set too low, the receiver will seem to be insensitive. Do not yield to the temptation to leave the slider set to maximum all the time. Using more gain than you need will make the radio sound noisy. Actually, you should not leave the RF gain turned full up on a conventional receiver either, but most people do.

If you have the G line turned on, you can drag the green square icon or adjust the AGC Gain slider so that the green line is a little above the noise floor. If the G line is not on, you can adjust the setting by ear. As you adjust the control, listen for the 'knee' where the audio level starts to reduce rapidly. The AGC Gain control should be set just before that point. If you are listening to a strong signal, you can reduce the AGC gain further to make the signal sound less noisy.

You can turn on the AGC G Line by checking the 'Display RX1 Gain Line' checkbox on the DSP AGC/ALC setup tab.

NOISE BLANKING AND NOISE REDUCTION

PowerSDR especially PowerSDR mRX has very good noise reduction and noise blanking filters. This is one of the big strengths of software defined radio and DSP based systems in general. Each of the noise filters in PowerSDR works in a different way; they are designed to work against different types of noise. The noise blankers are primarily for impulse 'ignition' noise and lightning crashes. The noise reduction filters are aimed more at wideband atmospheric noise especially on the low bands. To get the best results from the noise reduction systems it is important to have the AGC gain control set correctly (see above).

By introducing a very small delay, the filters are able to look ahead and modify the digital data streams to remove noise and interference before you hear it. This is not easily achievable with analog circuitry. It would require analog delay lines. The latest release of PowerSDR mRX has a new NR2 noise reduction filter, which I found to be amazing when listening to weak signals on 80m. On my radio, I do hear a slight Dalek / Darth Vader distortion to the audio, but it cuts the noise completely. When you turn it off or onto NR1, you realize just how well it is working.

The NR2 and NB2 filters are under development, so the setup settings mentioned below may differ from the PowerSDR release that you are using.

Noise blanking occurs very early in the receiver DSP process. It is performed on the wideband spectrum before any demodulation or other filtering takes place. Noise reduction is performed on the filtered signal i.e. within the receiver pass band indicated by the grey shaded are on the panadapter. You can select whether it is applied before or after the AGC section.

ADJUSTING THE NB AND NR SETUP CONTROLS

My first advice is "don't adjust them." The developers, most recently Warren Pratt, have done a lot of work on these filters and they have decided that the default settings work well. If you have an on-going noise problem that's been driving you nuts, then maybe you can tweak the settings a bit.

It is important not to make the threshold adjustment too low. If you do, the filter will act on the speech and not just the noise and you will make the received audio sound horrible. On the other hand, if you think that the current settings are already distorting the audio, you can raise the threshold a bit and make the filter less aggressive. Sometimes it is a trade-off. I find that the new NR2 filter does add a slightly electronic Dalek sound to the speech, but it also completely eliminates the background noise. Which do you prefer and which is less tiring to listen to? Some people leave it permanently enabled.

The following is an extract of the setup instructions recommended by the man who wrote the filter algorithms, Warren Pratt NR0V.

"THIS IS CRITICAL; I'LL SAY IT FIRST: Begin with a very high Threshold value, high enough that the blanker is having NO impact on the noise. Gradually reduce the threshold just until the blanker is catching the impulses. If you do not do this, you are very likely to introduce low frequency distortion into the signal stream.

Recommended adjustment steps:

- *If using NB2, select (one of the 5) modes of operation.*

- *Set all delay values to minimum.*

- *Adjust the threshold per the guidance given above.*

- *Try increasing the Lead to determine if any improvement can be obtained.*

- *Try increasing the Lag to determine if any improvement can be obtained.*

- *Try increasing the Slew to determine if any improvement can be obtained."*

BLOCKING NOISE BLANKER (NB)

Depending on the threshold setting, the blocking noise blanker can completely remove noise spikes, which are bigger than the average signal level, but it has no effect on noise spikes that are below the average signal level. The NB noise blanker does not act as a clipper. When it detects a large noise spike, it mutes the signal completely. Using NB introduces a very small, two sample, delay (latency) to the received signal. When it acts, it blanks the signal to zero for around six data samples. Hopefully by then the noise impulse has passed. At higher sample rates, the data stream is faster so the latency and mute period is shorter. You will not be able to hear the blank space it is much too short. What you will notice is the elimination of the impulse noise.

The basic concept of a noise blanker is to replace the signal during the impulses with either zero or some value much more representative of what the signal should be. The noise blanker algorithm depends upon the fact that the impulses are much larger than the signal to be able to detect them. It compares the signal at each sample with the long-term average value across a wide bandwidth. If the samples exceed a "Threshold" referenced to the average, it concludes this is an impulse. (NR0V)

- The software looks ahead to see if a noise burst is coming.

- When an impulse that is a preset amount larger than the average signal is detected, the signal level is decreased over a few data samples to zero. The time from full signal to zero is the 'Slew' rate.

- The signal is held at zero during the pulse and for a 'lag' time after the pulse. After the lag period, the signal ramps back to normal level over the 'transition' time.

- The slew, lag, and transition times are all adjustable on the DSP Options setup tab. The default is 0.1 ms for each. You can increase the times if you are experiencing longer noise bursts.

- The threshold setting adjusts the amount above the average signal level that the impulse noise has to be before the filter will operate. Too high and the filter won't work, too low and the blanker will try to work on voice peaks.

AVERAGING NOISE BLANKER (NB2)

The NB2 noise blanker is in development by Warren Pratt NR0V, so in the current software release there are many options that you can try. The aim is to improve on the original NB noise blanker. Any major advancement will be retained and less successful options will be removed from future PowerSDR releases.

At present NB2 supports five modes of operation. The differences relate to the way that the software manages an impulse when it is detected. Rather than muting the audio to zero amplitude when there is a noise pulse, the different routines attempt to mimic what the signal might have been without the noise. The different settings either set the audio level to an average of the incoming signal, to the level just before the impulse was detected, to the level just after the impulse was detected, or to an average of what the level was before and after the impulse. I expect that all of these methods will sound pretty much the same. Warren can use test software to evaluate how effective each method is, sample by sample. When he has decided which is best he will make that method the default for NB2. Until then you will be able to try all the methods and decide for yourself what works the best on the particular noise that you are experiencing.

- Zero: when an impulse is detected, the output signal is set to zero amplitude for the duration of the pulse. This is the method used in the NB noise blanker.

- Sample-Hold: the output is set to an average of the incoming sample for the duration of the impulse. This mode is basically the same as the old NB2 blanker.

- Hold-Sample: for the duration of the impulse, the output signal is held at the value occurring just after the impulse.

- Mean-Hold: for the duration of the impulse, the output signal is held at the average of the values occurring just before and just after the impulse.

- Linear: the output signal is a linear interpolation of the signal value occurring just before the impulse and the signal value just after the impulse.

NOISE REDUCTION (NR)

The noise reduction filters work to reduce annoying background noise. If you are experiencing noise impulses or bursts it is probably better to use a noise blanker. The noise reduction filters work best when the received signals have a good signal to noise ratio. Using a NR filter will probably not help you to pull an otherwise unreadable signal out of the noise. However, the NR2 filter, which uses a different type of noise reduction calculation, is very effective with weak signals.

Noise reduction is performed on the narrow band signal after the receive filter, rather than on the full panadapter. In other words, the NR filter only affects the approximately 3 kHz bandwidth you are listening to. You have a choice of applying the noise reduction before or after the AGC. I find that the NR2 filter works better if applied before the AGC, but you may prefer it the other way around. Post AGC noise reduction might be more effective in some situations such as when there is fast fading.

It is best to set the AGC Gain line just above the noise floor so that the AGC action doesn't undo what the noise reduction is trying to achieve.

If you have persistent noise problems or just like the way it sounds, you can adjust the filter settings. I suggest that you don't make large changes. It is better to make small changes and evaluate the effects that you are hearing before proceeding further. This is because the NR filters are adaptive filters. They take some time to settle. The noise level gradually reduces as the filters average the noise levels over time. I just leave everything at the default settings.

For a 192 kHz sample rate the recommended default settings are:

- Taps = 64 (256 on old PSDR versions). Taps is the number of LMS (least mean square) stages used in the calculation. You can increase the number of taps to expand the frequency range and reduce the noise. A higher number of taps increases the CPU load on the host computer while the NR filter is in use because more computations are being performed.

- Delay = 16 (64 on old PDSR versions). Delay changes how many samples back in the data stream the system works. Increasing the delay makes the filter act earlier, which should reduce the noise.

- Gain = 100. Decrease the gain to further the reduce noise. Lower values of gain may work better on CW signals.

- Leak = 100. Leak is the amount of signal that is applied to the next iteration of the software, i.e. how much the past noise level affects the current calculation. More 'leak' should reduce noise. But it also means the filter takes longer to respond to changes in the received noise level.

Technical description: The noise filter is an adaptive interference canceller. It finds a periodic (repeating) signal like speech and cancels out incoherent signals such as noise.

The data stream is passed through a delay line and an adjustable FIR (finite impulse response) filter, which is a band pass filter that automatically moves to the signal we want to keep, or in the case of a notch filter eliminate. The delayed signal becomes a kind of reference signal at the periodic frequency. It is subtracted from the current samples creating an error level. After some time the filter coefficient automatically adjusts in order to progressively, reduce the error level, meaning that the delayed signal is as close as possible, in phase with the current samples. When the error signal is at its smallest, the wanted periodic speech is enhanced and the unwanted non-periodic noise is suppressed. The technique uses a least mean square algorithm developed by Widrow and Hoff in the late 1950s. These adaptive filters work in the time domain, no FFT is required.

The automatic notch filter is very similar to the noise filter. In fact, the software code is almost identical although the reference variables have different values. But in this case the unwanted signal is more periodic constant signals like unwanted carriers and 'birdies' and the wanted signal is the less periodic speech. So this time we output the more incoherent 'error' signal rather than the coherent 'interference' signal. So the notch filter works the same way as the noise filter, but the output is taken from a different part of the filter code.

ADVANCED NOISE REDUCTION (NR2)

The NR2 noise reduction uses a new 'noise predictive equalizer' (NPE) algorithm. The filtered audio is reported to be less tiring to listen to than the typical LMS noise reduction used in the NR filter. I believe that it is also much better at bringing a weak signal out of the noise.

It is important to adjust the AGC gain correctly before turning on the NR or NR2 filters. AGC is the enemy of noise reduction algorithms because it tries increase the gain, thus increasing the noise level while the noise reduction is trying to reduce the noise level. I have found it better to use NR2 in the Pre-AGC mode, so that it is not competing with the AGC.

The NR2 filter is still under development. The settings and functions may change. I recommend using the default 'Gamma' gain mode, either OSMS or MMSE as the NPE-method, and leave the AE-Filter checkbox checked. I don't know what it does, but the audio sounds really weird if the AE filter is not selected.

I found that the NR2 filter is excellent on 80m. It cuts the background noise completely, but it does introduce a strange electronic sound to the speech. The NR2 noise filter is enabled by pressing the NR button, then pressing it again for NR2. It is certainly worthwhile experimenting with the filter settings. It is always a good idea to write down the default settings before making adjustments, so you can remember what they were.

The NPE adapts to achieve a minimum 'error signal' calculated using either the MMSE or OSMS calculation methods.

NPE = Noise Power Estimation
OSMS = Optimal Smoothing and Minimum Statistics
MMSE = Minimum Mean Square Error
AE = Artifact Elimination

AUTO NOTCH FILTERS (ANF)

PowerSDR includes an automatic notch filter. The ANF is extremely effective at removing constant interference such as a carrier signal within the receiver's pass band. This is a very common occurrence on the HF bands. ANF is not effective when you are listening to digital signals like RTTY or PSK because it will attempt to notch out the fairly constant wanted signal. It is not useful when receiving CW for the same reason. In both of those cases you can usually use a narrow receive filter and avoid the interfering signal that way.

The LMS algorithm used for ANF is very similar to the code used for the NR noise reduction although the aims are different and different time constants are used. In the noise filter, the aim is to keep the steady speech signal and eliminate relatively random noise signal. In the ANF filter, the aim is to eliminate the steady interfering carrier and keep the relatively random speech signal. The same type of filter is used, but the output of the filter is taken from a different part of the code. Using the automatic notch filter is CPU intensive. The CPU load increases with the number of taps and with higher sample rates.

Increasing the gain allows the ANF filter to lock onto offending carriers more effectively. But if you push the gain too high, you will begin to distort the wanted speech. I leave the ANF adjustments at the default settings.

For a 192 kHz sample rate the defaults are:

- Taps = 64 (256 on old versions), increase taps to expand the effective frequency range

- Delay = 16 (64 on old versions), lower to improve the maximum effective frequency

- Gain = 100 (200 on old versions), increase to more effectively lock onto offending signals

- Leak = 100: probably no point changing this. Less leak means it looks at less of the audio when working out what is audio and what is an offending carrier, so more leak should be better.

- Pre-AGC checked. Post-AGC may be better for fast fading or on AM when you are using the fade leveler.

MULTI NOTCH FILTER (MNF)

Version v3.3.6 of PowerSDR mRX introduced a new Multi Notch Filter (MNF). It replaces the FlexRadio 'Tracking Notch Filter,' which is included in FlexRadio versions of PowerSDR but not the versions intended for other radios.

"The, Multi Notch Filter (MNF), allows you to specify up to 1024 notches. The notches are specified by RF frequency and width and will be invoked, as needed, when they overlap the passband. This feature is useful for those who have interference that consistently appears on specific frequencies.

To avoid phase distortion, the notches are implemented with linear phase. Also, they introduce no additional processing delay nor do they consume any additional CPU cycles once you're on frequency and the notches are set up. This is all accomplished by simply "cutting" the notches into the existing bandpass filters rather than adding additional filters." Doug **Wigley**, W5WC and **Warren Pratt**, NR0V.

Notches are added on the DSP / MNF tab. To add a notch, click 'Add' then enter the center frequency and notch width then click 'Enter'. You can also enter the notch frequency by tuning VFO-A to the desired frequency and clicking the VFOA button. If you enter a very narrow notch width, less than 200Hz, the filter might not achieve the full attenuation of >100 dB. Leaving the 'auto increase width' checkbox checked will automatically increase the notch width to achieve 100 dB of attenuation when the notch is cut in.

DOLLY FILTERS

'Hello Dolly!' The Dolly Filters are 'double lobe' twin peak filters designed specifically for receiving RTTY. They have been included in PowerSDR mRX since version 3.2.12. These filters are very narrow and it is important that they are set to cover the same audio offset frequencies as the transmit profile that you use for RTTY. I have found them to be extremely effective. They have allowed me to decode RTTY signals that were completely illegible without the Dolly Filter. The DSP Audio setup tab includes three groups of Dolly filter settings, one for each receiver.

RTTY transmissions send a signal that alternates between two 'tone' frequencies that are usually 170 Hz apart. I changed the default 'standard' RTTY frequencies on my Dolly filters to 1400-1570 Hz because it suits the way I have my DIGU filter set up.

One annoying downside is that there is no front panel control to turn the Dolly filters on and off. Because they are very narrow, I find it nicer to turn them off while tuning to another signal. It would be great if the software developers could allocate a button on the GUI for the Dolly filters. It would also be handy if these filters were only enabled for the DIGU and DIGL modes. At the moment, they work on any mode setting. If you are on CW mode and you select both the CW APF and the Dolly filters at the same time, both filters will be in circuit and you will see no signals.

CW AUDIO PEAKING FILTER (APF)

The CW audio peaking filter was added to PowerSDR mRX PS about the same time as the Dolly Filter appeared. It is a very sharp adjustable filter great for pulling weak CW out of the noise. There is a handy 'APF' button to turn it off when you are tuning around the band.

The setup controls for this feature are located on the DSP Audio setup tab. There are three groups of APF settings, one for each receiver.

Selecting the CW APF filter causes a new set of controls to appear in the 'transmit audio settings' block of the main screen. You can control the filter gain, filter bandwidth, and fine-tuning of the frequency relative to the standard CW pitch. The front panel controls are the same as the ones on the setup tab. The CW pitch offset is set on the DSP CW setup tab.

The CW APF bandwidth is very narrow. It is adjustable from 10 Hz to 150 Hz. The frequency is centered on the standard CW tone offset and is adjustable plus or minus 250 Hz.

ZERO BEAT (0 BEAT)

The '0 Beat' button automatically pulls the frequency of the radio so that you are receiving CW signals with exactly the same tone offset as the transmitter will use when you are sending CW. This feature makes netting the received CW signal with the transmit frequency much easier. It is also handy if you use external software to decode CW.

I like to receive CW at a pitch of 690 Hz. If you operate CW regularly, I am sure you will have a favorite CW tone. The 'CW Pitch (Hz)' tone offset is set on the DSP CW setup tab.

AGC SETUP SETTINGS

The correct way to set the AGC gain control has been discussed earlier. It is very important to set it every time you change bands. The easiest way is to position the 'G line' just above the noise floor, but you can also set it by ear. It should not be left at maximum. This section is about the other AGC settings, which are more of a set and forget arrangement. PowerSDR offers six options for AGC, rather than just the fast, medium, or slow options on most conventional receivers. You can adjust the actual AGC operating parameters for each of the six AGC settings.

In a conventional receiver, the AGC performs two roles. It limits the audio output on strong signals by reducing the stage gain and it compensates for the limited dynamic range of conventional receivers by increasing the stage gain when weak signals are received. The AGC setting in PowerSDR reduces the gain on strong signals but there is no need to compensate for a lack of dynamic range. The dynamic range of the SDR receiver is large and the audio output level is directly proportional to the RF signal level. This makes big signals too loud, so the AGC limits the audio level when you are listening to a strong signal. It does not increase the gain above the normal level when you are receiving a weak signal.

According to the excellent paper written by NR0V (23Nov 2012) and available online, the AGC in PowerSDR is a single attack, dual decay system.

This means that the AGC responds quickly to large receive signals and it has two decay rates. If the input is a short burst of noise, the decay time is made short in order to restore the receiver output to a normal level quickly. On the other hand, if the input has a longer average for example, normal speech, the decay is longer and the threshold level is controlled by the AGC gain setting that you selected on the main SDR console.

The AGC dropdown on the console sets the AGC mode in use.

- Fixed – AGC is off, there is no limitation to the audio output on strong signals. Note that the DRM, DIGU, and DIGL modes automatically disable the AGC.

- Long – AGC attack time is 2ms, decay time is 2000ms and hang time is 2000ms.

- Slow - AGC attack time is 2ms, decay time is 500ms and hang time is 1000ms.

- Med - AGC attack time is 2ms, decay time is 250ms and hang time is not enabled. The H line will not display on the panadapter.

- Fast - AGC attack time is 2ms, decay time is 50ms and hang time is not enabled. The H line will not display on the panadapter.

- Custom - AGC times are as per the settings on the DSP AGC/ALC setup tab.

Another unique function is that the gain changes made by the AGC action lead (occur in advance of) the changes in the RF input signal, so there is never any AGC undershoot or overshoot. This can be done because the AGC is calculated numerically and applied to the signal. We tend to forget that all of the digital signal processing is performed by mathematically manipulating the data using computer software.

The AGC changes are not performed instantly because that would cause a choppy distorted audio output from the receiver. They ramp up and down following exponential curves, in much the same way as analog circuits with capacitors would in a conventional receiver. A 'hang' function is included to delay the onset of AGC action when AGC is set to long or slow modes. This prevents AGC ramping up the audio level during pauses in SSB speech or CW words. Without the hang function, pauses in the received speech could be accompanied by a 'swishing' sound as the noise level rises between sentences. Slope allows strong signals to sound a bit louder than weak signals, without blowing you out of the room.

You can configure PowerSDR to display two of the key AGC settings on the panadapter display either right across the panadapter or just within the light grey receive pass-band. I usually select the right across the panadapter option.

The green G line indicates the maximum AGC gain. Dragging the G Line on the panadapter has the same effect as changing the AGC Gain slider control on the console. For general listening, you would normally set it so that the line is just above the noise level on the panadapter. If you are listening to a particular station, you can reduce the AGC Gain until just before the wanted audio signal drops. As you reduce the AGC gain, the background noise level should reduce but the wanted signal should stay much the same. At a point usually about 10 dB above the noise floor there is a noticeable 'knee' and after that, the wanted signal level will begin to reduce at the same rate as the noise. The best AGC Gain setting is just before the point where the wanted audio begins to reduce. The background noise has been reduced, so the signal to noise ratio is at its best. If the signal is strong, you can raise the G line even more and this will reduce both the signal's audio level and the background noise.

The yellow H line is the hang threshold. It is only available if the AGC is set to long, slow, or custom. If the signal is strong enough to cross the hang threshold line, the 'hang mode' will activate. If the hang line is set above the peak signal level on the panadapter the hang mode will not be active.

The AGC is calculated using the AGC settings on the Setup tab.

- Slope dB - allows strong signals to sound a bit louder than weak signals. It is best not to be too aggressive with the settings I use the default slope of 0. You could try anything from 0 to 20 dB, but I would suggest a setting of not more than 6 dB

- Max gain dB – this is the same as the G line on the panadapter (if selected) and the AGC Gain slider control on the console.

- Attack time ms – Is not adjustable, it is fixed at 2 ms.

- Decay time ms – sets the normal (no noise spike) decay. 50 ms is fast 2000 ms is very slow. It can only be adjusted for the 'Custom' AGC setting.

- Hang time ms – delay before the hang allows the AGC to activate, usually 1 to 2 seconds. It can only be adjusted for the 'Custom' AGC setting.

- Fixed gain dB – stage gain when AGC is set to off (Fixed). This level is the same as the Fixed Gain slider that appears in place of the AGC Gain control if you select 'Fixed AGC'.

- Hang threshold dB – same as the H line. It sets the threshold that a signal has to exceed before the hang mode activates. The H line is only active if you have selected long, slow, or custom AGC.

Technical note: the AGC attack time constant is always 2ms. Decay time is a constant as well, but the time is different for each AGC mode. The time constants are used mathematically by the very complex AGC algorithm in the PowerSDR software. The AGC routine is one of the largest code blocks in the software, mostly because there are so many options available. Hang time is not a 'time constant' calculated from the data rate it is an absolute time interval.

SETTING TRANSMIT LEVELS FOR SSB

If you are planning to use your SDR radio to transmit SSB voice transmissions, it is essential that you setup PowerSDR correctly. In the earlier forks of PowerSDR, a failure to do this could result in a distorted transmit signal, which would be embarrassing, ineffective, and could cause interference to other band users. Luckily, the settings are much less critical with the latest PowerSDR mRX PS software and these days you can pretty much leave all of the settings except the Mic Gain at the default settings. PowerSDR mRX has been modified so that it is almost impossible to overdrive the transmitter to the point where distortion is caused. Even with the new mRX version, it is still important to check the levels to make sure that you are fully modulating the radio. A quick check is to adjust your MIC level so that the ALC meter is just bumping 0 dB on speech peaks. If it is hitting 0 dB occasionally then you have full modulation.

PowerSDR mRX PS now has completely new software algorithms for the compressor, ALC, and Leveler stages. You cannot turn off the ALC (automatic level control) and it will not allow the level at the ALC stage to exceed 0 dB.

Setting your transmitter audio levels only has to be done "once", although currently if you have deleted the database.xml file as a part of a software upgrade you will have to reset your settings for each new version. I suggest that you make a note of the settings at each stage before loading a new version of PowerSDR mRX, so that you can easily reset the levels. See the section on dealing with new software releases, below.

The transmitter audio level can be adjusted at four points in the audio chain, MIC, EQ, LEVELLER and ALC. The levels are adjusted using on screen slider controls and there is an individual meter reading for each adjustment.

It is important to remember that you are adjusting digital levels inside a software program, not physical levels inside the radio. Signals peaking a little higher than 0 dB on the meter will not cause flat topping or distortion if you are using PowerSDR mRX, but if you are using other PowerSDR variants, you should never let any of the stages peak above 0 dB. The transmit levels are quite easy to adjust if you follow the simple process listed below. There is a very good online video by G7CNF, on how to set the transmit levels on the old versions of PowerSDR with a Flex-5000 radio.

First, we prepare the radio before adjusting the transmitter audio levels:

1. If you are using a dynamic microphone, it is likely that you will need to enable the +20 dB mic boost setting on the Transmit setup tab. You can also set the maximum and minimum level for the Mic Gain slider on the main GUI screen. It defaults to a range from 0 to 70. I like to change that so that I have a maximum just a bit higher than the level that we will set when we adjust the levels. On my setup, with a dynamic microphone, I have the maximum Mic Gain set to 20 and the Mic gain on the front panel set at 16.

    TIP: there is a difference here between PowerSDR versions. Old versions of PowerSDR use the Windows Mixer control, accessed along the top left of the PowerSDR screen to set the maximum Mic level. On PowerSDR mRX PS the maximum level is set using the setting on the Transmit setup tab.

2. Select a transmit profile using the drop-down box on the GUI screen or on the Transmit setup tab. I usually setup the transmitter audio levels with the radio on the 'Default' profile setting. Later on, I setup the 'Default DX' to the same settings, but add 6 dB of compression and turn the 'down expander' on. That gives me the choice of using a 'standard' profile or a 'DX' profile.

3. While you have the Transmit setup tab open, turn on the '*Auto Save TX profile on PowerSDR close*' checkbox. You can click the other checkbox to on as well if you want to. Also, make sure that the 'Transmit Filter' bandwidth is suitable for the transmit mode, i.e. a low cut off between 100 - 300Hz and a high cut off around 2700 – 3000 Hz for SSB. Save the transmit profile by clicking the 'Save' button, under the 'profiles' drop down box. Ignore any warning message. I use the transmit default of 100 Hz to 3100 Hz for the 'Default' profile and a slightly narrower setting of 150 Hz to 3000 Hz for the 'Default DX' profile.

4. On the DSP AGC/ALC setup screen, make sure that the Leveler is checked to on.

    In most versions of PowerSDR, the Leveler should always be on, especially if you are using the Compressor. The only exception would be when you are using the line input and external audio processing using an external equalizer. Some people say that the Leveler should be set to off for digital modes, but it should never act when you are using digital modulation, so I don't think it matters if you leave it set to on.

The Leveler function has been re-written in PowerSDR mRX. With the normal audio levels that are expected if, you have adjusted the earlier audio stages correctly the Leveler only acts as a fixed gain amplifier stage. But if there is a peak of audio level coming that would exceed the threshold set within the software (currently +0.4 dB), the stage gain is gradually reduced. The Leveler only acts if there is an abnormally large audio level i.e. you are shouting.

5.   Return to the main screen and select USB, (or LSB if you are operating below 10 MHz). It does not matter which band the radio is set to, so long as you have a good 50 Ohm load. During the setup, you will probably be running full transmitter power at times.

6.   To avoid interference to other band users, connect your transmitter to a suitable 100 Watt plus, 50 Ohm load. You can use a 20 W load for a QRP transceiver.

If you don't have a suitable load, you can set the audio levels at a lower power level, or you can leave the radio connected to your antenna. If you do that, make sure the frequency is not in use and setup the levels on a closed band. Of course, if you are using an antenna, it must present a good, safe, impedance to the radio.

You can set the transmit audio at any transmit power level, but it is important that you do not exceed the rated maximum transmit power for your radio. On some radios, full power occurs at a drive level of exactly 100. On others, it may not have been calibrated, so it might occur at a lower drive level. (See the section on setting transmitter power). Many radios are not designed for 'full duty cycle' operation. It is generally better not to run your transmitter at full power for more than 30 seconds at a time. The following step makes sure that you do not exceed the operating parameters of your radio.

On the Setup, Transmit tab, enable the 'use drive power' check box. Set the meter to TX power, press Tune to key the transmitter and increase the drive level until the meter reads full power, (100 W for a 100 W rig, 5 W for a FLEX-1500, 10 W for an ANAN-10). Note the drive level. Turn off the Tune control, which will un-key the transmitter then ensure that the drive level control, is set to the same level as it was in tune mode at full power. It should only take a few seconds to adjust the drive level for full power.

7.   Make sure that the downward expander (DEXP) and compressor (COMP) buttons on the main screen are turned off.

8.   Set the Mic Gain slider to about 1/2 full scale/

OK, now we are finally ready to adjust the transmitter audio settings.

9.   Set the dropdown list on the S meter, top right of the main screen, to 'Mic.' This is the microphone level meter, it indicates the level of the first

transmit audio stage. It will show as greyed out because the transmitter is not keyed on yet.

10. Key your transmitter and speak into the microphone in your normal 'on air' voice. I tend to speak up a bit and project my voice as if I am talking to an audience because I work a lot of DX. You might be more interested in a conversational level for rag chewing. Just try to talk the way you typically would while transmitting 'on the air'. It is best to use the same sort of language. I normally make a CQ call or count to 10 and back. Nobody will hear it if you are using a dummy load. The counting to ten and back to zero is an old habit from my days as a 'Radio Technician.'

Adjust the Mic Level control on the front panel so that the Mic meter peaks to 0 dB. If it does not quite make 0 dB, you can increase the maximum mic level on the Transmit setup tab. But, it is no big deal as you can make up any deficit in the EQ and Leveler stages.

(On other PowerSDR versions set it to about -2 dB, it should never ever peak above 0 dB)

11. Now set the transmit meter to EQ. This is the equalizer (second) audio stage. Open the Equalizer tab on the menu bar at the top of the main screen. Click the check box to enable the equalizer otherwise there will be no meter indication when you transmit. You can leave it at three bands or click the radio button to change to a ten band equalizer.

Key your transmitter and speak into the microphone in your normal 'on air' voice, while observing the EQ reading on the meter. At this time just adjust the 'Preamp' control at the left of the equalizer sliders. Leave the other sliders in mid position. As before, you should adjust for peaks to 0 dB, *(or -2 dB on old PowerSDR).*

If, like my setup you end up with the preamp control set at 0 dB, you can leave the equalizer turned off.

Actually if you don't plan on making any adjustments to the EQ settings, you can leave the EQ turned off. The levels will be made up in the Leveler stage anyway.

TIP: The actual equalizer does not need to be adjusted at this stage. After the basic levels have been set, you can make small on-air adjustments to the 3 or 10 band transmit audio equalizer, so that your mates can all disagree as to which settings sound the most like "you." Some hams are passionate about transmit audio and use a variety of external hardware and software based audio equalizers amplifiers and filters. I just leave it flat. If you do adjust the equalizer controls, you will probably have to reduce the preamp level a bit to make sure that the peaks on the EQ meter stay under 0 dB.

12. The third stage is the Leveler. It provides an AGC action, just in case you get excited and start shouting. While talking, adjust the 'Max. Gain' control up or down from the default setting for a Leveler meter reading of 0 dB. Warren Pratt NR0V who writes much of the code for PowerSDR recommends leaving the Leveler set to 5 dB and that is good enough for me. But if the Mic gain is a bit low in preceding stages, you could make up the difference in the Leveler stage.

On old versions of PowerSDR, make sure that the meter never exceeds 0dB. You can also adjust the attack / decay / and hang times of the stage if you want a faster or slower response. This is a trial and error process and may take some time. Before adjusting, take a note of the settings you start with and if in doubt, return the settings to standard. Mike W5CUL who wrote the original instructions for this transmitter setup process, recommends reducing the decay and hang times.

13. The final stage is automatic level control. ALC should always be used. In fact, in the recent versions of PowerSDR it can't be turned off. Proper operation of the ALC is indicated by the fact that the ALC Meter will not exceed 0 dB on voice peaks. The only ALC setting that you can change is the 'Decay' which has a default level of 500 ms. *On PowerSDR mRX the new algorithm makes it impossible for the ALC to exceed 0 dB.*

If required, you can make a small adjustment of the Mic Gain to ensure that the ALC meter is just bumping to 0 dB on voice peaks. If it is, then the modulation is adjusted correctly. If it never hits 0 dB then you are under-modulating. If it never goes below 0 dB, then your levels are too high and you are operating with compression, but you are not over-modulating because the software won't let that happen.

On other versions of PowerSDR If all of the previous stages have been adjusted correctly, the ALC meter position should read a peak value less than 0 dB. Most often, it reads between about -5 and -1 dB. If the odd peak is exceeding 0 dB you can tweak the ALC attack / delay / hang settings on the DSP tab, AGC/ALC sub-tab, or reduce the mic gain control on the main screen a little. The standard settings for ALC parameters on other versions of PowerSDR are:

- *Attack = 2ms*
- *Decay = 10ms*
- *Hang = 500ms*

14. MOST IMPORTANT! Go back to the setup Transmit tab and Save the profile. Otherwise all your changes will be lost when you change the transmit profile. Each transmit profile saves; the transmit filter width, RF drive level, microphone gain, compressor, downward expander, equalizer, leveler and ALC settings.

TIP: if you want to do what I do, and set the Default DX up at the same time. Save the 'default' profile then change the profile dropdown to 'default DX' and save the current settings as default DX as well. Then on the front panel set the compressor to 6 dB or less and set the downward expander. Then save the default DX profile again to save the changes. Now, you can select either the default transmit profile or the DX transmit profile from the front panel. The only thing that should change when you switch between them is the compressor and downward expander buttons and levels.

15. Set the transmit meter to TX Power. Note that the transmit power level may not peak to full power on voice peaks. The meter is probably too slow to indicate the full peak power. In any case, it is better to have a nice clean transmission than to wring the last few mW of power out of the radio. A power meter with PEP measurement or a peak hold function should indicate that you are peaking to (or very near) the full PEP power of the radio.

When you have finished these adjustments, your modulation should sound smooth and clean when you turn the MON function on. You can adjust the 3 or 10 band equalizer to trim the frequency response to match your voice and microphone. Remember to do a quick check of the ALC meter after you have adjusted the equalizer, it should just hit 0 dB on voice peaks. Ask for a few on-air reports over your next few QSOs.

Golden rules:

1. Don't use 'mic boost' unless you need it to get 0 dB on the Mic meter. Too much level here could overdrive the Mic preamp and cause distortion.

2. It is strongly recommended that you leave the Leveler turned on. This is especially true if you are using the compressor.

3. On PowerSDR mRX, you can't turn the ALC off. With other versions, it is strongly recommended that you leave it turned on.

Technical TIP: The transmit ALC works by adding a small delay to the signal (data stream). This means that the software can look ahead and see an audio peak coming. If the audio level is going to exceed 0 dB, the gain is gradually reduced, following an exponential curve, until the audio peak hits exactly 0 dB. This means that the output signal sent to the radio modulator can never exceed 0 dB, so although the audio may be compressed it can never overload the modulator. There is never a situation where flat-topping, which would cause severe distortion, can occur.

THE DOWNWARD EXPANDER (DEXP)

The downward expander has been a feature of PowerSDR since the early days. However, many users don't know what it does or how it works. Its function is to reduce the amount of noise that you transmit between words and syllables. When you key the microphone in SSB mode without talking, you will notice some RF signal on the spectrum display. This is background noise from things like; fans, thermal noise, and other noise in your shack, modulating your transmitter. The downward expander works like a noise gate, but it is much smoother and less aggressive. It effectively increases the dynamic range of the microphone by decreasing the noise level when you are not talking. Traditional noise gates do not decrease the gain. Below the threshold, they just switch off the audio and they tend to 'chatter' on and off which causes a choppy sound on your transmitted signal.

The downward expander has two adjustable controls on the 'Transmit' setup tab. 'Threshold' which sets the level below which the microphone audio will be attenuated and 'attenuate %' which sets how aggressively the signal will be attenuated. The threshold control is the same as the DEXP slider control on the front panel.

Technical TIP: The threshold control sets where the downward expander stops operating. When the microphone audio level is below the threshold, the algorithm will reduce the microphone gain. When it is above the threshold, it has no effect. The attenuation % affects how much the system will reduce the audio level. If it is set to 0%, the downward expander does nothing at all. At 100%, it acts like a noise gate switch, i.e. either no microphone audio output or normal audio output.

The downward expander makes your signal sound better and it is something that most radios don't have. There is a document on how to set it up on the FlexRadio resource site, but here is my less technical method.

1. I set the 'attenuation %' to 80%. If it is set much higher the action becomes choppy, you can see this variation on the panadapter while transmitting with the microphone open but no speech. If it is set lower than 80%, you will get less effective noise reduction.

2. Key the microphone but don't talk. A green line will show on the DEXP slider control. It represents the microphone audio level. Set the slider control to just a little higher than the end of the green line.

3. Turn on the DEXP you should notice a reduction in the noise level within the transmit pass band while transmitting. This is indicated by a lower amplitude RF signal on the spectrum display.

THE COMPRESSOR (COMP)

If you plan to work DX, it is worthwhile using some compression on your transmit audio. The compressor increases the quiet levels in your speech in order to increase the average power of your signal. This reduces the dynamic range of your audio, but it makes your signal easier to copy. It stops the quiet parts of what you are saying disappearing into the noise, especially when the received signal strength is weak. Your signal will be more 'punchy' and more effective at cutting through the noise and QRM.

The compressor or 'compander' button on PowerSDR mRX activates a speech processor, rather more sophisticated than the compander in the earlier / other PowerSDR variants.

You don't want your signal to sound too compressed and unnatural. I usually operate with 6 dB of compression. Forum reports say that the signal will start to sound odd and unnatural at about 10 dB. I would not recommend using more than 10 dB of compression.

CONTROLLED ENVELOPE SINGLE SIDEBAND (CESSB)

Controlled envelope SSB is a hot new method of getting a higher average transmitter power from your SDR transceiver. It is another excellent example of innovative software development making your SDR transceiver even more effective.

Dave Hershberger, W9GR, published interesting articles on CESSB in the November/December 2014 issue of QEX and in the February 2016 edition of QST. The intent of his algorithm is to increase "talk-power" on SSB by bringing the average power/speech level closer to the peak level. Part of this method has been used in the compression (COMP) routine in PowerSDR mRX for around three years and the other part; 'filter overshoot control' has just been implemented. Apparently, the same algorithm is used in the FlexRadio 6000 series. FlexRadio has reported and average increase in talk power of 2.56 dB (x1.8). This increase is equivalent to stacking another identical antenna top of your main antenna!

David, states that overshoot is inevitable in SSB modulators. You have to either reduce the audio modulation to a level where the audio peaks do not drive the RF power amplifier to a level where clipping distortion occurs, or use ALC (automatic level control) to dynamically reduce the level of audio peaks. Both of these methods reduce the average talk power of your signal and ALC is only partly effective in reducing the effects of overshoot in the modulator. Traditional ALC systems reduce the amplitude of an SSB signal in response to overshooting envelope peaks. Slow ALC may result in clipping and splatter because it has failed to act fast enough. Fast ALC will significantly reduce the average transmitted power. The advantage of DSP and SDR systems is that the peaks can be measured and reduced before they get to the modulator. David's CESSB algorithm increases the average transmitted power without letting the signal go into distortion.

"Controlled Envelope SSB envelope control is accomplished by: 1) Pre-filtering and peak limiting the audio input signal. 2) Baseband "RF clipping" of the SSB signal to reduce Hilbert transform overshoots. 3) Overshoot compensating the remaining envelope peaks resulting from baseband "RF clipping." By accurately controlling SSB envelope peaks at the point where the SSB is generated, ALC is unnecessary. ALC, even with look-ahead, reduces transmitted power when it does not have to — before and after an envelope peak. Average transmitted power can be significantly higher, without introducing "speech processor" type artifacts. An SSB signal with well-

controlled envelope peaks makes more efficient use of the RF power amplifier, and produces higher average power for a given peak envelope power." (W9GR)

To start using CESSB, enable the "filter overshoot control" checkbox on the DSP/Options tab. CESSB will not operate unless the compressor (COMP) is also enabled. However, the compressor will still work without CESSB control if the filter offshoot control has been not selected.

Note that, *"CESSB is intended for use with speech signals. Although it is a nonlinear process, the nonlinearity has a negligible effect upon speech. For non-speech SSB applications, however, such as digital modes (PSK, JT65, SSTV, and others), CESSB should be tested to be sure that any average power increase is not offset by nonlinear distortion." (W9GR)*

DIVERSITY MODE

PowerSDR mRX includes a diversity mode, which will work with radios that have two synchronized ADCs and receivers. As far as I am aware the only dual ADC radios compatible with PowerSDR, are the ANAN-100D and ANAN-200D transceivers, and the Afedri AFE822x SDR-Net (Dual Channel) receiver.

Diversity mode is very useful, particularly if you operate on bands where wideband noise is a problem. There is an excellent online video by Nige Coleman G7CNF illustrating how effective it is. He demonstrates up to 20 dB of reduction in the noise floor when using diversity noise reduction while receiving broadband noise. This could make a previously unusable band workable and reveal stations that you didn't even know were there.

The diversity mode allows you to combine signals received from your main antenna with signals from a reference or 'noise' antenna in such a way that much of the wideband noise is cancelled while the wanted signal remains almost unaffected. A 'radar' control lets you adjust the phase and amplitude of either receiver one or receiver two, in relation to the other receiver. It is very quick and easy to adjust while watching the noise floor decrease on the panadapter display.

The system works best if the noise being received is similar and at the same or greater level as the levels from the main antenna. If you don't have enough noise being received off the reference antenna, the subtraction effect will be diminished and so the noise cancellation will be ineffective. There is no point in putting the reference antenna near power lines or machinery in order to, deliberately introduce noise that is not affecting your main antenna.

If the noise problem is power line noise or a plasma TV down the road, you will need an outside reference antenna, mounted outside. It can be close to your main antenna, but not so close that a lot of power from your transmitter will be coupled into it. The 'noise' or reference antenna does not need to be directional. It can be a long wire, dipole, or a multiband vertical, used in conjunction with your directional Quad or Yagi antenna.

If the noise problem is within your house such as your own plasma TV, low voltage lighting, ADSL modem, PC switch mode power supplies etc. Then the diversity system may work better with a small antenna inside the shack or up in the ceiling space. You may have to experiment with different options.

The diversity mode works best in situations where the interference signal is fairly constant, but it doesn't necessarily have to be wideband. It will not be effective against lightning crashes, static, or vehicle ignition interference. The diversity adjustment is manual and fixed, not dynamic so it is less effective against changing, non-repetitive noise sources.

If, like me, you don't have the right model of SDR, you can buy 'antenna phase change' devices, which do the same sort of thing. These have a reputation for being tricky to adjust, but I am sure that using one with an SDR, which has the benefit of a panadapter, would make adjustment much easier.

PURESIGNAL – TRANSMIT PRE-DISTORTION

Amplifier nonlinearity results in poor IMD (intermodulation distortion) performance, which is bad. Adaptive transmitter pre-distortion modifies the audio modulation signal to correct for the nonlinearity of the amplifier so that the net result is a flat linearity response. This improves the transmit IMD performance a lot. Maybe it sounds easy but it is not! Both phase and amplitude linearity errors need to be corrected and the nonlinearity characteristics change dynamically with changes of frequency, antenna load, temperature, power supply voltage and all sorts of other factors.

PureSignal is an innovation for PowerSDR mRX PS that makes use of the full duplex capability of the software defined radios. It also requires the wide bandwidth capability of the transmitter and the calculating power of the PC application.

Technical TIP: Full duplex is the ability to receive and transmit simultaneously. Most conventional architecture HF radios are not able to operate in a duplex mode. They tend to use the same local oscillator and I.F. amplifiers for transmit and receive and their receivers may not be able to cope with the high levels from the transmitter. Many VHF and UHF radios are able to operate in full duplex mode, but that is more often used for cross band operation. So far, there are very few ham radio transceivers with the ability to use adaptive transmit pre-distortion.

The program was developed by Warren Pratt NR0V. It dramatically improves the transmitter's intermodulation performance by adjusting the modulated RF signal going into the RF power amplifier so that the signal at the output of the amplifier is a more accurate but amplified representation of the input signal. It is so effective that when PureSignal is employed, it currently gives the ANAN radios better transmit intermodulation performance figures than any other HF ham radio transceiver tested by

ARRL labs, (based on published QST data). The ANAN-8000DLE claims a third order IMD typically -72dB below PEP @ 200W output on 20M.

Technical TIP: Warren's new "adaptive pre-distortion PureSignal" algorithms operate in real time rather than using the LUT (look up table) approach. Illustrations in the introduction to PureSignal document available from the Apache Labs web site indicate a typical improvement in IMD performance of 20 dBc, which is very impressive indeed.

Press the 'information' button on the new PureSignal tab in PowerSDR and it will load a very informative PDF file on PureSignal transmit pre-distortion which explains it all very well. I will try to add a (slightly) less technical introduction to the subject. More PureSignal documents can be downloaded from the Apache web site and from the Apache forum.

How does it work? A low level sample of the transmitter's output power is taken, usually from a coupler at the antenna port. It is received and demodulated by the receiver, which in an ANAN or Hermes radio is always running because the radio is full duplex. It is extremely important that this feedback signal be suitably attenuated to avoid damage to the sensitive receiver front end.

The demodulated sample signal is compared with the audio input signal being sent to the modulator. Phase and amplitude changes are applied to the modulated signal in order to dynamically reduce the IMD products. This is not straightforward because the amount of adjustment required changes continuously with the changing input signal. The level and phase adjustment needs to adapt. Also, the amount of nonlinearity caused by the amplifier will be different at different operating frequencies and when the transceiver is connected to different antenna impedances. If the radio was just sending an un-modulated carrier signal the phase and level adjustment would be easy. But then life would be boring because you can't convey any information with an un-modulated carrier signal. No, not even CW, which is an amplitude modulated digital mode, "carrier on, carrier off".

Inside the SDR software both the audio signal being used to modulate the transmitter and the audio from the received feedback signal are digital signals. The PureSignal adjustments can be calculated mathematically and applied by changing bits in the 'transmit' audio data stream. Over a short period, the software adjusts the modulation signal to compensate for the IMD created by the amplifier. It continuously compares the transmitted signal with the modulation and adapts to changing conditions.

The idea of using pre-distortion to improve the transmitter's linearity has been around for quite a while, but it is tricky to implement with conventional electronics.

In a software defined radio the problem can be resolved using a mathematical algorithm and that allows fast, dynamic, adjustment of the transmitted signal. The receiver needs to be working at the same time as the transmitter because you need to continuously receive and compare samples of the transmitted signal. The process needs to be able to apply adjustments over a wider frequency range than the normal SSB transmission bandwidth so that harmonics of the modulation frequencies are included. This is another problem if you are trying to implement adaptive transmitter pre-distortion on conventional architecture radios.

Adaptive transmitter pre-distortion could be implemented in the DSP chips of conventional transceivers. But, they do not usually have enough transmitter bandwidth and most are not able to transmit and receive on the same band at the same time. The reuse of circuit blocks such as the local oscillator limits the ability for many conventional radios to operate in a duplex mode. Future designs may use an embedded SDR receiver or a sub receiver to receive the required feedback signal.

What is transmitter nonlinearity? All RF power amplifiers introduce some nonlinearity into the transmitted signal. 'Nonlinearity' just means that the relationship between the input power and the output power is not entirely flat. In other words, the output signal is never a perfect but louder copy of the input signal. The power amplifier in your transceiver may have a little less gain when the input signal is small and it might not put out as much power as it should when the input signal is large. This is usually due to the power supply voltage drooping under high current load. Components heat up under high current conditions. This can cause them to have more resistance or to change their capacitance or inductance, which might de-tune the transmitter slightly. All of these factors combine to introduce two kinds of nonlinearity. Amplitude nonlinearity where the gain of the amplifier does not remain the same for all input levels, and phase nonlinearity is when the phase of the output signal is being affected by the input level or frequency.

Using a 'linear' amplifier after your transceiver adds an additional source of nonlinearity. If you place the feedback coupler at the output of the linear amplifier instead of the output of the transceiver, PureSignal can actually compensate for the overall nonlinearity of the transceiver and linear amp combination.

Why do we want good transmitter linearity? When we transmit a digital mode or SSB HF transmission, the last thing we want is complaints that our transmission sounds bad, or that it is causing splatter interference across the band. We are legally required to ensure that we do not cause interference to other band users and this includes making sure that our signal is mostly contained within the wanted bandwidth, usually less than 3 kHz for an SSB signal.

SDR transceivers are in general no better and no worse than any other kind of ham transceiver and using the standard 'two tone' test, the 3rd order IMD product is usually between 28 dB and 32 dB below the test tone level. In some cases this level of interference can be heard at the receiver's location and would interfere with a station operating very close to the transmit frequency. For example if you were transmitting USB on 14.200MHz and a station was receiving your signal at 30 dB over 9, then a station in the same locality listening on 14.203 MHz would hear interference at around S9. Improving the transmit IMD performance of your transmitter is a way of being "nice to the neighbors." Transceivers with higher voltage 50V output stages tend to have slightly better 3rd order transmit IMD performance than 12V transceivers. The improvement is typically dB to 8 dB. Transmit pre-distortion is able to improve the 3rd order transmit IMD performance by a massive 20 dB.

The technical background: Amateur radio transceivers use linear power amplifiers because the voice signals that we want to transmit vary in amplitude, causing the transmitted RF signal to range from zero to the full output power of the radio. You see this as the peaks on your transmit power meter during SSB operation. It is important that the output power of the amplifier accurately follows the changing level of the input signal. This is called the amplifier's amplitude linearity.

During AM or SSB transmission, the phase of the output signal should not be affected by changes in the level or frequency of the audio input signal, this is called the amplifier's phase linearity. Phase nonlinearity can be caused by components changing their inductance or capacitance when they are stressed due to high voltage or current causing heating. The change of value causes de-tuning of the RF power amplifier resulting in phase shift. Phase nonlinearity effectively causes a small amount of phase modulation when we want amplitude modulation.

Severe nonlinearity causes the different frequency components of the RF signal to mix together creating unwanted sum and difference frequencies. The result is known as 'intermodulation distortion.' The amount of degradation is dependent on the design and tuning of the output stage of the amplifier, the output filters, load impedance, drive level, frequency of operation, modulation signal, stiffness of the power supply and components like toroids, and the output transistors.

Linear amplifiers tend to be less linear at low input levels and the output power tapers off near full drive level. If you chart the output power vs input power you would see a slight S shape rather than the desired linear line.

Intermodulation products mixed into the wanted transmitter signal sound bad, because they interfere with the wanted speech. Intermodulation products that are created outside of the wanted transmit bandwidth are heard as 'splatter' and make the transmitted signal wider than intended. If your transmitter is only used for CW and digital modes like PSK and RTTY the audio modulation level does not vary. The modulation is either on, or off. With these modes, the RF amplifier does not have to be linear. They generate much less IMD but PureSignal can still be used.

How well does it work? The normal way to measure a transmitter's IMD performance is to apply two audio test tones to the SSB modulator at a level that causes full transmit power. The transmit signal is measured using a spectrum analyzer and the level of the 3rd, 5th, 7th and 9th order intermodulation products compared with the two tone level is recorded.

You might have seen the IMD products on pictures in transceiver reviews. A 3rd order Transmit IMD of -30 dBc compared to the two tone level is very good. PureSignal can produce a 3rd order Transmit IMD of better than   - 50 dBc, (-56 dBc using ARRL method).

What it can't do: PureSignal can improve amplitude and phase linearity problems, but is less successful with 'memory effects' because they are related to past events not the input signal that is currently being compared. 'Memory effects' are phase or amplitude distortions caused by earlier signal events affecting components in the radio. For example, a large input signal could cause the RF transistors and heatsink to get hot resulting in an amplitude and /or phase change in the amplifier output signal. When the input signal level drops, the devices take some time to cool so the distortion persists even though the input signal has reduced. Another example is a high input level causing the amplifier to run at near full power, drawing maximum DC current. This may cause the power supply voltage to droop and the lower supply voltage will affect the amplifier linearity. When the input signal level reduces, the DC supply voltage takes some time to return to full voltage, so again the distortion persists even though the input signal has reduced.

Adaptive pre-distortion can only improve IMD caused by nonlinearity that is attributable to the input modulation signal. It may not be able to adjust for fixed sources of IMD such as saturated Toroids in the output filter, badly tuned linear amp stages, or IMD occurring in the antenna system, i.e. after the feedback coupler.

The feedback coupler: The feedback level from the transmitted signal is quite critical. It has to be quite large but not so big that it causes the receiver ADC to overload. The Apache Labs ANAN-200D 'Orion' transceiver has been designed with adaptive pre-distortion in mind. It includes an internal coupler to sample the transmit signal. Other models need an external coupler.

If you place the coupler on output of your linear amplifier, you will need to be able to switch in additional attenuation to reduce the feedback level when operating QRO and then increase it again when operating bare foot. Maybe two couplers with suitable attenuators could be used with a switch connected to the 'operate' control of the amplifier.

SHED YOUR SKIN

One of the very cool things about PowerSDR is the ability to change what the operating interface 'GUI' looks like. This is called changing the skin. The buttons and controls all remain in the same place and have the same functions, but you can change what they look like. You can also change the background image of the radio and the panadapter. There are several skins bundled with PowerSDR. They can be selected by using the dropdown box on the Display setup tab. You can download other skins off the Internet, but sometimes they are for older versions of PowerSDR and you may need to add image files for any new buttons. You can replace the image files with other pictures of a similar size. The skins are a collection of small graphics files. There is a separate graphics file for every button and control on the console and larger image files for the background pictures.

How to make or change a PowerSDR skin:

These instructions work with the current version of PowerSDR mRX and they will probably work with most PowerSDR variants (forks). It is best not to mess up an existing skin. I recommend that you copy the files from an existing skin into a new folder so you can experiment safely.

A): find where the skins are stored on your computer (or download one from the Internet) and make the new folders.

1. Find the old Power SDR skins. They are not in the program directory, you can usually find them in the;

    C:\Documents and Settings*your logon*\Application Data\FlexRadio Systems\PowerSDR Skins, folder.

    Or they might be in the;

    C:\Documents and Settings*All users*\Application Data\FlexRadio Systems\Power SDR\Skins folder.

2. When you have located the skins folders, you will see that each skin name has a 'Console' subfolder containing all of the image files.

3. Make a new sub folder called anything you like e.g. *mySkin_name*." Then make a subfolder under that called 'Console'. Copy (don't move) all of the files from another skin or download them and save them in the new Console subdirectory. Other than the Console subdirectory, the *mySkin_name* directory will have no files in it.

After you have done the three stages above, start PowerSDR mRX. The new skin should appear on the 'Setup', 'Appearance', 'Skins' dropdown list in PowerSDR MRX. If it is not on there then it is probable that you have not placed your new folder in the correct place, or the files are not in the 'Console' subdirectory. You can make as many folder pairs, *skin name and subfolder called Console*, as you like. Now you can play with a copy rather than messing with a working skin. All the .png files for a skin must be in the relevant Console sub folder.

Now you can replace any missing controls (section B) or change the background and spectrum display background images (section C).

B): If the new skin was downloaded, it is likely to be missing some buttons or controls. Here is how to add the missing controls.

The skin will be working, but you may find that the MIC button next to the Mic Gain slider is not there and neither is the 'TX FL' button, or the 'Rx1 AF' and 'Rx2 AF' slider controls. This is fairly easy to fix, you just have to copy and rename eight files. Browsing the Console folder in Windows 'thumbnail' view shows what the items look like.

1. To add the Mic button, go to the new console folder:

    a. Make a copy of *chkVOX-0.png* file and rename the copy to *chkMicMute-0.png*

    b. Make a copy of *chkVOX-1.png* file and rename the copy to *chkMicMute-1.png*

    One image is displayed when the button is unselected. The other image is displayed when the button has been pressed.

2. To add the TX FL button, go to the new console folder:

    a. Make a copy of *chkMUT-0.png* file and rename the copy to *chkShowTXFilter-0.png*

    b. Make a copy of *chkMUT-1.png* file and rename the copy to *chkShowTXFilter-1.png*

    One image is used to show the unselected button and the other image is displayed when the button has been pressed.

3. To add the Rx1 AF slider, go to the new console folder:

    a. Make a copy of *pbtAF-back.png* file and rename the copy to *pbtRX1AF-back.png*

    b. Make a copy of *pbtAF-head.png* file and rename the copy to *pbtRX1AF-head.png*

    One image is used to show the slider control background and the other image is the control knob.

4. To add the Rx2 AF slider, go to the new console folder:

    a. Make a copy of *pbtAF-back.png* file and rename the copy to *pbtRX2AF-back.png*

    b. Make a copy of *pbtAF-head.png* file and rename the copy to *pbtRX2AF-head.png*

    One image is used to show the slider control background and the other image is the control knob.

Now the skin should work perfectly. Select it using on the Setup / Appearance, Skins dropdown box in PowerSDR MRX.

C: Changing the background image and the spectrum display background.

Just for fun or for a demo to your radio club, it is possible to change the look of the radio. I made a 'Matrix' skin and a 'Spotty' skin. You can even have your own smiling face, a photo of your shack, or a picture of your dog.

Figure 19: change the skin to customise the look of PowerSDR

You can use any image that has been saved as a .png file. Most graphic editors can open a .jpg file and save it as a .png file. Try to get an image the right shape or it will get stretched to fit.

Background images need to be very simple, so that the buttons don't get lost in the detail. I like to use a "texture" file like gravel or a wood-grain image. It is easy to download suitable images from the Internet.

To change the GUI background image:

1.   Save a copy of *console.png* (so you can restore things to the way they were). Rename it to *Console_old.png* or similar

2.   Use a graphic editor to open the .png or .jpg photo that you want to use as the background image and save it as *Console.png*

3.   Place the new *Console.png* file back into the Console directory of the skin that you want to use, start PowerSDR and select the skin.

4.   Next; decide you don't like it, find another image file and go back to stage two.

5.   Repeat items 2, 3, and 4, until your wife/husband/partner calls you for dinner.

Spectrum images sit behind the spectrum display. They can be of anything but they will be stretched to fit, so a wide image is preferable. If you use Panafall, the waterfall will cover the lower half of your picture. Dark images look better underneath a white spectrum display and grid.

To change the image in the spectrum display area:

1. Save a copy of *picDisplay.png* (so you can restore things to the way they were). Rename it to *picDisplay_old.png* or similar

2. Use a graphic editor to open the .jpg photo that you want to use and 'save as' *picDisplay.png*

3. Place the new *picDisplay.png* file back into the Console directory, of the skin that you want to use, start PowerSDR and then select the skin.

4. Decide you don't like it, find another .jpg and go back to stage two.

5. Repeat 2, 3, and 4, until your wife/husband/partner calls you for dinner.

NOTE: You can't overwrite the image file if PowerSDR is currently using it. Closing down PowerSDR mRX should not be necessary. Usually temporarily selecting another skin and hence a different background image file, allows you to overwrite the file.

D: Changing other screen controls.

You can change other images such as buttons but they need to be the right size and of course, they need to have the right text on them. One option is to copy button or slider image files from another skin. I imported a complete skin with 3D buttons that I liked and then changed the background image.

CHANGING THE FREQUENCY LABELS

Beneath the frequency indication on both VFO-A and VFO-B there is some text displayed which describes the band segment that you are in. It can also identify spot frequencies such as beacons, shortwave station names, or net frequencies. The US amateur radio band plan, WWV, and the NCDXF/IARU beacon frequencies are loaded by default. These labels are contained in the 'BandText' table inside the database.xml file. It is possible to edit the band segments and to add new spot frequencies using a Band Text utility or an XML file editor. Note that there are many other setup keys and settings included in database.xml. Do not edit the other data tables unless you know exactly what you are doing, (see the section about database.xml below).

Band Text entries should not overlap. Be careful with the high and low frequencies. If the high frequency is the same as the low frequency then a spot frequency is described. If there is a gap between the high frequency of one record and the low frequency of the next record, then "Out of band" is displayed. This never happens within the ham bands, as the BandText table has entries covering all of the amateur bands. I added several beacons and the PSK sections to my Band Text table.

Figure 20: band text data is displayed below the VFO frequency

USING POWERSDR WITH DIGITAL MODE SOFTWARE

PowerSDR has special DRM, DIGU, and DIGL buttons for use with external digital mode software. Selecting one these modes disables the AGC and provides separate banks of ten receive filters. You can customize the receive filters to the widths that you need for the digital mode you are using. I like to have a wide filter for spotting PSK signals and then move to a narrow filter while operating a QSO. Recent versions of PowerSDR mRX also have special double peak 'Dolly' filters especially for use when receiving RTTY signals. These are very effective and increase readability (printability?) of RTTY signals significantly. If you are an RTTY operator, I recommend that you try them. Unfortunately, they are a recent addition and so far, they can't be turned off and on from the main PowerSDR screen.

To configure your station for digital modes, you need to setup some virtual com ports so that the digital mode program can control the radio and so that it can display the operating frequency. You also need a virtual audio cable (or a pair of them) to connect the audio from the receiver into the digital mode program and the digital audio modulation from the digital mode program to the radio transmitter. Selecting DIGU or DIGL selects the display of the audio levels for the VAC output and input. Note that, 'VAC' must be set to 'on' for audio to be sent to the digital mode software. It trips me up pretty much every time! You should save a separate transmit profile for digital modes and I recommend using the option to show the transmit filter width on top of the grey receiver bandwidth on the panadapter. It places yellow lines at the transmitter high and low frequencies. For PSK (DIGU) operation, I have one of the receive filter buttons set to exactly the same width as the 1 kHz transmit bandwidth and I turn the '*show transmit bandwidth for digital modes*' option on. Then I know that any signals that are between the yellow lines on the panadapter will be inside the receiver passband when I switch from a wide filter, to the narrow filter that matches the transmit bandwidth. My DIGU mode 'transmit profile' creates a 1kHz bandwidth between 1000 Hz and 2000 Hz. Note that the actual width of your transmission is set by the digital mode that is in use. The narrow PSK31 transmission can be placed anywhere within the 1 kHz transmit bandwidth. For RTTY I created a special 'RTTY' transmit profile with the transmitter bandwidth from 1960 Hz to 2460 Hz. This gives me a 500 Hz wide filter centered on 2210 Hz. The minimum bandwidth required to send a 45.45 Baud, 170 Hz shift, RTTY signal is about 250 Hz.

SETTING YOUR TRANSMIT LEVELS FOR DIGITAL MODES

Most digital modes run your transmitter at a higher average power level than the SSB or CW modes. It is important not to stress or overheat the radio. Unless the radio is rated for a 100% duty cycle, I recommend using about half the rated power of the radio, i.e. 50 W for a 100 W radio, for transmitting digital modes. Note that FlexRadios are designed to run full power on all modes, so you can run a higher average power if you have a FlexRadio. Refer to your user guide for the manufacturer's recommendations. The same rule applies to linear amplifiers, some of them are designed to run full power on any mode, and others must be down rated for digital modes.

Remember that transmitting half power only reduces the received signal from your station by 3dB. In most cases, the other station would not even notice the reduction from 100W to 50W.

It is also very important that the digital signal does not over modulate the transmitter. You don't want to cause interference to other band users or to transmit a distorted signal that is difficult or impossible to decode. I often see over modulated PSK31 signals on my digital mode program's waterfall display, it shows as a wider than normal PSK signal with horizontal streaks. A clean PSK signal looks like a fuzzy railway track.

When you select the DIGU or DIGL modes, the audio level slider controls for the VAC audio input and output are shown in the space on the GUI that the Mic gain and compressor controls occupy when you are in in SSB mode.

My method for setting the transmit level for digital modes like PSK and RTTY is to;

1. Connect your transceiver to a dummy load or to a correctly matched antenna on a quiet band. Never tune up into an antenna on a frequency that is inside the digital mode segment of the band.

2. Click the PowerSDR Tune button and slowly increase the drive level until you reach full power. 100 Watts on a 100 Watt rig or 10 Watts on a 10 Watt rig. Note the drive level then to avoid inadvertently transmitting at fill power, set the drive slider back down to about 10% of maximum. Turn off the Tune mode.

3. Set the transmit drive level to the same setting as the figure you noted while you were in the Tune mode. This means that a clean test tone on SSB would drive the transmitter to full power.

4. Now select DIGU (or DIGL) mode. Set the 'transmit audio slider' control to a low setting and activate your digital mode program to transmit a PSK or other digital mode signal. Slowly increase the audio 'transmit audio slider' control until the transmitted level rises to ½ its rated RF power, (3/4 or even full power on a FlexRadio).

5. This method ensures that the transmitter is not over modulated and your transmit signal should be clean. Ask another station to comment on the quality of your transmission as a final check. A PSK signal may transmit a slightly higher power when letters are being sent but the increase will not be significant. If in doubt, lower the drive a little.

VIRTUAL COM PORTS

Conventional radios have RS232 COM or USB ports for CAT control and connection of devices like CW or voice Keyers. But PowerSDR is usually running on the same PC as the programs that issue the CAT commands. It is pointless using hardware com ports and serial cables to connect together two programs working on the same PC, so 'virtual' com ports are created. These virtual ports are created in pairs by a utility program. There are several free options. I use com0com. You use the program to create back-to-back virtual com ports, with port numbers outside of the range used by your PC for hardware com ports. VSP (virtual serial port) Manager from Eterlogic is another option. See http://www.eterlogic.com/Products.VSPE.html. VSP is available as freeware for a 32 bit Windows platform and as shareware for the 64 bit version.

It is usually a good idea to name the com port pairs in a way that is easy to remember. For example, I created com pairs; COM6 to COM16 and COM7 to COM17. You can use other arrangements such as COM8 to COM9. Whatever you find easier.

Once the com port pairs have been defined, they stay connected. You should never have to set them up again. To use the virtual com ports, set PowerSDR to COM6 and the digital mode program to the paired port, in my case COM16. As usual, the data speed, parity, and number of stop bits must be set the same on both software applications. Because the com ports are 'virtual' you can use very fast speeds up to 57600 bps, but for CAT control 9600 bps is adequate.

Computer serial ports use binary signaling, so the data rate in bits per second is equal to the symbol rate in Bauds.

VIRTUAL AUDIO CABLES 'VAC'

Just like the com ports mentioned in the last section, we need a way to connect the audio input and outputs from the radio to our digital mode or CW software. We don't want to have to install a second sound card and connect cables between the two, so we use a virtual audio cable. Unfortunately, the capability to route audio signals between software applications is not usually built into the SDR software. FlexRadio Systems has included their own 'DAX' audio router with Smart SDR, but if you are using PowerSDR you will need a third party application. There are three or four commonly used virtual audio cable programs.

One is called **VAC** (virtual audio cable) by Eugene Muzychenko. See, www.software.muzychenko.net/eng/**vac**.htm. VAC is shareware, you have to pay a nominal sum and register VAC to avoid a voice message that is embedded in the trial version. **VB-Audio Cable** is a similar Windows utility, available at www.vb-audio.pagesperso-orange.fr/Cable/. VB-Audio Cable is donation-ware. There is a MAC equivalent called **Soundflower** available from www.macupdate.com/app/mac/14067/soundflower. **Sound Siphon** is another possibility for MAC PCs. I have tried VB-Audio cable and it works fine, but I had already setup and paid for VAC so I am still using that. VAC is possibly a little more difficult to configure, but like the com port utility, once it is configured you should never have to do it again.

To use the VAC function in PowerSDR you must first use the virtual audio cable utility to create two virtual cables, one for audio from the radio to the digital mode software and the other for audio from the digital mode software to the radio. If you were only interested in receiving, for example using a CW reader like Skimmer, you would only need one virtual cable.

Once you have created the cables, you have to connect them correctly. For example, set Power SDR VAC1 audio output to 'virtual cable 1' and VAC1 audio input to 'virtual cable 2.' The digital mode software should be set to receive audio from 'virtual cable 1' and send audio to the radio over 'virtual cable 2.' This is the same concept as connecting two physical cables but it can be a bit confusing.

When you initially create the cables, you set the audio sampling rate that is used. It is best if this matches the sample rate used by the digital mode software and PowerSDR, usually 48,000 samples per second. A setting of 24,000 provides a more readable, wider display on MixW.

PowerSDR can use the WDM audio driver or the MME audio driver for VAC. On my PC the other selections will not work.

If you wish to use both VAC1 and VAC2 in PowerSDR in order to send and receive audio to two different applications, it is best to create four virtual audio cables. I believe that the ANAN-100D and 200D radios link the receiver on ADC1 to VAC 1 and the receiver on ADC2 to VAC 2 by default.

The cables created by VB-Audio Cable are named differently. No configuration is required. Again, the cables cross over. Set PowerSDR to send audio to the digital mode software on VB-Audio Cable-A, and receive audio from the digital mode software on VB-Audio Cable-B. Note that VB-Audio Cable requires that PowerSDR use the WDM audio driver. The other selections will not work and are likely to cause an error.

Technical TIP: Virtual audio cable programs are Windows Audio Drivers. They work by creating a fake sound card device on your PC, which most digital mode programs can select as their audio input or output device. The digital mode software and PowerSDR use the standard Windows WDM or MME audio streaming. Some primitive digital mode and CW software, designed for use with conventional transceivers, can only receive input from and output to, the Windows 'default sound card.' In that case, you would have to configure the fake VAC sound card as the Windows default sound card using a selection in the Windows Control Panel. That will probably mess up the connection to your PC speakers for other audio applications such as you music player and web browser. It will work to connect the program to the radio (PowerSDR), but it is a clumsy solution.

CHANGE YOUR FILTER SETTINGS AND LABELS

Many PowerSDR users do not realize that you can customize the receive filters for each mode. Simply right click any of the filters and select 'Configure.' From there you can change any of the ten fixed filters and even the two variable filters. However, the variable filters will be overwritten if you manually change the filter width or shift, so there is not much point setting them with the 'Configure' menu.

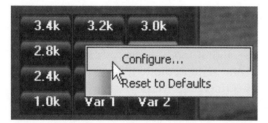

This is another example of the flexibility of software defined radios compared to the fixed filters in most conventional transceivers.

Figure 21: you can change the filter names and settings for each mode

You can change the button labels as well, so you could, rename the digital filters to RTTY, PSK, Narrow, or Wide, etc. I reset my USB SSB filters so that I have filters at 3.0, 2.9, 2.8, 2.7, 2.6, 2.5, and 2.4 kHz. I also changed the lower cut off from 150Hz to 180Hz, which seems to suit my hearing better.

THE STEP ATTENUATOR

This section only applies to Open HPSDR Hermes and ANAN transceivers. Other radios using PowerSDR have different attenuator arrangements.

The ATT drop down list is situated below the Drive slide control and above the Squelch slide control on the main console GUI. If the Enable Attenuator checkbox on the General / Options setup tab is selected, the label above the drop down list will be S-ATT to indicate a 0-61 dB attenuator with 1 dB steps. If the check box is not selected the label will show ATT to indicate that the attenuator is adjustable in 10 dB steps. You can also switch between these two modes by double clicking the ATT / S-ATT label on the console.

Both of these attenuator controls actually activate three different attenuators. There is a Mini Circuits 0-31 dB, 1 dB step, attenuator on the Hermes / Angelia

/ Orion board and if you have a radio that includes the Alex filters, (i.e. not an ANAN-10 or a bare Hermes board) there are 10 dB and 20 dB fixed attenuators that are switched into circuit by relays. You can hear them switch in or out as you adjust the ATT / S-ATT controls past the 31 dB point. These two attenuators on the Alex board are connected in series so they can provide 0, 10, 20, or 30 dB of attenuation to the received signal before it reaches the ANAN or Hermes radio board.

The Hermes and ANAN radio boards have a 20 dB pre-amplifier after the 31 dB attenuator and 50 MHz LPF and before the LTC2208 ADC. This amplifier cannot be turned off. It is used in conjunction with the attenuator to provide a pre-amplifier / attenuator function.

In S-ATT mode, the attenuator is adjustable in 1 dB steps from 0 to 31 dB. If the Alex filter is present then the attenuator is adjustable in 1 dB steps from 0 to 61 dB, using the 0-10-20-30 dB attenuator on the Alex board (PA / Filter board on ANAN) as well as the 0-31 dB attenuator on the radio board. You can hear the Alex attenuator switch in, as you increase they S-ATT level from 31 to 32 dB. It does not happen again, so I believe that the full 30 dB is switched in at once.

In ATT mode, the attenuator is adjustable in 10 dB steps from 0 to 50 dB. The list is a bit odd because 20 dB is on it twice.

- **20 dB** attenuation using the 31 dB attenuator on the radio board.

- **0 dB** no attenuation. This is the normal default setting

- **10 dB** attenuation using the 10 dB attenuator on the Alex filter or ANAN PA/Filter board.

- **20 dB** attenuation using the 20 dB attenuator on the Alex filter or ANAN PA/Filter board.

- **30 dB** attenuation using the 10 dB and the 20 dB attenuator on the Alex filter or ANAN PA/Filter board.

- **40 dB** attenuation using the 31 dB attenuator on the radio board and the 20 dB attenuator on the Alex filter or ANAN PA/Filter board.

- **50 dB** attenuation using the 31 dB attenuator on the radio board, the 10 dB and the 20 dB attenuator on the Alex filter or ANAN PA/Filter board.

Technical TIP: Unlike many conventional radios, the PowerSDR S meter always indicates the level being received at the antenna connector. Unless the signal drops below the noise floor, the meter indication should not change as the attenuator settings are adjusted.

TRANSMIT PROFILES

PowerSDR allows you to store an unlimited number of transmit profiles. These govern the bandwidth of the transmitted signal and the status of the, transmit audio equalizer, microphone level, compressor, VOX, downward compressor, and display settings. The system defaults to a choice of two options, 'Default' and 'Default DX'. If you select the 'More Options' checkbox on the Transmit

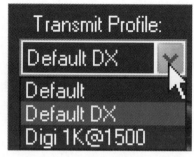

setup tab you can choose from a range of other options each tailored for a specific type of operation. I use the 'Digi 1k @ 1500' and 'Digi 1k @ 2210' options for PSK and RTTY operation. You can create your own transmit settings and save them with a unique name. Once a transmit profile has been saved it can be selected from the main PowerSDR operating console using the dropdown list near the microphone and compressor controls. I use the 'Default' setting for general SSB operation and the 'Default DX' setting for SSB contests and working DX. On my setup, the only difference between default and default DX is that I use 6 dB of compressor, activate the DEXP, and a slightly narrower transmitter bandwidth for the DX option. You might consider creating different TX profiles with different EQ settings for DX, or for different microphones. I use the standard default settings for CW, but a proficient CW operator might prefer a custom profile for CW.

Technical TIP: Each transmit profile stores:

- *transmit filter high and low frequencies,*
- *equalizer settings,*
- *compressor settings,*
- *microphone level,*
- *microphone level for FM mode,*
- *Leveler settings,*
- *ALC settings,*
- *transmit power level,*
- *downward expander,*
- *'Tune' power,*
- *transmit meter mode,*
- *transmit audio monitor level,*
- *AM carrier level,*
- *show TX filter on panadapter setting,*
- *VAC1 enabled and levels,*
- *VAC2 enabled and settings and*
- *DSP buffer sizes.*

DITHER & RANDOM

The LTC2208 ADC used in the Hermes / Apache Labs transceivers have internal Random and Dither controls and these can be selected in PowerSDR mRX. These functions are covered in detail in the ADC section. While the benefit of these functions may be measurable in the test lab, I don't see any real improvement when the radio is connected to an antenna. I find that there are enough mid-range signals on the bands and that I see no improvement with either or both functions turned on. Try it out for yourself.

DEALING WITH NEW SOFTWARE RELEASES – DATABASE.XML

Conventional radios store the current state of the radio so that when you turn the radio on, it will restart on the same band, with the same mode, filter widths, and other settings. This information, along with setup menu options and saved frequencies are stored in non-volatile memory inside the radio.

In most software defined radios these user interface, 'persistence' settings are stored on the hard drive of the PC not in the radio. PowerSDR saves all of this useful data in a computer file called 'database.xml.' It saves other database files as well, notably 'memory.xml' which holds all of your saved frequencies and related data. The others are 'CAT Structs.xml', which holds the CAT commands and a file for Midi control.

The following section applies to PowerSDR mRX versions, but the information should also apply to most PowerSDR forks.

Currently, nearly every time a new version of PowerSDR mRX is installed, it is necessary to delete the database.xml file and let PowerSDR mRX automatically build a new one when the new release is run for the first time.

There are three ways to delete the database.xml file.

a. Using database reset on the PowerSDR setup screen. On my PC, this causes PowerSDR to delete the database.xml and then shut down.

b. If you run a new release of PowerSDR, which requires a newer database than the current one, it will ask if you want to reset the database. Or it may just crash.

c. You can find the file and rename it or delete it.

After you start the new release, the database.xml file is automatically updated any time a setup option is changed and every time that Power SDR is shut down. The requirement to delete the database file when a new software release is installed is because, unlike a hardware radio, the database structure changes if new on-screen controls are added or deleted from PowerSDR. Also, the software is under active development so new settings and defaults may be required.

Having to go back to a default database is a real nuisance because it means that the radio forgets any custom filter settings, skins, equalizer settings you have defined and more importantly if forgets your transmitter audio levels. You have to go through all of the setup screens and enter any non-default preferences again. After most software updates you cannot simply restore from a previously saved database, because it would not have the revised database format. It would be very good if the developers can find a way to update database.xml without losing all of your custom settings. Perhaps the settings that you are likely to set, like your transmit audio and equalizer settings, the custom screen header, VAC settings and skins could be stored in a different database.

Technical TIP: It is well worth writing down your settings or taking screen shots of your setup tabs before doing a PowerSDR mRX update. This will make it easy to set things the way you had them before the update.

OK from here on this chapter gets quite technical, so you can jump to the next chapter if the going gets too tough.

A database utility program can restore settings by copying individual xml keys from a previously saved backup database, but you have to be extremely careful not to delete any of the new keys that the upgraded PowerSDR version requires. Also, you don't want to copy old settings when the defaults have been changed due to a coding update. I had this happen when the noise reduction filters were revised. To make updates easier for myself, I wrote a database manager in C# but I have not released it to the public because of the risk of adversely affecting someone's setup.

Many of the settings interact, for example there are database 'keys' for each band, but only one should be set to True at a time, since RX1 (or RX2) can't be on more than one band at the same time. Some default settings might be changed by the developer due to re-coding of the software and of course, you would not want to overwrite the key that holds the current software version number. It is possible to change keys so that the transceiver is in transmit mode when the radio starts, un-calibrate the transmit power metering, or reduce the setting of the receive attenuation while transmitting. So editing the database.xml file needs to be approached with knowledge and caution. However, careful editing is acceptable and if you do mess up the settings, you can just delete the database.xml file and PowerSDR will rebuild a new default one. It is best to save a backup before attempting any editing. You can do this using the export database function in the setup.

The following list shows what is inside database.xml and some notes about changing the data using a utility program. Some of the data tables listed are not included in the database.xml file unless you open the relevant screens in PowerSDR and then close them again. This is because when PowerSDR builds a new default version of database.xml it does not include some of the information tables if they are at default status. For example, the CWX table is only added to database.xml if you start the newly upgraded PowerSDR and then open the CWX setup screen. The same applies to the Diversity, XVTR, and Equalizer tables.

Database tables that are commonly included in PowerSDR database.xml		
Band Stack	The radio saves the last three frequencies that you used on each band. Clicking the band button cycles through the three saved frequencies. Band Stack holds three frequencies for each band.	You can change this data but it will be overwritten each time you change bands. After a database reset, the radio defaults to the bottom of the CW section of each band and to CW mode. The radio will start on 10MHz WWV. Updating Band Stack from a backup modifies this behavior.
Band Text	Band Text: holds the text that is displayed underneath the frequency on the VFO display. It also determines what frequencies you can transmit on.	It is good to edit this data. You can add net frequencies, beacons, and shortwave station identifiers. You can also revise or rename band segments. For example, I added the PSK segments.
CWX	CWX: holds the CW macros from the CWX screen.	It is really helpful to copy these from a backup to save you writing them all in again.
Diversity Form	Diversity Form: holds the settings of the Diversity screen accessed a tab on from the main console.	I don't use this mode as I don't have a radio with two ADCs, so you are on your own with this one. My recommendation is to reset the data using the PowerSDR setup screen.
EQ Form	EQ Form holds equalizer settings relating to the Equalizer setup screen accessed from a tab on the main console.	The table data includes a choice of, 3 or 10 band EQ, preamp level and EQ settings. It also holds the size and starting position of the EQ Form window. It is OK to copy these EQ settings from a backup file.
Group List	Group List: holds the different modes that are available for CAT commands.	This never changes so there is nothing to edit. It always contains 0=AM, 1=FM, 2=SSB, 3=SSTV, 4=CW, 5=PSK, 6=RTTY.
Memory	Memory: always seems to be an empty table. But it is always included in the database.	Nothing to edit. Maybe it is used for short term storage?

Memory Form	Memory Form only holds the screen position and size for the memory form accessed from a tab on the main console.	There is no need to edit this table.
Options	Options, is a 'key/value' table. It holds the setup screen settings; check boxes, slide controls, radio-buttons and drop down list selections.	You can make changes, if you are very careful. My database manager allows an update from a list of selected default settings.
PureSignal	The PureSignal table holds the setup information from the Linearity setup screen accessed from a tab on the main console.	My recommendation is to reset the data using the PowerSDR setup screen rather than editing the database.
State	State, is a 'key/value' table. It holds the persistence settings for the radio, i.e. what state the radio was in when you turned it off.	You can make changes, but they may be overwritten the next time you turn off the radio. It is important to be careful with logic states. Some values are dependent on, or interact with other settings. For example, the two RX1 audio controls are ganged. Only one band, filter, and mode should be selected at the same time.
TX Profile	TX Profile: holds the selected transmit profiles. In a new database.xml it only contains 'default' and 'default DX' profiles.	It is helpful to load any other transmit profiles that you normally use.
TX Profile Def	TX Profile Def: holds the list of all of the default profiles.	It does not normally change between software releases, so it should not be edited.
Wave Options	The Wave Options table holds the wave recording setup data from the Wave setup screen accessible from a tab on the main console.	My recommendation is to reset the data using the PowerSDR setup screen. The table also holds the setup screen, start position and size.
XVTR	XVTR: holds the transverter setup screen data.	I don't use this screen, but if you do, it should be safe to update it from a backup.

CUSDR

cuSDR is an excellent, open source software project, which has been developed for the OpenHPSDR / Apache ANAN radios by Hermann von Hasseln. Unfortunately, Hermann has been in poor health and the last Beta update of cuSDR is dated 17 Feb 2013. The program was written using the Visual C++ 2010 programming language. It has a modern look, which emphasizes the use of multiple panadapters. Most control functions remain hidden until required.

Older SDR software like PowerSDR tends to emulate the appearance of a conventional radio with all of the controls drawn to imitate real radio controls. This was important while we all got used to the idea of operating the radio via software and it stemmed directly from radio remote control programs, like Ham Radio Deluxe. Modern SDR programs like, cuSDR, SDR#, and SmartSDR, have abandoned that outdated approach and treat the SDR console as a software application rather than pretending to be a radio front panel.

cuSDR can display up to seven panadapters simultaneously. However, my PC can only reliably show five panadapters from my ANAN-100 transceiver. An ANAN-100D or 200D may be able to display all seven. The panadapter and waterfall displays are stunning and you can change the colors of the spectrum and spectrum fill individually for each panadapter.

Currently PowerSDR mRX is able to display three receivers on two panadapters. A main and sub receiver on the RX1 panadapter and a second receiver on the RX2 panadapter.

Each panadapter can display a receiver slice, but you can only listen to one of them at a time. You are not able to listen to two or more frequencies at the same time. Each panadapter also includes a waterfall display. There is also an optional wideband spectrum display to show the whole HF band from 1 MHz to 59 MHz. You can click on it for instant band changes. Note that you will probably have to turn the Alex filters to the manual mode if you want to display panadapters on different bands at the same time or for the wideband display mode. You can undock each panadapter so that they are in separate windows and you can even move them onto another monitor.

The program has some of the controls for a transmitting function, but they are not yet active. So at present cuSDR is for receiving only. Noise blankers, auto notch, and noise reduction filters have not been implemented yet. On radios that have dual ADCs, the second panadapter defaults to ADC2. This is similar to PowerSDR mRX. At the last software release, cuSDR was in the process of being updated to use the same DSP engine as the newer versions of PowerSDR mRX.

SETTING THE ALEX FILTERS FOR WIDEBAND RECEPTION

cuSDR can display up to seven 'receivers' (panadapters) and it can also display the full HF spectrum using the 'wideband' function. But the operation is somewhat confusing. For example if you have the first panadapter on the 20m band and you open another panadapter on 15m, the second window may not display any signals. Open a third panadapter on the 10m band and it is deaf as well. When you click on panadapter three it bursts into life, but the signals on the 20m receiver disappear! What is going on?

This problem can be avoided by disabling the automatic switching of the high pass and low pass filters inside the ANAN radio. The low pass filters are used on transmit to limit harmonics and they are used on receive to provide additional protection from aliased signals from the VHF spectrum above the wanted band. The high pass filters protect the dynamic range of the receiver by cutting out signals below the wanted band, particularly AM broadcast signals. It is not very useful to have seven panadapters unless they can all display signals at the same time. To do that you need to bypass the filters. In most situations the receiver will work perfectly well on receive without either the high pass or the low pass filters.

cuSDR operates differently to PowerSDR mRX. I think that this mostly because the default settings for the HPF and LPF are not contiguous in cuSDR. They are aligned to the ham bands and not to general coverage. The way that the filter switching works is quite confusing and there is no handbook.

In the default (automatic) situation, the second and subsequent receivers are likely to display no signals until you click on the spectrum display, which shifts the focus and rearranges the filter switches in the radio to that receiver. This is a bit counter-intuitive since you would expect that every time you open another receiver (panadapter) that it would be working.

- If you have an ANAN-100D or 200D the second panadapter will always show the signal from the 2nd ADC which is connected to the RX2 antenna port. If you want another receiver on the main antenna, simply open a 3rd panadapter and then close the second panadapter.

- If you click on a panadapter, the filters will change to the settings for that band. For example if panadapter one is on 20m and panadapter three is on 10m, clicking on panadapter one will cause signals on the 20m band to display, but the signals on panadapter three will disappear.

One of the very neat features of cuSDR is that you can see the effect of the selected filters on the wideband display. As the filters are changed, you can see the spectrum display respond.

MAKING CUSDR RECEIVE SIGNALS ON ALL SLICES

The best way to make all receiver slices work is to select 'Alex Man' (with no blue border) on the main cuSDR display and also turn on the Bypass button (blue) on the HPSDR filter setup tab.

These settings will show on the HPSDR filter setup tab and will affect the wideband spectrum display.

DEFAULT HPF AND LPF SETTINGS – 'ALEX MAN' SETTING ONLY

Filter name	Band	HPF default settings
1.5 MHz HPF	160m, 80m, 60m	1.500 MHz to 5.500 MHz
6.5 MHz HPF	40m	7.000 MHz to 7.300 MHz
9.5 MHz HPF	30m	10.000 MHz to 10.150 MHz
13 MHz HPF	20m, 17m	14.000 MHz to 18.168 MHz
20 MHz HPF	15m, 12m, 10m	21.000 MHz to 29.700 MHz
50 - 61.66 MHz BPF	6m	50.000 MHz to 54.000 MHz

Note that unlike PowerSDR mRX the default filter settings have gaps where the radio will default to bypass.

Filter name	LPF default settings
160m	1.800 MHz to 2.000 MHz
80m	3.500 MHz to 4.000 MHz
60/40m	5.330 MHz to 7.300 MHz
30/20m	10.100 MHz to 14.35 MHz
17/15m	18.068 MHz to 21.450 MHz
12/10m	24.890 MHz to 29.700 MHz
6m	50.000 MHz to 54.000 MHz

As with PowerSDR the cuSDR filter settings do not change the tuning of the high pass or low pass filters on the Alex board or the Apache Labs PA/Filter board. The settings only change the frequency at which the Alex filters are switched in or out of circuit. Low pass filters are always switched to suit the transmitter band. Although cuSDR does not support transmitting anyway. If the filters are switched to bypass, the receiver will operate in wideband mode.

KISS KONSOLE

Kiss Konsole is one of the few SDR software programs for the OpenHPSDR and Apache Labs ANAN radios that supports the ability to transmit.

It was never designed to be a full featured SDR application. The intention is for it to act as a learning tool for budding software developers. It is an open source project and the software code is extensively commented so that it is easy to understand. Kiss Konsole was written using the C# computer language. All of the code is available from the OpenHPSDR downloads site. When it is running, the program looks and works like a simple version of PowerSDR. It only supports a single panadapter and waterfall, but it works very well. I even had a go at modifying the code by making a small change to slow down the display of the received signal strength meter.

If you are interested in learning more about how a basic SDR software application works, I cover the major Kiss Konsole code blocks in my other book; 'An introduction to HF Software Defined Radio.' The book also covers the three data frame structures that are used to carry information between the radio and the PC.

After by reading a lot of information from many websites, magazine articles, and papers I gained a fairly good understanding of how the hardware side of software defined radios work. But the hardware is only half the story. I also wanted to understand the SDR software.

Strangely, my online research hit a wall when I tried to find out how the PC software works. I thought that this was rather odd because there are many SDR software applications available and most of them are open source. I expected there to be a lot of reference information, but explanations even at a block diagram level are pretty rare. I seemed to fall into a small group (of one?) who wanted to know how it works, but who did not want to create my own software. I spent a lot of time studying the C# computer code that makes up Kiss Konsole. Now I know why there is so little information about SDR software online!

My approach in other the book was to explain how the Kiss Konsole software works with no mathematics and as little software code as possible. I did include a few small code snippets to demonstrate how efficient some of the code actually is. For example, an AM demodulator can be achieved with a single line of C# code. I found the analysis very interesting even though it took a very long time because I had never done any software coding in C#.

Kiss Konsole uses the SharpDSP dll written by Phil Covington. The rest of the Kiss Konsole code was developed over several years by a team of developers, notably Phil Harman VK6PH and Warren Pratt NR0V who are still actively developing PowerSDR mRX.

SDR# (SDR SHARP)

SDR# "SDR Sharp" was developed using the C# computer language. It is rapidly becoming the preferred software for a wide range of USB and sound card based software defined radios.

The software is for receivers only. It can demodulate; AM, FM narrow, FM wide (stereo) with embedded RDS text, USB, LSB, DSB, and CW. Not many SDR programs can demodulate FM stereo.

SDR# has extensive control over the waterfall and spectrum displays, digital noise reduction, and a noise blanker. It supports unlimited memories grouped into user defined banks and recording of either the IQ signal or the demodulated audio. You can show all of the controls or hide them leaving only the panadapter and waterfall displays. The screen controls, (zoom, contrast, range, offset), frequency, and the volume control also remain visible. If the I.F. spectrum, FM MPX spectrum, or audio spectrum displays have been selected they show as well.

The program is open source and extendable. It comes with some standard plug-ins and several others can be added.

The standard plug-ins are;

- Zoom FFT – zoomed IF spectrum display (I.F and FM MPX)

- Audio FFT – audio spectrum display

- Noise blanker

- DSP noise reduction

- Baseband IQ or audio recording

- Frequency manager – memories in groups

SDR# can include several plug-ins contributed by other developers;

- Frequency scanner (by Jeff Knapp)

- Frequency scanner (by Vasili rtl-sdr.ru)

- CTCSS tone decoder (by Vasili rtl-sdr.ru)

- Baseband IQ or audio recording (by Vasili rtl-sdr.ru)

- Digital audio processor (by Vasili rtl-sdr.ru)

- DDE client for Doppler correction when receiving signals from satellites

SDR# is from the same developer as the Airspy SDR receiver. It supports a wide variety of software defined radios, including;

- AIRSpy One

- SoftRock

- FiFiSDR

- FUNcube Dongle Pro

- FUNcube Dongle Pro+

- Cross Country Wireless SDR-4

- LazyDog LD-1

- RFSpace SDR-IQ

- RFSpace SDR-IP / NetSDR

- HackRF

- RTL dongles TCP or USB

- SoftRock or other sound card based SDR front end

- Any ExtIO based SDR front end

I like SDR#. I use it with my FUNcube Pro+ dongle. Admittedly, it spends most of its time on the FM Broadcast band. For FM broadcast reception, you must turn off the low noise amplifier in the dongle, which you can do from within SDR#.

I have also used the SDR# and FUNcube Pro+ combination for monitoring local 2m and 70m repeaters, and for receiving aircraft ACARS, automatic air traffic control messages and maritime VHF AIS beacons. There is free software for decoding AIS and ACARS signals available online.

The SDR# developer has also published ADSB# and ADSB Spy which are used to decode the signals from 1090 MHz ADS-B aircraft position beacons.

AIS = automatic identification system (VHF ship ID, status and position beacons)

ACARS = aircraft communications addressing and reporting system (basically a text messaging system for pilots, often used to report faults to the ground crew)

ADS-B - Automatic dependent surveillance – broadcast. It is a rebroadcast from the aircraft of satellite sourced position information. The received and decoded transmissions can be sent to sites on the Internet, which plot aircraft movements on maps.

EXPERTSDR2

ExpertSDR2 is supplied free of charge for the Expert Electronics, SunSDR2 transceivers and the ColibriDDC receiver. It is closed source software and as far as I am aware, it cannot be used with other SDR hardware. I am including this description because it has some interesting features and because I am familiar with using it. In addition, I have a couple of troubleshooting tips, which may help you, if you are new to using it.

ExpertSDR2 is functionally quite similar to PowerSDR although a lot more colorful. It is able to support transmit operation and it has two panadapters. Each panadapter can have two receivers active, so you can operate split and hear both sides of the QSO. In fact, you can hear all four receivers at the same time. On each panadapter, you can shift the audio from the receivers to separate them left and right in the stereo audio field. I like to place the audio from the high RF frequency on the right side and the lower RF frequency on the left side. There is some ability to customize the look of the software including changing the image behind the panadapter, the grid line, spectrum display colors, and the waterfall. If you do change the background image, choose a darkish picture so that the spectrum display can show clearly in front of the image.

One of the unusual features of ExpertSDR2 is that the wideband scope has a waterfall as well as the spectrum display and you can zoom the wideband image so that it only shows the range of frequencies that you want. I believe that this is unique to this software. Another novel feature is that each of the two panadapters has its own VAC (virtual audio cable) connectivity and its own CAT command port. So you can route the panadapters to different digital mode programs and run them both at the same time. The program uses the Kenwood TS-480 CAT command set.

The 'quick memory' automatically remembers the last 16 frequencies. There is a memory bank as well which you can tag with a description for each frequency entered. The main console shows the temperature of the radio, DC voltage applied, current draw, cpu loading, day and date, local and UTC time. On transmit the 'S meter' shows both transmit power and reflected power along with a numeric indication of the SWR. On receive it shows the received signal strength within the receiver passband, in S points and dBm.

The program can automatically launch other applications when it starts. This could be used to launch your favorite digital mode program, rotator controller, propagation, or logging program. Or all of them! You can start up to 10 other applications.

Technical TIP 1: Initially I had a problem with the CAT control. This was not a fault in ExpertSDR2 or the radio and it was quickly addressed by the manufacturer.

Here are the details of what happened, in case a reader has a similar problem. The symptom was that the frequency and band control could not be changed from the digital mode software. It worked fine from the radio to the digital mode software and other functions seemed OK. Every time I moved the frequency, it would bounce back. I think that this was caused by the radio sending the frequency back to the digital mode program before it had settled on the revised frequency.

I managed to fix the problem by changing settings on the com0com virtual Com ports. Unselect the two 'emulate baud rate' check boxes and the two 'enable buffer overrun' check boxes leaving all options unselected.

Technical TIP 2: This problem was not a fault, just "operator error" on my part. The wideband display, equalizer, S meter and mixer controls all show in boxes that are initially docked to the main GUI display. They can be dragged off the GUI so that they are displayed in their own windows, which you can place anywhere on your desktop, or even on a second monitor. Once undocked, I was not able to get them stuck back onto the GUI again. Another email to the helpdesk resolved the issue. If you move the window to the left edge of the spectrum display, it will dock on the left side. If you move the window to the bottom center of the GUI, it will dock at the bottom of the screen.

The SunSDR2 Pro transceiver uses a static IP address, rather that accepting an address from your Internet router via DHCP, like an ANAN transceiver does. This means that when you first plug in your transceiver and start ExpertSDR2, the program may be able to see that the radio is on the network, but be unable to send and receive data. The radio is on the network but has an incorrect subnet address. The procedure to fix this is included in the equipment user guide. I found an alternate way that was easier for me.

Technical TIP: I fixed this one myself. Setting the radios address only has to be done once and after that, it will work with no problem. The radio ships with an address of 192.168.16.200. If your computer uses a different sub-net, the ExpertSDR2 software will be able to locate the radio but it will not be able to receive or send any data. You can find the subnet by looking at the IP address of your PC or a connected printer in the computer management settings or in your Internet router LAN (not WAN) settings. The subnet number is the third set of digits in this case 16. It is likely that your network's subnet address will be 1.

There are a couple of ways to resolve the problem. You can connect the radio directly to the Ethernet port on the computer and then use the setup page of ExpertSDR2 to set the address of the radio so that it is in the correct sub-net, or you can take the approach that I did. I left the radio connected to my Ethernet switch, the same as the ANAN. Then I set up a static route in my Internet router to 192.168.16.200. It is actually easy to do. That let the radio communicate with the PC over the network. I could have left it that way, but instead I used the ExpertSDR2 software to change the address of the radio to 192.168.1.20, which is in my subnet. After that, I could disable the static route in the Internet router and the radio continues to work fine.

GNU RADIO

What's GNU Baby?

GNU Radio is a clever new way to write your own SDR software. It is an open source project with hundreds of collaborators. You can take advantage of software code blocks, which have been written in computer languages like C++ or Python and then made available for other developers to use in their applications. Apparently, GNU is pronounced 'Guh New.'

The really neat feature is that using CRC (GNU Radio Companion), the GNU graphical user interface, each software code block is represented on the worksheet as a rectangle. Each rectangle has one or more inputs called 'sources' and outputs called 'sinks.' Using GNU Radio Companion you can combine the blocks in the same way as building a Lego kit. This means that you can create your own SDR software application without knowing or writing any software code. You just link the graphics blocks together.

If you do want to write your own Python or C++ code blocks, you can expand on the open source examples to create whatever you want. You might design an improved filter, or a demodulator for a particular digital mode, and share it with the group.

There is a version of GNU Radio for Microsoft Windows, but most users use the Linux operating system. You can use compiled GNU Radio applications with a variety of SDR radios. It is very popular with people using experimenter's boards like Ettus USRP, Blade RF and HackRF One.

"GNU Radio is a free software development toolkit that provides the signal processing runtime and processing blocks to implement software radios using readily-available, low-cost external RF hardware and commodity processors. It is widely used in hobbyist, academic and commercial environments to support wireless communications research as well as to implement real-world radio systems.

GNU Radio applications are primarily written using the Python programming language, while the supplied, performance-critical signal processing path is implemented in C++ using processor floating point extensions where available. Thus, the developer is able to implement real-time, high-throughput radio systems in a simple-to-use, rapid-application-development environment."
http://gnuradio.org/redmine/projects/gnuradio

The GNU Radio software suite is not only used by SDR enthusiasts it is also used as a development platform by scientists, military, and commercial developers. Not all GNU applications are related to software defined radio. I noticed that one project is called 'Magnetic Resonance Force Microscopy (MRFM).'

I AND Q SIGNALS

In any technical discussion about software defined radio, it is not long before I and Q streams are mentioned. It is at this point people's eyes glaze over and they decide that SDR is too complicated for them. Don't panic, it is not really that difficult.

In a direct sampling receiver, the ADC converts the incoming RF signal from an analog signal into a digital signal. Then it is split into two data streams; one representing the original analog signal and the other representing the same analog signal with a 90 degree phase delay. The non-delayed digital audio signal is known as the 'I' or 'incident' stream, meaning that it is in phase with the input signal. The delayed digital audio signal is known as the 'Q' or 'quadrature' stream, meaning that there is a 90 degree phase difference from the input signal. If you have both the I data and the Q data, you can demodulate any kind of modulation and you can cancel out any image signals. For transmitting, the modulating signal is applied to, I and Q data streams, which are then up converted to the wanted frequency and changed from a digital to an analog signal. Then the resulting analog RF signal can be amplified by the RF power amplifier and passed through standard low pass filters to the antenna.

Technical TIP: The I and Q signals both contain the same signal amplitude information. You can demodulate AM modes like AM, SSB and CW from either individual stream because the mathematical algorithm only needs the signal's amplitude over time. You need the second stream to eliminate image signals using the phasing method and to demodulate phase or frequency modulated modes like FM and PSK. To demodulate modes based on phase or frequency changes you need to detect the phase difference between the streams, as well as the signal amplitude.

The older QSD radios mix the RF signal down to two audio streams, which are then converted, to digital bit streams using two analog to digital converters. The two analog to digital converters are often the left and right stereo channels of a PC sound card. One of the resulting digital bit streams is the, I stream and the other is the Q stream. The phase and amplitude relationship between the I and the Q signals is used to demodulate the signals. In QSD receivers, the IQ phase difference is also used to eliminate the image signals that arise from the single conversion mixing process.

With hybrid type HF software defined radios and VHF or UHF SDRs, the RF signal is usually mixed down to an I.F. frequency which is either sampled directly using an ADC or mixed to audio using a QSD. After that, the DSP process is the same as other software defined radios. Sometimes the hardware mixer and oscillator and the analog to digital processor are located inside a tuner chip that outputs IQ signals for processing in the DSP stages of the radio. The RTL and FUNcube Dongle receivers are based on this type of arrangement.

So in summary;

- QSD receivers mix the RF signal down to two audio streams, which are then converted to digital signals using two ADCs.

- DDC digital down conversion receivers use a single ADC to sample the HF spectrum directly with no mixing or down conversion. The resulting high speed data is split into I and Q streams inside the DSP stage of the radio.

- Hybrid SDR receivers mix the RF signal down to an I.F. (intermediate frequency) that is within the range of a digital conversion DDC stage. The I.F. signal is sampled with a single ADC and converted to I and Q digital signals in the DSP stage. Alternatively, some hybrids use a fixed tuned QSD system connected to the output of the I.F amplifier.

IQ signals are also used in the transmitter. The wanted modulation is coded into the two data streams and then they are mixed together in a quadrature mixer in the same way as the received signals are in the receiver. The output of the mixer is an RF signal at the final operating frequency. The signal is carrying the wanted modulation. All that remains is to amplify it and to filter out any harmonics using standard power amplifier and low pass filter circuits. In the older QSE quadrature sampling exciter, the mixer is a Tayloe detector. In a digital up converting (DUC) transmitter the mixer is software code running on the FPGA or DSP stage. The single output data stream is passed to a digital to analog converter, which outputs the modulated RF signal.

If you look at the audio I and Q streams from a QSD detector on an Oscilloscope they look almost identical. The only differences are the result of the slightly delayed sampling of the Q signal. The signals can be represented using a vector diagram, which depicts the phase and amplitude of signals rather than the amplitude over time representation of an Oscilloscope.

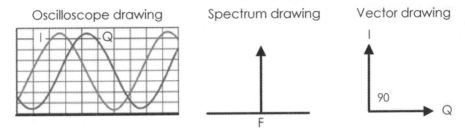

Figure 22: a vector diagram shows the phase relationship of the signals

Note: for convenience I often refer to the I and Q data streams as 'IQ streams', it just seems less cumbersome and it stops the grammar checker having a fit.

QUADRATURE SAMPLING

QSD (quadrature sampling detector) receivers usually use a Tayloe detector to detect the RF signal and turn it into two audio signals. Since it converts directly from RF to audio, it is acting as a single conversion receiver. The advantage of this is that it does not include the oscillators and mixers that can introduce noise and distortion to the wanted audio output. Also, it is very cheap to make, only requiring a few very cheap integrated circuits. The disadvantage is that all single or 'direct' conversion receivers are very prone to image signals.

The Tayloe Detector was patented by Dan Tayloe N7VE in 2001. The same design can be used in reverse as a quadrature sampling exciter (QSE) to make a signal which can be amplified to create a transmit signal. Gerald Youngblood AC5OG, the CEO of FlexRadio stated in a March 2003 QEX article that the Tayloe detector is the same in concept as modulator designs published by D. H. van Graas, PA0DEN, in 1990 and by Phil Rice, VK3BKR in 1998. However, he also says, *"Traditional commutating mixers do not have capacitors (or integrators) on their output. The capacitor converts the commutating switch from a mixer into a sampling detector (more accurately a track-and hold)."* In other words, the earlier circuits did not have the capacitors on the mixer output, which act as the sample and hold mechanism. Anyway, Dan holds the patent and most if not all amateur radio / short wave listener QSD based receivers use the Tayloe design.

Tayloe detectors receive a band of frequencies above and below the nominal local oscillator frequency. In this case, the oscillator is a square wave signal. It is generated by dividing a clock signal.

Technical TIP: Oscillators are used when you dealing with analog signals, clocks are used when you are dealing with timing signals such as ADC sampling or passing data signals through registers. In the digital world, everything happens at distinct times, which are governed by one or more clock signals. The time that the data signal changes state is usually when the clock signal transitions from low to high. This is the rising edge of the clock pulse. The time that the data is sampled is when the clock signal transitions from high to low. This is the falling edge of the clock pulse.

In the DSP part of the radio, you can represent an analog signal such as a Sine or Cosine wave as a stream of digital numbers. Such a stream would still be an oscillator, not a clock, since it will be acting in the same way that an analog signal would in a hardware mixer. Combining the numbers representing the Sine or Cosine wave with the numbers from the ADC has exactly the same effect as using a hardware oscillator and mixer. You get an output stream of numbers representing the difference between the two signals. Unlike a hardware oscillator and mixer, you do not get sum products or either of the original signals. The digital process adds no noise or intermodulation products.

THE TAYLOE DETECTOR

The Tayloe QSD detector is very simple and cheap to make. It uses three very basic integrated circuits, a dual Flip Flop D type latch configured to divide the local oscillator signal by four, a multiplex switch, and a dual low noise Op-Amp.

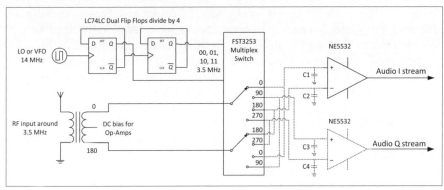

Figure 23: double balanced Tayloe quadrature sampling detector schematic

Take a look at the schematic diagram of the 'double balanced' Tayloe detector above. The two flip flops in a 74LC74 chip are configured to divide the 14 MHz clock signal by four. The two outputs generate a 00, 01, 10, 11 binary pattern which is used to switch the two multiplex switches in the FST3253 chip, to each of the four outputs in turn. If the VFO signal is from a variable device like a Si570 chip, the receiver can be made to cover a wide range of frequencies.

The Tayloe design can be used up to around 1 GHz, but in this example the local oscillator signals to the switch are at 3.5 MHz and the received signals are also centered around 3.5 MHz. This means that the signal from the input transformer is switched to all four outputs during every cycle of the input frequency. A pulse of the input signal voltage is applied to each of the four capacitors in turn.

The capacitors store the voltage on the inputs to the Op-amps and end up averaging the input levels over time. This is called a sample and hold circuit. It works as an envelope detector in the same way that the capacitor following the diode in a crystal set does. You get an audio frequency output. In a double balanced Tayloe detector, the signal from the other side of the input transformer is not wasted. Because it is anti-phase it is used to top up the capacitor that is 180 degrees out of phase. So for each of the four switch positions two of the capacitors are charged up with the input signal. As Dan Tayloe states in his article titled 'Ultra Low Noise, High Performance, Zero IF Quadrature Product Detector and Preamplifier,' "... *two separate detectors are driven with the inputs 180 degrees apart using an input transformer. The two detectors use a common set of four detector caps. Since the outputs of the two detectors are 180 degrees out of phase, the detector capacitors are now driven two at a time.*"

A DC bias voltage for the Op-Amps is applied to the transformer center tap. It passes through the switches to the Op-Amp inputs.

Because the signal on the 180 degree capacitor is the same as the 0 degree capacitor but with reverse polarity, the 0 and 180 degree signals can be combined using the differential inputs of the Op-amp. This gives a 6 dB increase in the, I stream signal level without adding any noise to the signal. Likewise, the 90 degree and 270 degree inputs are combined in the other Op-Amp to create the Q signal, also with a 6 dB enhancement. Just like the 1950s phasing receivers, both of the audio outputs contain the same signals but the Q signal is sampled 90 degrees later. The audio signals at the I and Q outputs extend from 0 Hz up to the bandwidth of the detector.

The bandwidth of a Tayloe detector is limited by the RC time constant of one of the capacitors multiplied by the overall resistance of the network. In the double balanced Tayloe detector, the capacitors are topped up twice as often. They can be smaller because they only have to hold their charge for half as long. Smaller capacitance means that the bandwidth is wider than the original single balanced detector. The other factor limiting the bandwidth is the sample rate of the analog to digital converter following the detector. In this type of first generation SDR, the ADC is usually the PC sound card. The I and Q signals are connected to the Left and Right line input on the PC. Do not use the microphone input because it is often not stereo.

THE QUADRATURE SAMPLING EXCITER

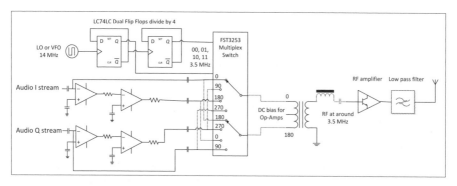

Figure 24: QSE quadrature sampling exciter

The QSE or quadrature sampling exciter is the transmit version of a Tayloe detector. It is virtually the same circuit in reverse and it works in much the same way. Audio signals that have been created from the data are sent to the QSE via the sound card DAC (digital to analog converter). The digital signals feeding the DAC carry the modulation added by the DSP software. In the QSE, the I stream is split into 0 and 180 degree signals. The Q stream, which already has a 90 degree lag, is split into 90 and 270 degree signals. The FST3253 is switched at the 3.5 MHz rate causing a 3.5 MHz RF signal to be created. This is amplified and passed through a suitable low pass filter, then connected to the antenna.

The QSE circuit is simple but effective. Similar designs are used in all generation 1, 2, and 3 SDR transmitters. The Elecraft KX3 and the SoftRock Ensemble use the circuit above. The Genesis design uses more Op-amps and eight individual 74HC4066N switches rather than the FST3253 multiplex switch, but at a functional block level, the design is the same.

THE IMAGE PROBLEM

Direct conversion receivers are similar to Superheterodyne receivers except the I.F. output is directly at audio frequencies extending from 0 Hz up to the bandwidth of the receiver. The local oscillator (LO) is at the same frequency as the receiver center frequency (Fo). In the mixer an upper sideband signal that is 10 kHz above the local oscillator frequency becomes an upper sideband audio signal at 10 kHz. See the lighter colored signal on the drawings below.

This is great except that the Tayloe QSD is a mixer. It works both above and below the local oscillator frequency. An RF signal that is 5 kHz below the local oscillator frequency cannot become -5 kHz. It becomes reflected into the audio range with a phase change of 180 degrees. See the darker colored signal on the diagrams. So now, we have a wanted signal at 10 kHz and an unwanted 'image' signal at 5 kHz. The image signal becomes a lower sideband audio signal due to the 180 degree reflection. The problems arise when an image signal from below the local oscillator frequency appears right on top of a wanted signal.

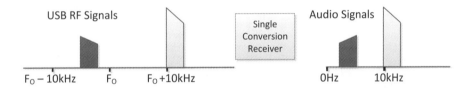

Figure 25: single conversion creates image signals in the audio output

Traditionally this image frequency problem is managed in one of two ways; either the signals below (or above) the LO frequency are filtered out before the mixer, in the same way that image signals are filtered out before a mixer in a Superheterodyne receiver, or the 'phasing method' is used to eliminate the image frequencies. SDR receivers use the phasing method for image frequency cancellation.

This is not a new idea. Direct conversion 'phasing' receivers such as the Central Electronics CE-100v were popular in the mid-1950s until improvements in filter design made Superheterodyne receivers the preferred design. In the phasing method, the signal is split into two streams before the mixer and one stream is delayed by 90 degrees. This should sound familiar!

After the mixer the two streams are added back together which cancels the unwanted image signals.

The Tayloe QSD detector creates I and Q audio frequency signals in quadrature. The two audio signals are converted to digital data using the PC sound card or a dedicated analog to digital converter (ADC) chip. Software in the PC creates the second 90 degree phase change, allowing image cancellation using mathematics rather than circuitry. The left side of the drawing is the hardware Tayloe detector. The right side shows what happens inside the PC. Note that one output has the signals from above the LO frequency with cancellation of image signals from below the LO frequency. The other output has the signals from below the LO frequency with cancellation of image signals from above the LO frequency. Combining the output onto the same panadapter shows all of the signals above and below the receiver center frequency with no image signals.

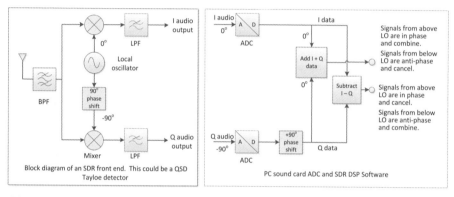

Figure 26: typical QSD software defined receiver including image cancellation

The process could be done in hardware, but in a software defined radio, everything after the analog to digital converters is done using computer programming.

The drawing on the next page shows how the panadapter display is created from the incoming RF signal. First, there is the single conversion receiver front end, which creates I and Q audio signals. Both streams are virtually the same and both contain unwanted image signals. However, the phase relationships are different.

We want to create a panadapter that displays the signals above and below the nominal center frequency Fo, with no pesky image signals. We use the I+Q signal to supply the high end of the panadapter and cancel the image signals from below Fo. The I-Q signal provides the lower half of the panadapter and cancels the images from above Fo.

By selecting the data from a different part of the FFT output buffer, we get a reversal of the I-Q part of the signal. This corrects the sideband reversal and places the signal at the proper frequency offset from the center of the panadapter. Then the data can be combined to display a panadapter.

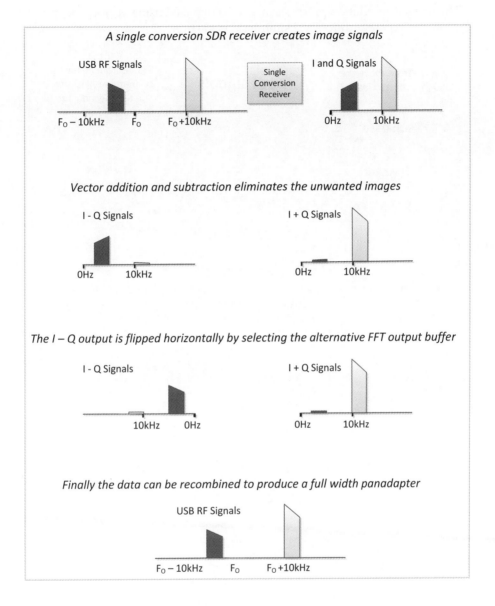

Figure 27: using the I and Q streams for image cancellation

The image cancellation process can also be depicted using vector diagrams to show the vector addition and subtraction in action.

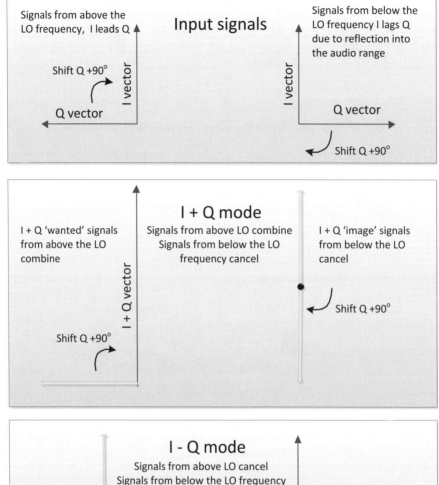

Figure 28: vector diagrams illustrate the image cancellation process

To get good image cancellation the audio level of the I and Q streams must be the same and the phase difference must be exactly 90 degrees. To achieve 40 dB of image cancellation requires the difference between the I and Q levels to be within 0.1 dB and the phase error to be less than 1 degree. For 60 dB of image cancellation, the levels must be within 0.01 dB and the phase error less than 0.1 degrees. The PC software is able to compensate for phase and amplitude errors to minimize the display and reception of image signals but the correction is not perfect across the whole spectrum.

If you have a QSD type receiver, you can see the effect of the image cancellation by disconnecting or turning down the level of either the I or the Q stream, thus disrupting the IQ balance. With the streams unbalanced, each wanted signal will have a mirror image on the other side of the spectrum display, equidistant from the center frequency. The mirror images will have the sideband(s) reversed, which is not a problem and not visible for CW, AM or PSK signals but obvious with SSB signals. Using a mono rather than a stereo sound card input will have the same effect i.e. no image cancellation.

THE RECEIVER

As well as creating the data for the panadapter display, the IQ digital signals are used to determine the amplitude and phase of the received signals at the times they were sampled. The phase differences are used to decode FM or other phase modulated signals and the amplitude information is used to decode amplitude modulated signals like CW, AM and SSB. In fact, if you have I and Q signals you can demodulate any type of modulation.

A 48 kHz or 96 kHz bandwidth is enough to display quite a few SSB signals or the entire CW or digital mode section of the band. You can click your computer mouse on any displayed signal and hear the QSO. Another function unique to SDR receivers is that you can record the full panadapter bandwidth and play it back later. You can listen to QSOs anywhere on the recorded band segment even signals you didn't listen to earlier.

Some other statistics for the Tayloe detector include a conversion loss of 0.9 dB (a typical conventional receiver mixer has 6 to 8 dB), a low Noise Figure around 3.9 dB, (the NF of a typical HF receiver can be anything up to 20 dB), and a 3rd order intercept point of +30 dBm. It also has 6 dB of gain without adding noise and it is very cheap.

The Tayloe QSD SDR provides very good receiver performance at a much lower cost than conventional receivers and it achieves the goal of making the modulator and demodulator a part of the digital signal processing, bridging the gap between IF DSP and AF DSP. But it still has one mixing process, which is a potential source of intermodulation distortion. The next logical step is to eliminate the QSD mixer and sample the RF spectrum directly at the antenna. This is the basis of 4th generation SDRs. The process is known as direct digital synthesis (DDS). It uses digital down conversion (DDC) and for transmitters digital up conversion (DUC).

DIRECT DIGITAL SYNTHESIS

In a direct sampling receiver, the RF signal is directly sampled by a single very fast analog to digital converter. The digital data output is then split into the I and Q streams by the software or 'firmware' running on an FPGA (field programmable gate array), or on a microprocessor, or a dedicated DSP chip.

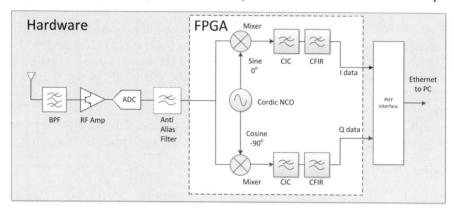

Figure 29: typical digital down conversion (DDC) HF receiver

The block diagram of the mixer in the FPGA looks the same as the mixer in a QSD Tayloe detector, but it is constructed purely in software code. The oscillator and mixer stage is called the 'CORDIC' after the software algorithm that is used to generate the oscillator signal. The difference is that in a QSD receiver the mixer is before the analog to digital conversion and works at audio frequencies. In the direct sampling receiver, the mixer is after the analog to digital conversion and it works on the digital signals.

The NCO is a numerically controlled oscillator. It creates data streams of numbers that are equivalent to a Sine wave and a Cosine wave.

A CIC filter is a type of FIR filter that either interpolates or decimates. What? I hear you gasp! OK, CIC stands for cascaded integrating comb filter. They are multi stage filters with the advantage that the mathematics governing the filter's operation is easy and efficient to code in software. The drawbacks are a certain amount of latency (delay) and they are not completely flat. They have a slight roll off at the top end. The more CIC stages employed, the more roll off occurs and that is why the last filter in each of the two receiver chains are CFIR (compensating finite impulse response) filters. They are trickier to implement in the FPGA because they use more FPGA elements and resources. The CFIR acts as a filter that has a rise at the high frequency end which compensates for the droop in the earlier filters. The result is a flat panadapter across the band. Without the CFIR filter, you would see a drop off at the far left and right ends of the panadapter. You sometimes see this drop-off in level at the edges of 'sound card' SDR panadapters.

Decimation in the DDC receiver involves throwing away a whole lot of the ADC output bits. In some radios, the data rate from the ADC is too fast to send to the PC. The combination of the CORDIC mixer and decimation selects a subset of the input spectrum and sends it to the PC at a much reduced data rate. The CIC filters shown in the receiver block diagram slow the data rate down from the ADC rate to the sampling rate that is sent to the PC. For example, in an ANAN radio the CIC filters slow the data from the ADC sample rate of 122.88 Msps to 384 ksps or lower. As the sampling rate is reduced, you must apply a low pass filter at the Fs/2 frequency to stop alias signals appearing in the wanted pass-band. The CIC filters do both the decimation and the filtering. Note that not all direct sampling receivers use decimating filters. Onboard DSP may process the entire output of the ADC.

The direct up conversion transmitter is quite similar to the receiver design. A modulated IQ signal is sent from the PC via Ethernet. The IQ data from the PC is at a much lower speed than the rate required for the DAC. It only has to be at least twice the highest modulating frequency. The CIC Interpolation filters speed the data up to the DAC sampling rate. Then the CORDIC mixes the resulting data up to the RF frequency. The DAC converts the signal from digital data into an analog signal at the RF frequency, which is amplified and filtered before being sent to the antenna. There will usually be several stages of amplification and filtering because the output from the DAC is only about 1 mW of RF power.

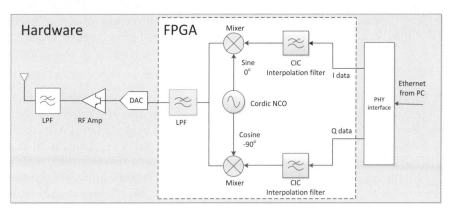

Figure 30: typical direct up conversion (DUC) HF transmitter

Interpolation in the DUC transmitter is a mathematical way of filling in the gaps. The data rate of the IQ signals carrying the modulation is much lower than the data rate required by the DAC. This means that every 16 bit sample applied to the CIC interpolation filter results in a whole lot of 16 bit output samples. The output could just repeat each input sample two thousand five hundred and sixty times to interpolate between the 48 ksps transmit IQ stream and the 122.88 Msps DAC stream of an ANAN transmitter, but that would cause sudden signal level changes. The interpolation filter uses mathematics to smooth the rate of change.

THE ADC

The heart of any software defined radio, or indeed the DSP stage in a conventional receiver or transceiver, is the conversion of the analog signals that we receive on our antenna into digital signals that we can process with computer technology. We do it because manipulating the digital signal adds none of the noise and distortion that happens in the amplifiers and mixers of a conventional radio. The analog to digital converter (ADC) reads the voltage at its input, decides what the closest voltage step is, and then outputs a number representing that voltage step. This happens very fast. For example, the ADC used in the new FlexRadio FLEX-6500 and FLEX-6700 samples the input voltage 245,760,000 times per second.

When we need to convert a signal from digital back to analog, we use a digital to analog converter (DAC). This integrates voltages between samples to create a smoothed analog output signal.

WHAT ARE BITS?

I keep talking about bits. But what are they exactly? Computers are stupid but they work very fast. They do not understand decimal numbers or the text on this page. At the particular time that the clock signal changes from a high state to the low state, the computer looks at the data lines or internal storage 'registers' and reads whether there is voltage present or not. It can also set registers, data, or address lines to combinations of high and low logic levels. The digital data that represents this, "is it high or is it low?" measurement, is called a 'bit' of information. In this logic structure, there are only two possible levels, so it is a 'binary' bit.

A 'binary' bit is the smallest amount of digital information possible. In most logic systems if the voltage is high, the data bit is a 'one' and if the voltage is low then the data bit is a 'zero'. A bit can only be a 1 or a 0. One bit at a time does not get you very far and a computer that could only handle a bit at a time would not be very useful at all. But, if we look at two bits side by side, the combination of the two bits can represent 4 different numbers. Four bits can represent 16 numbers, eight bits 256, and sixteen bits can represent 65,536 numbers.

2 bit Binary	4 bit Binary	8 bit Binary	Decimal
0 0	0 0 0 0	0 0 0 0 0 0 0 0	0
0 1	0 0 0 1	0 0 0 0 0 0 0 1	1
1 0	0 0 1 0	0 0 0 0 0 0 1 0	2
1 1	0 0 1 1	0 0 0 0 0 0 1 1	3

With 16 bits, you can do some pretty fancy mathematics and you can use combinations of bits to instruct the computer to do something like add two other numbers together, or that a particular number is equivalent to a text character. Modern computers work with huge numbers that are 64 bits wide, but most analog to digital converters are 8 bit, 14 bit, or 16 bit devices.

Note that I grouped the 8 bit binary numbers into groups of four digits to make them easier to read. An 8 bit ADC has eight output pins so the smallest number that can be output is zero, represented by 0000 0000 on the output pins and the largest output number is 255 represented by 1111 1111.

That means that the output of an 8 bit ADC can represent 256 different voltage steps, because that is the maximum number of different numbers that can be fitted into 8 bits. If the input range is an analog signal with a minimum level of 0 and a maximum level of 1 Volt, then the voltage steps are 3.9 mV apart. That means that every sample has an error, which could be as much as 3.899 mV. An input level just over the 1000 0001 level will be represented as 1000 0010, which is the next step up. The error is known as quantization error because it is a mistake in quantifying the input level. Quantization errors cannot be recovered. When you convert the signal back to an analog level, the output for that particular sample will be wrong by the amount of the quantization error. This manifests itself as noise on the recovered signal. The only way to reduce quantization errors is to make the sampling voltage steps smaller. To do that you need to use more bits. However, that adds to the complexity of the device. Using 14 or 16 output pins instead of 8 means a larger chip size with more internal buffers.

TIP: Actual quantization errors are minimized by pipeline sampling in the ADC. This is a sort of successive approximation methodology.

A 16 bit ADC can represent 65,536 individual voltage levels, so if the input is in the same 0 to 1 Volt range, the voltage steps are now 0.015 mV apart. This means much higher sampling accuracy i.e. much lower quantization noise. Alternatively, we could extend the range of the input signal, for example 0 to 1.5 Volts.

Adding more bits increases the data rate that we need to transfer over the serial USB or Ethernet interface between the radio and the SDR software running on the PC. Doubling the number of bits from an 8 bit data packet to a 16 bit data packet doubles the data rate required. The actual serial data rate is not quite, double because the number of overhead bits in each data frame remains constant.

Technical TIP: What is serial and parallel data? The ADC outputs the sample as a 16 bit number with each of the 16 bits appearing on a separate output pin. The pins are connected to other devices (digital chips) via tiny parallel wires or 'traces' on the circuit board. This is called a parallel data bus. Like a real bus, it carries many data bits (passengers) together. This works well on a circuit board, but it is less convenient when you want to send the data to your PC across a cable. You could use a cable with 16 wires, one for each bit, but that would need 16 data transmitters, 16 data receivers, and a fat cable. It is more usual to convert the data into a serial stream where each of the 16 bits is sent in turn. Then you only need one signal wire and a ground return. But of course, you need to send at a rate that is 16 times as fast, so that you don't lose any of the information.

ARE ADC BITS IMPORTANT?

Is the number of bits used by the ADC important? The answer is yes, but not as important as some people think. There is a large amount of misinformation on the Internet about how much the number of bits used by the digital sampling process affects the performance of software defined radio receivers. Some critics have claimed that SDR receivers cannot technically achieve the signal to noise and dynamic range statistics that are claimed in lab reports. They are dead wrong. I have taken it as my mission to try to clear this up.

DYNAMIC RANGE AND SIGNAL TO NOISE RATIO

The analog to digital converter in the SDR receiver creates a stream of data words, which represent the signal at the ADC input at very specific instants in time. In other words, the ADC looks at the input signal and outputs an 8, 14, or 16 bit number, which represents the voltage step that is nearest to the input voltage at that time. This is called sampling. An 8 bit ADC can describe 255 voltage levels and a 16 bit digital number can describe 65,536 voltage levels, although in practice internal noise performance reduces the number of usable bits. The noise performance confuses the reading of very small input signals and this reduces the effective number of bits. For example, a 16 bit ADC may only be able to output 12 bits of usable data. This is known as the 'effective number of bits' or ENOB.

It is the ENOB of the ADC, and the process gain from decimation, that determines the maximum dynamic range of a SDR receiver, not the number of bits in the output stream. That is why radios with 14 bit ADCs often have very nearly as good dynamic range as radios with 16 bit ADCs.

QSD RECEIVERS AND ADC BITS

I have a QSD based SDR and my PC sound card uses 24 bit sampling. Does that make it better than a direct sampling receiver that only uses 16 bits? Is it better than a receiver dongle that has an 8 bit tuner chip? The answer to both questions is no.

The ADC for a QSD receiver is working on audio signals not I.F. or RF signals. Yes, the 24 bit sound card has lots of accuracy and therefore low quantization noise, but its sample rate is only 96 ksps. The low sample rate limits the QSD receiver to a maximum panadapter bandwidth of 96 kHz. Noise near the center of the panadapter and imperfect image cancellation are limitations of the QSD design.

The QSD receiver is a direct conversion receiver so the audio streams contain image signals, which must be cancelled by the DSP software. Direct conversion receivers tend to be noisy near the DC point, which is in the center of the panadapter display and there is a risk of some intermodulation noise from the mixing process. The sound card ADC also has limitations at very low audio frequencies. This often results in a pronounced noise spike in the center of the panadapter display. Some SDR software, notably SDR#, has 'DC cancellation' to reduce the noise spike.

If you are using a QSD receiver, a 24 bit sound card is better than a 16 bit sound card, particularly if it can sample at 192 ksps. A 192 ksps sample rate will result in a panadapter display that is 192 kHz wide. This is a pretty useful size of panadapter display and of course, you can zoom in for more detail. Even though my ANAN-100 can display wider panadapters, I find that 192 kHz suits my needs pretty well. A 96 ksps sample rate will result in a panadapter display 96 kHz wide and a 48 ksps sample rate means a maximum panadapter display only 48 kHz wide. I find a 48 kHz panadapter a bit too limited.

On VHF and UHF frequencies, the bands are much bigger and repeaters may be several MHz apart, so the ability to display a wide panadapter is very useful. Some direct sampling SDR boards can provide bandwidths of up to 20 MHz.

ADC SAMPLING RATE

The ADC sampling rate is very important because it sets how much of the radio spectrum the radio can cover in one chunk. In most cases the faster the ADC can sample, the better.

If the receiver uses a mixer to down convert VHF or UHF frequencies to an intermediate frequency, or from HF to audio in the case of a QSD receiver, the ADC sampling rate defines the maximum panadapter display bandwidth. For example, a receiver with an ADC sampling rate of 192 ksps can display a 192 kHz section of the RF spectrum. That might be from 14.100 to 14.292 MHz or from 10,000.000 to 10,000.192 MHz. You get a 192 kHz wide band centered on the receiver's nominated frequency.

In an HF receiver using digital down conversion, the receiver will be able to cover frequencies from a few kHz up to a frequency set by the Nyquist limitation, (one half of the ADC sampling rate). For example, the ANAN-100 uses a sampling frequency of 122.88 Msps, so the maximum frequency that can be sampled reliably is 61.44 MHz. The receiver is specified to cover up to 55 MHz and has a low pass filter to block any signals from above that frequency. The ADC used in the Perseus receiver is clocked at 80 MHz giving a maximum frequency of 40 MHz. The Perseus is specified to cover 10 kHz to 30 Mhz. You will note that the 6m band is not included due to the lower ADC sample rate.

With digital down conversion, the maximum radio bandwidth is ½ of the sampling rate. Very often, the whole of that bandwidth is not sent to the DSP section. CIC filters decimate the data down to a narrower bandwidth such as 384 kHz. This would result in a 384 kHz wide panadapter.

- SDR with a mixer before the ADC: the maximum bandwidth (MHz) can equal the sampling frequency (Msps), but might be less.

- SDR with no mixer before the ADC: the maximum bandwidth (MHz) equals half the sampling frequency (Msps).

Technical TIP: ADCs typically have a much wider frequency response than the Nyquist bandwidth. For example, the LTC2208 ADC used in the ANAN / Hermes receiver has a frequency response up to 700 MHz. You might wonder why anyone would design a chip with a 700MHz frequency response if the Nyquist frequency is only 61.44 MHz. The reason is to facilitate the deliberate use of the 'alias frequencies.' Using appropriate band pass filters any 61.44 MHz wide band of frequencies can be sampled all the way up to the 700MHz cut off. Each chunk of spectrum is called a Nyquist zone. You might elect to use the receiver on the 3rd Nyquist zone 122.88 – 184.32 MHz to receive signals on the 2m amateur band.

The LTC2208 ADC as used in the ANAN / Hermes receiver has a frequency response up to 700 MHz, so without filters ahead of the ADC, large signals anywhere in the 2nd to 11th Nyquist zones could be sampled by the ADC. Once sampled, they would end up being heard in the receiver and shown on the spectrum display. You will note that the 2nd Nyquist zone includes the FM broadcast band. In the Hermes design, a 55 MHz low pass filter is incorporated to attenuate alias signals and ensure they are not sampled by the ADC.

The idea of deliberately receiving frequencies above the first Nyquist zone is called 'under sampling.' It is used in some receiver designs. For example, the SunSDR2 pro radio has an ADC sample rate of 160 Msps. It uses its 2nd Nyquist zone to provide coverage of 80-160 MHz. The radio switches automatically between HF and VHF modes when you select any frequency above 80 MHz.

You can only use one Nyquist zone at a time, i.e. HF or VHF and you must provide filters in front of the ADC to prevent signals from other Nyquist zones being sampled. If you try to cover more than one zone, the signals from both zones will be sampled and they will overlap on the Panadapter. Once signals are sampled, they cannot be removed. Without filters on the SunSDR2, a signal sampled at 10 MHz would appear right on top of a signal sampled at 150 MHz.

ADC NOISE PERFORMANCE

It is very important that the ADC used for a direct sampling radio has the ability to distinguish wanted signals from the background noise. This is such an important factor that the manufacturer's data sheets include tables of the results of several different measurements of the noise performance. The tests are done at several different input frequencies across the first Nyquist zone. If the ADC is being used in an under sampling mode the noise performance will translate up into higher Nyquist zones.

Unless you are building your own software defined radio you won't have any control over the choice of ADC but it is worth while discussing these measurements because the ADC noise performance is the ultimate limitation of how well your SDR will be able to receive weak signals. And strong signals too. These measurements also shed some light on why 14 bit ADCs work very nearly as well as 16 bit ADCs.

Prepare to enter acronym heaven!

DECIBELS, dBFS AND dBc

All of the noise measurements on the ADC data sheet are expressed in decibels (dB). Measurements in decibels are always a logarithmic ratio. They have to be a value referenced to something else. You can say that a voltage is a certain number of decibels above or below another voltage reading, or a standard value. The same goes for power measurements. If you are referring to an attenuator of an amplifier, the amount of loss or gain is expressed in decibels referenced to the level at the input of the device. i.e. an attenuator may have 10 dB of loss or an amplifier may have 20 dB of gain. Ohms law gives us the relationship of Power to Voltage. $W = V^2/R$. So given the same Resistance:

For power: dB = 10 x log$_{10}$ (power measurement 1 / power measurement 2) Twice the power is a 3 dB increase. Ten times the power is a 10 dB increase.

For voltage: dB = 20 x log$_{10}$ (voltage measurement 1 / voltage measurement 2) Twice the voltage is a 6 dB increase. Ten times the voltage is a 20 dB increase.

Common dB scales include; dBm, which is power compared to 1 mW, dBc which is power or voltage compared to the input 'carrier' level, and dBFS which is a level compared to the 'full scale' input level for the device.

dBFS is used to denote the maximum input level for the ADC because the actual maximum level is adjustable. Typical input levels are 1 V peak to peak, 1.5 V peak to peak, or 2.25 V peak to peak.

The ADC data sheet usually has performance data compared to dBFS or a set value below the maximum level such as -1 dBFS. But your input signal may be much smaller than the full scale value and you want to know how the ADC will work at the actual input level. So, the data tables also include dBc measurements, which are referenced to the input level.

CLIPPING LEVEL

The clipping level is the maximum input signal that the ADC device can handle without catastrophic distortion. The full scale figure 0 dBFS is set a little under the clipping level so that it can be reached without distortion. The actual level that your SDR receiver can manage without clipping is affected by the loss in any front end filters or attenuators and the gain of any pre-amplifiers, added to the ADC clipping level.

SPURIOUS FREE DYNAMIC RANGE (SFDR)

The dynamic range of the ADC is the difference between the noise floor and the maximum input signal of 0 dBFS. Nonlinearity in the front-end circuits of the ADC can cause harmonics of the input signals or intermodulation products, which will be sampled by the ADC. These harmonics and any other spurious signals such as interference resulting from clock signals show as spikes on the spectrum display. They are commonly referred to as 'spurs.'

The actual usable dynamic range of the ADC is affected by any harmonics or other spurious signals. This is recorded on the ADC data sheet as the 'spurious free dynamic range'.

The SFDR quoted on the data sheets is the dynamic range from the highest spurious or harmonic signal compared to either the level of the input test tone level (dBc) or to the 'full scale' clipping level (dBFS). Some data sheets quote SFDR at a variety of input frequencies measured against both dBc and dBFS. Typically, there are also separate tables showing SFDR relative to the larger 2nd and 3rd harmonics and SFDR relative to the 4th and higher order harmonics.

The SFDR tends to degrade fairly linearly as the input signal level increases and also as the frequency of the input test signal increases. For digital down conversion HF receivers, we are only using a small fraction of the overall frequency response of the device, so the roll off in dynamic range is not noticeable.

The SFDR also gets worse at very fast sample rates, but with most of our receivers, the ADC sample rate is fixed and less than the maximum allowable rate, so this effect is not important either.

SIGNAL TO NOISE RATIO (SNR)

The maximum signal to noise ratio of a software defined radio receiver is directly related to the dynamic range. It is the range between the maximum 'clipping' level the ADC can sample and the noise floor of the device. The ADC data sheets show measurements of the SNR compared to the noise floor. The SNR measurements exclude or ignore the first five harmonics of the input signal from the measurement. This is probably because the noise performance including the harmonics is covered by the SFDR test.

SIGNAL TO NOISE PLUS DISTORTION RATIO (SINAD)

SINAD is the Signal to Noise Plus Distortion Ratio [S/(N+D)], it is the ratio between input level of a test tone and all of the noise, harmonics and distortion products in the band of frequencies below ½ of the sampling frequency (i.e. the first Nyquist zone). For HF receivers the 1st Nyquist zone is the band of frequencies we are interested in receiving, so SINAD is the best indicator of the achievable signal to noise ratio.

Spurious free dynamic range (SFDR) measures the dynamic range between full scale or the input signal and the level of the highest harmonic.

Signal to noise ratio (SNR) measures the dynamic range between full scale or the input signal and the noise floor, ignoring any large harmonics.

Signal to noise plus distortion ratio (SINAD) measures the dynamic range between full scale or the input signal and the average noise level, including any harmonics or spurious signals within the first Nyquist zone.

EFFECTIVE NUMBER OF BITS (ENOB)

The ADC cannot describe very small input signals due to the limits of its internal noise performance. Very low-level signals might be recorded as 0000, or 0001, or 0010, or 0011. This makes the lowest few bits of the output data unreliable. ENOB is the number of bits, which contain usable information. It can be calculated from the quoted SINAD of the ADC.

ENOB = (SINAD-1.76)/6.02.

- The ANAN / Hermes board uses a 16 bit LTC2208 ADC, which has a SINAD of 77.4 dB giving an ENOB of around 12.6 bits.

- The Perseus receiver uses a 14 bit LT2206 ADC with a SINAD of 77.1 dB giving an ENOB of around 12.5 bits.

- The AD9467 ADC used in the new FlexRadio SDRs has a published SINAD of 76.2 dB and an ENOB of 12.4 bits.

You can see that the SINAD ratio of all three devices is pretty similar. This means that even though the Perseus uses a 14 bit ADC, the actual dynamic range performance is almost the same as the 16 bit ADCs used in the other two radios. The main difference between the three radios is the ADC sampling speed, which allows the FlexRadio to work to around 77 MHz, and the ANAN to work to 55 MHz, while the Perseus only works to about 40 MHz.

Technical TIP: The number of bits that the ADC uses to describe the signal is not a reliable indicator of the receiver's dynamic range and noise performance. It is the ENOB that is important. 14 bit or even 12 bit radios may actually work just as well as 16 bit radios.

ADC GAIN COMPRESSION

Very large incoming signals appearing at the input of the analog to digital converter can cause ADC gain compression. This temporary reduction in the dynamic range, results in a higher noise level being displayed right across the panadapter. Typical indications of ADC gain compression are a high or jumping noise floor. If the noise floor is regularly jumping a few dB, the ADC is probably being affected by AM or FM broadcast signals. Or it could be other large signals such as a nearby radar installation. Adding a band pass filter to the receiver antenna port or selecting internal high pass and/or low pass filters should fix the problem. Noise from lightning crashes will also cause the whole panadapter noise floor to jump, for the same reason.

An ADC with more bits describing the input voltage will usually have a wider dynamic range to start with, so they are less susceptible ADC gain compression. This is another reason that 16 bit ADCs are definitely better than 8 bit ADCs.

You can sometimes see the effect of ADC gain compression when you switch out the receiver band pass filters and operate the receiver in wideband mode. If the noise floor of the panadapter rises when you switch to the wideband filter, the dynamic range is being reduced by large signals that the ADC is processing. You may not be able to see the large signals on the panadapter; they may be outside of the displayed panadapter span.

Technical TIP: ADC gain compression should not be confused with 'Digital Gain Compression', which is an optional feature built into some analog to digital converters (but not the LTC2208 used in ANAN radios). Digital gain Compression is an AGC action that is applied to the analog signal inside the analog to digital converter before the signal is sampled. It limits the input signal so that it always swings between 10% and 90% of the maximum input level. This ensures that the input signal can never get to the clipping level or into the fuzzy noise floor where the level might be incorrectly sampled (see ENOB).

DITHER

Some ADC chips have a dither function built in. Others do not. If it is available, the SDR software will have a check box to select or de-select the function. The ADC used in the Apache ANAN series has a dither option and the ADC used in the FlexRadio Signature 6000 series does not. I don't believe that dither is particularly relevant in a ham radio or SWL receiver, but it does no harm so I usually leave it turned on at my QTH.

Dither improves the intermodulation performance of the ADC by ensuring the input signals are well spread across the analog to digital transfer characteristic of the ADC. Noise is deliberately added to the analog signal and then removed from the digital signal after the analog to digital conversion.

The ADC samples everything that is presented to its input, so unless you have a particularly poor antenna there will usually be enough medium size signals to ensure that the signals at the ADC input will transverse most of the ADCs input range. In that case, dither does not provide any advantage.

Dither could be helpful if you were using external narrow band filters for contest operation and it does improve the IMD performance when a two tone test signal is used, as part of lab testing because there are no other signals present. It could be a useful feature for weak signal work on VHF or UHF frequencies because the ADC will only be presented with very low strength signals right across the receiver's bandwidth.

When you are using the SDR as an HF receiver there are many signals at varying levels and frequencies, so selecting the dither function is not necessary. Switching the dither function on will probably not provide any noticeable improvement and it may degrade the receiver noise floor by a couple of dB.

Technical TIP: In the LTC2208 ADC the noise is generated as a pseudorandom digital code inside the ADC. The code is converted into an analog signal and mixed with the incoming signal from the antenna.

After the combined signal has been sampled and converted to digital data the original digital code is mathematically subtracted back out again. The result is better IMD performance with only a small degradation in noise performance.

RANDOM

Some ADC chips have a 'random' function built in and others do not. If it is available, the SDR software will have a check box to select or de-select the function. The ADC used in the FlexRadio Signature 6000 series does not have a random function and the ADC used in the Apache ANAN series does. I don't believe that the random is particularly useful in a ham radio or SWL receiver. At my QTH, I can't see any difference on the panadapter with random turned on or off.

"The ADC is a small device with a big problem." On the antenna side, there are very small sub microvolt signals which we want to hear in our receiver and on the other side, there are very high speed 3.3 V square waveform data and clock streams. Inside and around the chip both signals are in very close proximity. In the Hermes receiver, the ADC samples at 122.88 Msps and the same clock drives the FPGA. Capacitive and radiated RF coupling of the large 3.3 V signal into the sensitive analog input stage is a problem even with very good circuit board design. The effect, particularly when there are a limited number of input signals such as during testing, is that the coupling could cause fixed signal spikes called spurs, which would be visible on the spectrum display.

The generation of spurs is a particular problem when the radio is being used in a situation where the receiver is being used to receive signals at fixed levels or frequencies such as on a fixed radio link or a cellular base station. Spurs build up over time due to recirculating coupling from the digital signals to the ADC input.

Technical TIP: The problem with fixed levels and frequencies on the ADC input is the repetitive nature of the data coming out of the ADC. Harmonics and related intermodulation products can be coupled into the ADC input. These unwanted signals and harmonics right up to the 700 MHz bandwidth of the ADC can be aliased back into the wanted bandwidth as they are being generated after our front end filters. The answer is to randomize the data coming out of the ADC so any coupling back into the input becomes noise rather than visible and audible spurs.

The LTC2208 ADC does this by applying an Exclusive OR function to bits 1 to 15 of the output signal based on the value of bit 0. This produces a randomized output bit stream resulting in a clean spectrum display with no spurs. As soon as the scrambled signal gets to the FPGA it can be converted back into usable data by simply applying another Exclusive OR function to bits 1 to 15 based on the value of bit 0.

The output of bit 0 is random due to the noise performance of the ADC so the scrambling function really does produce a randomized output. The number of output bits is 16 but the ENOB is 12 so the bottom few bits just toggle randomly.

The creation of fixed spurs is not a problem on the ham bands or for shortwave AM reception. The random nature of the received signals means that the input signal at the ADC is fairly random and so the digital output signal is quite variable. Any coupling from the digital output of the ADC into the sensitive analog input just degrades the overall noise performance. No fixed spurs build up because the digital signal is not repetitive.

As far as I am concerned the use of dither and random is a personal preference. You might notice some small improvement in the displayed spurs and IMD performance at the expense of a minimal degradation of the noise floor. On my ANAN radio I see no improvement using the dither and random settings, but your experience may be different. Many software defined radios don't even have the ability to use dither and random.

PROCESS GAIN

Process gain is a trade-off between the dynamic range and the bandwidth of the signal. The ADC might have an SFDR at 30 MHz of around 95 dB, but that is while sampling the entire 700 MHz bandwidth of the ADC. The noise level is spread out. When you filter out the frequencies you don't want and just look at the signal in a narrow bandwidth such as the 2.4 kHz receiver bandwidth required for an SSB signal, or a 500 Hz wide bandwidth for CW there is much less noise and so the dynamic range and SNR is much improved. The improvement in signal to noise ratio is directly proportional to the reduction in bandwidth. It is normally expressed in decibels, as a gain in signal level, because an increase in the signal to noise ratio is equivalent to an increase of the dynamic range. Process gain = $10 * \log_{10}(BW1/BW2)$ dB.

Process gain is the reason that an SDR can deliver more than 120 dB of dynamic range from an ADC that might only have around 77 dB SINAD. Because of process gain, narrower filters result in better dynamic range. But the panadapter is much wider than the receiver bandwidth and it displays a lower noise floor. This is due to the FFT (fast Fourier transformation). The panadapter is effectively made by plotting the levels of thousands of very narrow 'bins' each only a few Hz wide. Because each individual bin is so narrow, they each have more process gain than the much wider receiver bandwidth. By plotting the level of each bin side by side, the displayed noise level is lower than the noise level in the receiver bandwidth.

The theoretical maximum dynamic range of an ADC is (N bits x 6.02) +1.76. For a 16 bit ADC, it is (16 x 6.02) +1.76 = 98 dB.

The typical 'real world' dynamic range of an ADC is (ENOB bits x 6.02) +1.76. For a 16 bit LTC2208 ADC, it is (12.6 x 6.02) +1.76 = 77.6 dB.

Process gain for an SDR is 10 x log (Fs/2 / B), where Fs/2 is the Nyquist bandwidth and B is the receiver bandwidth. [Fs is the sample rate].

For an ANAN radio on SSB with a filter of 2.4 kHz, the process gain is 10 x log (122880000 / 2 / 2400) = 44 dB. Therefore, the theoretical maximum dynamic range of an ANAN receiver in a 2.4 kHz bandwidth is 98 + 44 = 142 dB. The real performance is less because the ENOB of the ADC is less than 16 bits. Typical ADC dynamic range + process gain =77.6 + 44 = 121.6 dB. The real performance of an ANAN-100 is better than 120 dB in a 2.4 kHz bandwidth and 128 dB in a 500 Hz bandwidth. So its performance compares well with the theory.

FREQUENCY FOLDING AND ALIASING

As discussed above, the ADC can sample signals well above the Nyquist frequency of Fs/2, where Fs is the sampling rate. This can be useful if it is managed properly because it can extend the frequency range of your receiver. But you must ensure that you have bandpass filters before the ADC so that the ADC can only sample frequencies from one Nyquist zone at a time. Otherwise, received signals will interfere with each other.

The way that the signals are aliased back into the first Nyquist zone depends on whether the sampled signal is in an even, or an odd, numbered Nyquist zone. Signals from odd numbered zones are 'folded' back. This means that they will appear on the panadapter at an offset related to multiples of the Fs/2 frequency. Signals from even numbered zones are 'reflected' back. The reflected signals will be inverted. An upper sideband signal becomes lower sideband. In fact, the whole panadapter will be backwards, with high frequencies at the left and lower frequencies to the right. This is easy to fix in the SDR software because the buffer at the output of the FFT stage contains both a 'normal' and a mirror image 'inverted' copy of the panadapter data. To show the 2nd (or other even numbered) Nyquist zone panadapter you just use the data from the other half of the buffer. Software intended for receivers that deliberately use the 2nd or other 'even' Nyquist zones would automatically select data that displays a correct panadapter. Signals received on frequencies in odd numbered Nyquist zones are not inverted.

- For odd numbered zones the alias frequency = MOD(F_{RX},Fs/2)
- For even numbered zones the alias frequency = Fs/2-MOD(F_{RX},Fs/2)

In a spreadsheet, you can create the following simple calculator:

- *Cell A1 "ADC Sample Rate," enter the sample rate into cell B1 e.g. 100*
- *Cell A2 "Nyquist Frequency Fs/2", type formula =b1/2 into cell B2*
- *Cell A3 "Received Frequency," enter the receive frequency into cell B3 e.g. 123*
- *Cell A4 "Nyquist Zone," type formula = ROUNDUP(B3/B2,0) into C4*
- *Cell A5 "Alias Frequency", type =IF(MOD(INT(B3/B2),2)=0,MOD(B3,B2), B2-MOD(B3,B2)) into B5*

The example above should give answers of, Nyquist zone 3 and an alias signal displayed on the panadapter at 23 MHz.

Here is another way of looking at frequency folding.

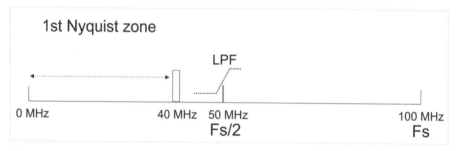

Figure 31: receiving in the first Nyquist zone

This is the standard configuration for a direct sampling HF receiver. Signals in the 1st Nyquist zone are sampled by the ADC and displayed on the panadapter. Signals from above the 1st Nyquist zone are not sampled because they are attenuated by the anti-alias low pass filter centered on the Fs/2 frequency.

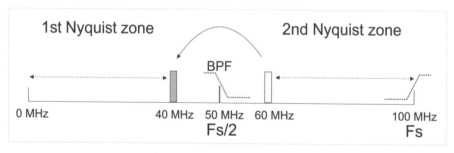

Figure 32: receiving in the second Nyquist zone

If we want to receive signals in the 2nd Nyquist zone we replace the low pass filter with a bandpass filter that covers the zone from around 50 MHz to 100 MHz. The 60 MHz signal is reflected back and it appears on the panadapter at the 40 MHz position. In a real SDR receiver the panadapter would be adjusted (flipped) to show 50 to 100 MHz and the inverted sideband would be corrected as well.

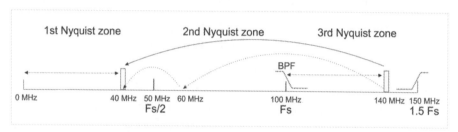

Figure 33: receiving in the third Nyquist zone

To receive signals in the 3rd Nyquist zone we move the bandpass pass filter so that it covers the zone from around 100 MHz to 150 MHz. The 140 MHz signal is folded back. It appears on the panadapter at the 40 MHz position. It is not inverted so no correction to the sidebands or panadapter is required, although the panadapter frequency labels will be changed. You can think of this as a double hop i.e. inverted twice if it makes it more understandable, but really it is just the way that the ADC under-samples the input signal.

The filters are essential to prevent signals from multiple Nyquist zones appearing on top of each other on the panadapter. Switching out the anti-alias filter on an HF SDR typically results in lots of FM broadcast stations appearing on the wideband scope.

The Nyquist zones are rather like a semi-transparent fan folded paper map. If you look through page one, the second page folds over and is reversed but the third page folds over the right way around.

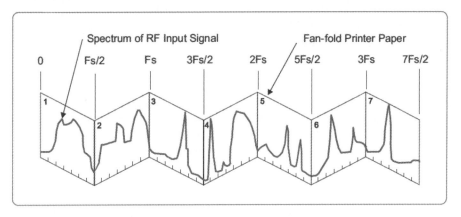

Figure 34: Nyquist zone folding

(Drawing from Pentek document, 'Putting under-sampling to work')

This drawing illustrates the way that 'even' numbered Nyquist zones are reflected or folded back in an inverted way where the panadapter would appear to be reversed. The 'odd' numbered zones are folded the same way as zone one so the panadapter and sidebands are not inverted.

Note that except for modes that only use a single side band, or which carry different information on each of the sidebands, the sideband reversal does not matter. AM and FM are unaffected by the sideband reversal since the sidebands are identical. SSB, digital modes carried as audio on a single sideband, ISB and some phase shift modes would need to be corrected because USB becomes LSB. PSK31 will decode OK because the information is carried by the phase changes, but the operating frequency would be offset below rather than above the nominal 'carrier' frequency. RTTY would be affected as it uses high and low tones, which would become reversed.

OVER SAMPLING AND UNDER SAMPLING

This is a subject that confuses a lot of people. I have even seen product brochures from leading SDR manufacturers that get this wrong. So let's sort it out!

When you use an ADC to sample frequencies above the Nyquist frequency, you are using under-sampling. As shown in the drawings above, if the sampling frequency Fs is 100 MHz, the 1st Nyquist zone is 0 to 50 MHz. When you deliberately receive a signal at 60 MHz, from inside the 2nd Nyquist zone, it becomes reflected back. The signal has been sampled accurately using a sampling frequency that is under (less than) what would be required if you were not using the aliasing mode.

Over sampling is completely different. It is the practice of using a higher sampling frequency than necessary. Taking the example used above. If you increased the sample rate to 200 Msps instead of 100 Msps, the signals below the wanted range of 0 to 50 MHz would be sampled twice as often. In that case, an input signal of 50 MHz gets sampled four times per cycle rather than the two times required by the Nyquist theorem. Why would you want to do that?

Remember that every time the ADC samples an analog waveform there is a small amount of error called quantization error (or quantization noise). These errors cannot be recovered or compensated for. Increasing the number of bits that the ADC uses to describe each sample reduces the level of the quantization errors. That is because the steps between each voltage level described are smaller.

Over sampling by a factor of two means that the signal is sampled twice as often. This averages the quantization errors. Say for example the error of sample one is 0.1 Volts and the error of sample two is 0.01 Volts. The average quantization error over two sample periods is 0.055 Volts. Over sampling minimizes quantization errors, giving you the same advantage as using an ADC with more bits. More bits means, better dynamic range and signal to noise performance.

This technique is used by FlexRadio Systems in their Signature series radios. They use an ADC sample rate of 245.76 Msps. Because you need to average the output samples, the sample rate for over sampling is usually an integer multiple of the basic Nyquist sample rate, i.e. two times Fs or three times Fs.

- Under sampling is the practice of using an ADC to sample signals above the Nyquist frequency.

- Over sampling is the practice of sampling the signals at a higher rate in order to improve the receiver's dynamic range and Signal to Noise performance by reducing quantization noise.

THE FPGA OR MICROCOMPUTER

Many direct sampling receivers use an FPGA (field programmable gate array) to manage the data coming from the ADC. Some also include a microprocessor or similar microcomputer to manage controls or display functions. Sometimes the microcomputer is a 'soft processor,' which is a software emulation of a microprocessor running on the FPGA fabric. Some radios also include dedicated DSP processors or radio tuner chips.

If the radio has real knobs, buttons, and a display, the microprocessor manages those functions. It may also handle filter and antenna switching, PTT, CW keying, band switching and the sending and receiving of control and signal data between the radio and any attached PC. The FPGA is an interface between the data coming from the analog to digital converter and the data being sent to the DSP stage of the radio. It is used to create the IQ data streams and for decimation and filtering.

There is a very large amount of digital information coming from the analog to digital converter. In the typical case of an Apache ANAN radio, there are 122,880,000 sixteen bit, samples every second. A FlexRadio creates twice as many samples per second. This amount of data is difficult for the DSP stage to manage and in the case of the ANAN radio, it is impossible to transport it all to the PC over the Ethernet connection. An FPGA is used to break the data into chunks that are more manageable. The process is called decimation and filtering. The software in the FPGA also creates the IQ data streams.

FPGA chips are very good at parallel processing. In the ANAN transceiver the signal data is copied into as many as seven streams, which are all decimated and filtered at the same time, creating up to seven panadapters.

The Apache ANAN-100D is able to send seven, 384 kHz wide segments, and the data for a low resolution 0-55 MHz wideband panadapter, over the Ethernet connection to the DSP in the PC software. Excluding the wideband display, this allows for a total display of 2.688 MHz of RF spectrum using seven panadapters. The actual number of panadapters that can be displayed is dependent on the SDR software you are using.

The FlexRadio 6000 series radios have onboard DSP so they not as constrained by the bandwidth of the Ethernet interface to the PC. They are able to display between two and eight, 14 MHz panadapters. Astute readers will note that the total bandwidth is actually wider than the original 0 - 77 MHz band sampled by the ADC. The FLEX-6700 can display up to eight panadapters, but only the dots making up the spectrum and waterfall displays are sent to the PC, not the raw IQ data. The radio can also send eight receiver audio signals and eight audio bandwidth IQ signals to the PC software. Each of the FlexRadio 'slice receivers' is created in the FPGA using parallel processing. The resulting signals are processed in the DSP section inside the radio.

You can split the incoming signal inside the FPGA seven or eight ways without causing any loss of level or introducing any noise or distortion. This is different to splitting a signal with an analog RF coupler, where you get a 3 dB loss of signal every time you split the signal into two paths. Actually, the data is not really split in the FPGA. It is copied into seven or eight input buffers, one for each parallel processing stage. This is much the same as using your PC to make a copy of a document or a photo except the process is continuous while the radio is running.

I have not mentioned the transmitted signal so far. It is relatively easy for the DSP stage and the Ethernet connection to manage the transmit signal because it is only a narrow band data stream carrying the modulation signal. In an ANAN transceiver the transmit signal to the radio is at 48 ksps. The speed up to the clocking rate of the DAC is done by software in the FPGA. Then the signal is shifted to the correct RF frequency in the CORDIC stage and finally it is converted back to an analog RF signal by the DAC.

Different radio models use varying amounts of signal processing inside the FPGA. Some radios don't even have an FPGA. They use a tuner chip or some other form of computer. I will describe the FPGA firmware used in the Hermes board as an example of how a FPGA can be used.

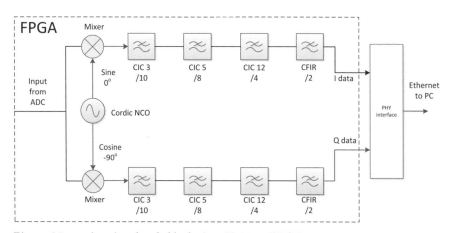

Figure 35: receive signal code blocks in a Hermes FPGA

The picture above shows the FPGA code blocks that are used in the Hermes / ANAN transceiver. Everything inside the dotted line is done using software. It is repeated for each of the seven possible panadapters.

I did not show the de-randomizer code block which is used to remove the effect of the ADC random function if it has been turned on. The de-randomizer is right at the input from the ADC, before the data is split into up to seven paths. It uses an 'exclusive OR' function to remove the randomization of the data signal.

CORDIC

The first code block is the CORDIC. It consists of a numerically controlled oscillator and two mixers. You should recognize the circuit; it is a single conversion receiver, the same as the Tayloe detector. But it is implemented by software working with numbers not hardware working with analog signals.

Technical TIP: You might ask, "won't the single conversion stage create image signals on the IQ streams?" Yes, it will and just like the QSD receiver, they will be removed by using the phasing method in the DSP section of the radio. When we use the Tayloe QSD method, imperfections in the phase and level relationship between the, I and Q signals make it impossible to completely eliminate the image signals right across the band. But inside the FPGA, the CORDIC works in software. The IQ phase and level relationship is perfect so the image signals can be completely eliminated.

The numerically controlled oscillator (NCO) creates two streams if 16 bit numbers, which represent a sine wave and a cosine wave, at a frequency of up to the incoming data rate of 122.88 Msps. These signals are 'mixed' with the incoming data, which shifts the spectrum, downwards by the difference between the NCO and the incoming frequency. It is all done with mathematics but the result is the same as using a hardware mixer and then converting the data to a digital format. You end up with the frequencies below the NCO frequency being discarded and the frequencies above the NCO frequency being passed on to the next stage, which is the first of the CIC filters.

CIC FILTERS

The following example is based on the Hermes radio with the panadapter set to the 192 kHz bandwidth. As we pick up the story, the signal has been mixed down in frequency by the CORDIC stage.

After the CORDIC stage, the data is still at the 122.88 Msps rate, but it has been shifted by the mixer, so the output only contains frequencies in and above the panadapter, we want. Say for example that the radio is tuned to 14.2 MHz. The output of the CORDIC mixer stage is numbers representing the signals sampled by the ADC that are from 14.2 MHz up. In other words 14.2 MHZ becomes 0 Hz and will be plotted in the center of the panadapter.

Because the CORDIC is a mixer the output data will have numbers representing signals both above and below 14.2 MHz, just the same as the Tayloe detector. A signal received at 15.2 MHz will end up at the 1MHz point and so would a signal received at 13.2 MHz. As discussed earlier the signals and images are sorted out by using the phasing method in the SDR software on the PC.

We don't need to keep the frequencies that are above the wanted panadapter bandwidth and we don't need such a high data rate to describe a 192 kHz bandwidth so we throw a lot away. This is done in four stages using a process known as decimation and filtering. Decimation means dividing the sample rate by an integer amount.

To get from a sample rate of 122.88 Msps to a sample rate of 192 ksps, we need a decimation ratio of 122880 / 192 = 640 so we are effectively throwing away 639 out of every 640 samples. One of the advantages of the CIC filters is that the decimation can be built into the same code block as the filter.

Reducing the sample rate causes a problem for Mr Nyquist. The low pass filters before the ADC removed all of the signals above 55 MHz, but each stage of the decimation process causes new alias signal problems.

CIC filters are 'cascaded integrating comb filters'. They are multi stage filters with the advantage that they are easy to code in mathematics. The drawbacks are a certain amount of latency (delay) and they are not completely flat. They have a roll off at the top end. The more CIC stages, the more roll off occurs and that is why the last filter in each of the two receiver chains are CFIR filters. CFIR stands for compensating finite impulse response. They are trickier to implement in the FPGA because they use more FPGA elements and resources.

There are three CIC filters in each of the, I and the Q signal paths. They are relatively easy to implement in the FPGA since they do not require a multiplier, just shift registers and addition. The numbers beside 'CIC' on the *'receive signal code blocks in a Hermes FPGA'* drawing above, indicate how many stages of filtering are inside each software code block. The number below is the decimation ratio of the stage. For example, the first CIC filter is a 3 stage filter that divides the sample rate by 10.

The first CIC filter has a decimation ratio of 10. It reduces the sample rate from 122.88 Msps to 12.288 Msps. The Nyquist bandwidth of a signal sampled at 12.288 MHz is 6.144 MHz. That means that any signals above 6.144 MHz are unwanted and they could be aliased back into the new receiver bandwidth. To prevent that from happening, the three stage CIC filter works as a low pass filter at a little above 6.144 MHz.

After the decimation at every CIC filter, we need to eliminate any signals from outside of the resulting Nyquist bandwidth. Once alias signals get into the data they can't be removed. They need to be filtered out before the decimation. This happens every time we decimate the sample, all the way down to our final rate of 192 ksps. Finally, we want a 192 kHz wide panadapter spectrum display, centered on the local oscillator frequency, with all signals above the 192 kHz bandwidth filtered out.

A side effect of the decimation process is an improvement in the receiver's dynamic range resulting from process gain. The output of the first CIC filter is at 12.288 Msps, one tenth of the original rate. Reducing the sample rate by a factor of 10 gives us 10 dB more dynamic range.

Process Gain = $10 * \log_{10}(122.88/12.288)$ = 10 dB.

We need more bits to describe the additional dynamic range so the number of bits per sample is increased from 16 bits to 24 bits. This is enough for all further stages so it remains at 24 bits throughout the rest of the process.

The decimation ratio of the second and third CIC filters can be changed by commands from the PC software in order to select the wanted output bandwidth; 48 kHz, 96 kHz, 192 kHz or 384 kHz.

For a 192 kHz panadapter, the second (5 stage) CIC filter will decimate by 8, down to 1.536 Msps and the third (12 stage) CIC filter will decimate by 4, down to 384 ksps.

At the end of this block, there have been a total of 20 stages of CIC filtering which is enough to reduce aliased signals from above the wanted panadapter by more than 100 dB. One more decimate by two stage will bring us down to the wanted 192 ksps sample rate and bandwidth. The final stage uses a different kind of filter.

THE CFIR FILTER

The CIC filters are easy to code and they don't use too many FPGA elements but their output pass band is not flat. After the 20 CIC filter stages, the output will have a roll off, of about 8 dB at the high frequency end. This is not desired, as it would show on the panadapter as a roll off in the noise floor and receiver sensitivity at both edges of the spectrum display. The final filter and decimation by two, down to 192 ksps in our example, is a CFIR (compensating finite impulse response) filter.

A standard FIR filter has a flat response and a sharp roll off above the wanted pass band. The compensating 'CFIR' filter is designed to have a shape, which rises at the higher frequencies and then has a sharp roll off. Combined with the CIC filters the output is flat across the wanted receiver panadapter with at least 100 dB rejection of signals from above the cut off frequency.

HOW ARE THE FILTERS DESIGNED?

All of these filters were designed using software like MATLAB and the resulting Verilog code is loaded into the FPGA as a firmware file. They operate mathematically on the data bits representing the signals, which were sampled by the ADC, but their performance can be measured and displayed just like hardware filters. Verilog is a 'hardware description language' (HDL) with a syntax similar to the C programming language.

RECEIVER CHAIN

For the ANAN receiver, IQ signal creation, frequency translation, decimation and filtering is all that happens inside the radio. After the CFIR stage, the IQ signals for each of the seven panadapters are combined into data fames and sent over the Ethernet connection to the DSP software running on the PC. The data also contains control signals, mic audio, and the wideband scope data.

Data from the PC to the radio contains the audio signal from the demodulators, which is sent to the amplified speakers, various control signals, and the transmit baseband signal.

OTHER FPGA FUNCTIONS

The FPGA manages other signals including, microphone audio, received signal audio for the speakers coming back from the PC to the radio, CW keying and CW modulation. Control signals sent to and from the PC are processed using software inside the FPGA and it generates the 128.88 MHZ clock signals for the ADC and DAC.

TRANSMIT CHAIN

The code blocks for the transmit side are much simpler than the receiver software. Again this example is based on The Hermes / ANAN design.

The IQ data arriving from the PC is at a much lower speed than the rate required for the DAC. It only has to be at least twice the highest modulating frequency. In the Hermes radio the transmit data is at 48 ksps so the transmitter has a maximum bandwidth of 24 kHz. This is more than enough for amateur radio signals, which are typically less than 3 kHz wide. The 24 kHz wide transmit bandwidth carrying the modulation signal is referred to as the 'transmit baseband' signal.

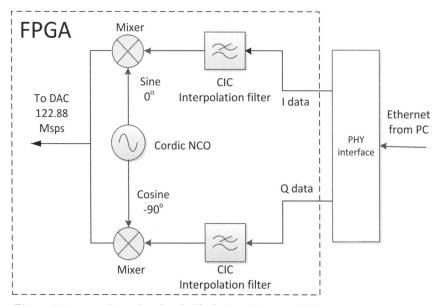

Figure 36: transmitter signal code blocks in a Hermes FPGA

The 48 ksps IQ streams received from the PC software are decoded from the Ethernet packets in the PHY interface. Interpolation CIC filters increase, the data rate up to 122.88 Msps. The full speed signal is mixed using a CORDIC stage so that the DAC will generate an RF signal on the wanted RF frequency. The transmitter CORDIC uses the same algorithm as the CORDIC used in each of the seven receiver stages. Outside of the FPGA, the DAC creates an analog signal at the RF frequency, which is amplified and filtered before being sent to the antenna.

SERVER / CLIENT ARCHITECTURE

There is a strong trend towards using a server / client architecture for future software defined radios. With this new approach, the traditional SDR program is split into two new programs with different functions. The server program resides on the PC that is physically connected via USB or Ethernet to the radio hardware. Or it might be running on a computer board or a microprocessor housed inside the radio, or on a stand-alone 'single board computer' like the NVIDIA Jetson TK1. The sever program usually has no direct user access. Its job is to act as a channel and interface between the radio and the client software.

The SDR client software may be running on the same computer as the server, or on another computer connected to the same computer network via an Ethernet cable or Wi-Fi. It might even be on a computer at a remote location connected to the server via the Internet. It is often possible to have more than one client application connected to a server application at the same time.

The SDR client does all of the display and control 'GUI' functions and the server typically does the DSP and signal routing. An API will be written to describe the data requirements and controls between the client and the server. You could use different SDR client programs to talk to the same SDR radio via the same server application. For example, you might use PowerSDR and cuSDR at the same time, to monitor different bands on different computer devices. You might listen for 6m band openings on your phone, while talking to a ham radio station on 20m SSB in your shack, while your children are listening to the BBC on a notebook PC in the lounge.

OK maybe you do not want to do all of that, but the client / server architecture does have several advantages. Firstly, the server can do much of the computer intensive digital signal processing. There will be a large continuous amount of data flowing between the radio hardware and the server program. The data flow between the server application and the client can be much reduced. It only has to carry the graphics for the actual panadapters being displayed, audio in both directions, information data like the S meter, frequency readouts, and the control commands (PTT, volume, filter selection etc.)

Developers will be able to provide a range of different client software applications designed to work with the server. This should mean shorter development times, as they would only need to create a GUI. The difficult DSP and FFT code resides in the server program. You could have a choice of user interface styles based around using the same server program and radio. Digital mode or specialist programs could interface directly with the radio.

FlexRadio Systems has already followed this route for their Signature 6000 range of transceivers and the 6700R receiver. Their developers wanted to create a radio that was capable of being used in a computer network situation.

They were aware that transferring a huge amount of data would be a severe limitation especially for wireless and Internet networking so they moved to a server / client design. The FlexRadios have a powerful ARM processor and DSP chips inside the radio. Firmware running on these chips acts as the server. The SmartSDR software running on the PC is the client. The data requirement between the radio box and the PC is much reduced compared to a traditional 'DSP on the PC' approach and this allows for flexible networking options and the 14 MHz wide panadapters.

The OpenHPSDR group is also experimenting with a server / client approach. They are working on the idea of using a powerful Jetson TK1 single board computer as a DSP server alongside the Hermes or Angelia SDR board.

THICK CLIENT

This is not a slur on the operator, it is a term used to describe a type of data connection between the radio and the PC. It does not refer to the actual electrical connection, usually Ethernet or USB, but rather to the amount of data traffic that is required. The thick client model is the situation where the DSP functions are performed by DSP software running on the PC. The PC also manages the control functions and displays the panadapters. This model of operation requires much more data to be transferred between the radio and the PC than the thin client model used by FlexRadio Systems. It also requires that the data flow is continuous, it can't be in bursts, or the latency will be too variable, possibly resulting in interrupted audio or disruptions in the spectrum or waterfall images. The thick client model tends to have a faster development cycle since PC software is easier to write than embedded software.

The thick client model is neither better nor worse than the thin client model, although the manufacturers and supporters of various radios may have a differing opinion. Both methods have advantages and disadvantages.

THIN CLIENT

No, this does not mean that you have to be a thin person to use the radio. That would rule out a lot of hams, including myself. Thin client is the flip side of the thick client model. The term is used to describe a data connection, which requires a low amount of continuous data. The 'Signature 6000 series' radios work on the 'thin client' model where the DSP functions are performed by DSP and computer chips inside the radio. The PC is only required for control functions and to display the panadapters. This model requires less data to be transferred between the radio and the PC than the thick client model used by Apache Labs and almost all other SDRs. Thin client connections allow the use of less powerful client computers, including Netbooks, tablets, and phones. It will ultimately make remote operation over the Internet easier to achieve.

The downside is that performing the DSP inside the radio makes the radio more complex and hence more expensive.

FFT MAGIC

Arthur C Clark wrote that, "*Any sufficiently advanced technology is indistinguishable from magic.*" He meant that if somebody demonstrates a device to you and you are completely unaware about how it works, such as showing a cave man a car, or your neighbor your ham radio transceiver, then "it works by magic" is as good an explanation as any other.

As far as I am concerned, Fast Fourier Transformation (FFT) is mathematical magic. It uses very complex mathematics including 'real' and 'imaginary' numbers to convert signals in the 'time domain' into signals in the 'frequency domain' or back the other way. This is essential for the creation of the panadapter spectrum display. What the heck are time and frequency domains? I hear you ask.

All software defined radio receivers use an analog to digital converter to sample the incoming RF (or down-converted to audio) signals and represent them as a series of digital numbers. The analog to digital converter samples the level of the incoming wideband received signal at instants in time and each sample is represented by a digital number appearing on the ADC output pins. On the next clock cycle, another sample is read and its level becomes the next number on the output pins. At some stage, the parallel data signals representing these numbers are converted to a serial stream of digital data bits. Since the data coming from the analog to digital converter represents the signal at specific 'sample' times, it is in the 'time domain.' This serial data is ok for decoding the modulation and for DSP functions like filtering and noise reduction, but it is no good for the spectrum display. We want to see a display showing signals represented at their operating frequencies across the band, not signals at different times. The FFT converts the data into a form that can be displayed on the panadapter.

Instead of a series of numbers representing the signal level at different times, FFT creates a series of numbers representing the signal level at different frequencies.

After the FFT process, each digital number in the output buffer represents the signal level of a narrow section of the frequency spectrum called a bin. As well as being able to display the spectrum on your panadapter, having the signal represented in terms of frequency is useful for some DSP functions. For example to create something like a low pass filter, you could progressively reduce the level of the bins above the cut off frequency. By altering the level in individual bins, you can make fine adjustments to the shape, or the high and low cut off frequencies of a filter. Frequency translation can be done simply by moving the position of bins in the software buffer. Amplification or equalization can be achieved by multiplying the level in each bin by a calculated amount. Or, you could create a notch filter by simply reducing the level in a few bins.

The spectrum display is made by plotting the level of each bin across the bandwidth of the panadapter. Because each bin is only a few Hertz wide, they each have a large dynamic range, due to process gain. Stacking thousands of bins side by side gives you a wideband display with a low noise floor. The same technique is used in modern spectrum analyzer, test instruments. Without FFT, a wide panadapter display would have less process gain and therefore a higher noise floor than the noise level within the receiver bandwidth. Using FFT, the panadapter can display a lower noise floor than the noise being heard within the receiver bandwidth.

The mathematics used in the FFT process is outside the scope of this book. It is for serious 'Boffins' only. Even though they are very smart, it is a bit too hard for some of the SDR software developers. Luckily, there are open source FFT algorithms available in the form of already published open source .dll files. Software developers can write SDR applications that make calls to the FFT.dll file and get the converted data back in a data array or buffer. They send the FFT routine time related data and it returns frequency related data, or they send frequency related data and it returns time related data.

I believe that most amateur radio SDR software uses a .dll library called, FFTW, 'Fastest Fourier Transformation in the West.'

Technical TIP: A .dll file contains reusable software subroutines that can be used by other programs. This allows software developers to avoid having to reinvent the wheel. Under license conditions they can incorporate code that another developer has written, to into in their software applications.

TIME DOMAIN

An oscilloscope displays signals in the 'time domain.' It shows the signal voltage on the vertical Y axis and time on the horizontal X axis. If we sample the analog signal using an analog to digital converter, the 8, 14, or 16 bit samples at the output of the ADC represent the received signal voltage at sequential times. The digital signal is still in the 'time domain,' it represents the original analog signal as, 'samples per second'. A digital to analog converter can recover the original analog signal.

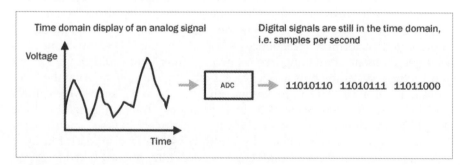

Figure 37: analog and digital signals in the 'time domain'

FREQUENCY DOMAIN

The panadapter spectrum display on your favorite SDR software shows voltage on the vertical Y axis and frequencies on the horizontal X axis, essentially the same as a spectrum analyzer display. Because the display shows signals at different frequencies instead of at different times, the digital signal and the display are said to be in the 'frequency domain'. Before the FFT stage, the analog and digital signals are in the time domain. After the FFT stage, the digital bins are in the frequency domain. If you used a DAC to convert the post FFT signal from digital to analog, you could display the analog frequency domain signal on an analog spectrum analyzer display.

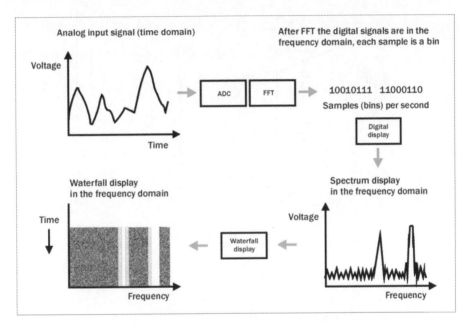

Figure 38: analog and digital signals in the 'frequency domain'

To build the panadapter, the FFT stage outputs numbers representing the level of each bin into a software buffer. As the buffer is read, the level of each bin is displayed as a dot on the panadapter. The higher the level, the higher the dot is placed on the screen. Then the FFT program looks at the next input sample and calculates the frequency spectrum relating to that. This allows the spectrum display to be updated at a nominated number of frames per second. The spectrum line is drawn left to right across the panadapter and overlaid when the spectrum relating to the next ADC sample is drawn. The level of the bins is also used to calculate the brightness and color of each waterfall pixel. A whole line is calculated, then the entire waterfall picture moves one line down the screen and the new line is inserted at the top.

The waterfall display is very useful because it indicates higher signal levels by using more brightness and color, in the time domain down the screen, and in the frequency domain across the screen, at the same time.

ANOTHER WAY OF LOOKING AT FREQUENCY AND TIME

I know this is a bit of a repeat of the above, but I think that this diagram really illustrates the way you can imagine yourself looking through the "time window" on the left or through the "frequency window" on the right.

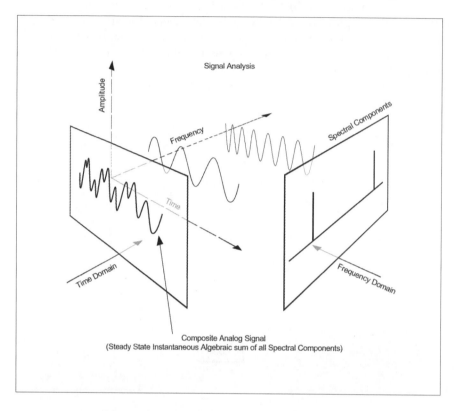

Figure 39: time and frequency domains

The image above comes from 'Understanding Data Converters Frequency Domain Specifications,' Datel application note AN-4 by Bob Leonard. It shows how you can look at the same signal in two different ways. The picture on the left is the time domain signal, which shows the signal as you would see it on an Oscilloscope. The picture on the right is the frequency domain display of the same signal as viewed on a Spectrum Analyzer or a panadapter.

If we consider radio signals being input to an ADC. When you look at the time domain signal on the left, you see the composite vector sum of all of the frequencies being sampled. When you look at the frequency domain, panadapter spectrum display, you can see the amplitude of each individual signal. The frequency domain (panadapter) image is a much more useful display. A waterfall display shows a history of the frequency domain signals. The top of the waterfall is very recent history and the data gets older as you look lower down.

PANADAPTER AND WATERFALL DISPLAYS

This chapter provides more detail about how the panadapter and waterfall displays are created. The panadapter looks very complex with noise at the bottom and a lot of signals across the band. It is always changing. In fact, it changes so fast that it is usually better to select an averaging function to make the rate of change smoother and less flickery. The waterfall flows down the screen, showing a history of the spectrum display. But these two displays only show a small fraction of the information that is being converted to digital by the ADC and then processed by the DSP. There is too much data arriving much too fast. The panadapter screen does not have enough pixels across it to display all of the bins that are being created by the FFT process and the sample rate is far faster that the rate that we need the spectrum and waterfall images to be refreshed.

THE SPECTRUM DISPLAY

The IQ data contains the level of the signals at the sample times. However, this is no good for display on a panadapter spectrum. It must be converted to a series of samples or 'bins' that contain the level of the signal at different frequencies. The panadapter spectrum display shows these levels as dots on the screen. The higher the level, the further up the panadapter the dot is placed. Each dot is called a pixel.

As discussed in the last chapter, the conversion from time domain, data samples, to frequency domain samples or bins is done using FFT. To keep things going without losing any of the information coming from the radio, the FFT processes the samples at the same rate as the input data. It takes a chunk of the incoming data, for example, a 'frame' of 2048 or 4096 samples, converts each frame to bins and then goes back for the next frame.

If we use the example of a 192 kHz wide panadapter, the sample rate being managed by the digital signal processing is 192 ksps. That means that the FFT is calculating the spectrum bins at 192,000 samples per second. Each 16 bit time domain sample that is sent to the FFT becomes a 16 bit frequency domain sample or 'bin' in the FFT output buffer.

To make the programming easier and more logical, the panadapter is often but not always designed to display a submultiple of the frame size. For example if the frame contains 2048 samples, the display might be 1024 pixels wide. Each pixel or dot shown on the panadapter display is at the level of the larger of two samples. At full scale, when the display is not zoomed in, PowerSDR plots the level of every second bin as a pixel on the screen. It only uses data from one of the IQ data streams, as the other stream is 'almost' identical. If the frame contained 4096 samples, the display might still be 1024 pixels wide. In that case, each pixel or dot shown on the panadapter display is at the level of the largest of four samples.

The spectrum display does not update at the same rate as the data stream. If it did, the spectrum information would be updated at 192 lines per second. That is much too fast. Depending on the refresh rate that you choose, the software may only display every 10th or 20th frame. The full data rate is not required for the panadapter, but it is necessary for the DSP and demodulator.

A 192 kHz wide panadapter displayed on a screen with 1024 pixels shows a pixel for every 187.5 Hz of the input spectrum. A 14 MHz wide panadapter on the same panadapter only displays a pixel dot every 13.675 kHz across the band. As you zoom in, the resolution improves. This is called the panadapter resolution.

The maximum range of frequencies that can be displayed on the panadapter is the 'panadapter bandwidth'. It could be 192 or 384 kHz on an ANAN radio or 14 MHz on a FlexRadio. The range of frequencies that you can actually see on the screen when you zoom in, or out, is called the 'span'.

This is not the whole story! The panadapter displays the amplitude of the received signals on a logarithmic dBm scale, not the linear scale that comes out of the FFT. This is adjusted mathematically before the pixels are displayed on the panadapter.

The number of frames displayed per second is usually adjustable. If you set the frame rate to one second, you will see each spectrum line update once per second and the waterfall will add a new line every second. On PowerSDR, it will take 256 seconds for the waterfall screen to scroll all the way down.

THE WATERFALL

The waterfall display is usually updated at the same rate as the spectrum display. It is created from the same data samples as the spectrum display. If we continue to assume a 1024 pixel panadapter screen, the value of each of the 1024 displayed samples is recorded as a dot across the top line of the waterfall display. Large value numbers (big signals) are displayed as bright colors and small values (weak signals) are displayed as dark colors. Every time a line of spectrum information is displayed on the spectrum display, a new line is added to the top of the waterfall display. In PowerSDR, the waterfall is stored as an image file that has 1024 pixels by 256 lines. Unlike the spectrum, which is drawn across the panadapter like the trace on an oscilloscope, each waterfall line is added as a complete line.

In SmartSDR, the waterfall is stored in a matrix that is much larger than the amount of lines that are displayed on the screen. You can drag the whole waterfall display up to see what the signals looked like as far as 10 minutes in the past. If you change the panadapter bandwidth or center frequency, the whole displayed waterfall is recalculated so the waterfall lines stay straight. In PowerSDR, the lines once written to the image are not recalculated, so the vertical traces indicating traces will appear to bend if you change the panadapter center frequency or bandwidth.

DIRECT FOURIER CONVERSION

Direct Fourier Conversion (DFC) is an exciting new method of digital down conversion for SDR receivers. Instead of using firmware code in the FPGA to select the data for the wanted panadapters, DFC uses a 'forward' FFT calculation to convert the ADC samples into frequency domain bins. The selected band of frequencies for each panadapter are taken from the FFT output buffer. This is not quite as easy as it sounds. After the band selection, the bins relating to the wanted panadapters are converted back into time domain signals using 'inverse' FFT calculations, combined into data frames, and then sent on to the DSP stage of the software. There is a single forward FFT stage, but each panadapter or 'receiver' must have its own inverse FFT.

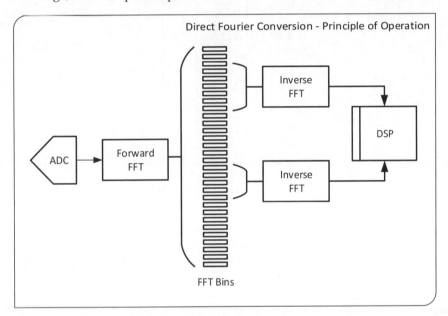

Figure 40: DFC sampling - principle of operation

The trend for new DDC receiver designs is towards using DSP chips or microcomputers to perform all of the digital signal processing inside the radio. DFC turns this 'on its head' by moving all the digital signal processing out of the radio hardware and into computer software. In a DFC receiver, the only essential hardware is an anti-alias low pass filter, the clock, and the ADC.

At this experimental stage, DFC is being performed by software running on either a NVIDIA PC graphics card or a single board NVIDIA Jetson computer. These cards contain multi CUDA core graphics processor (GPU) chips. They are excellent for DFC because their multi-core architecture allows parallel processing for several DFC receivers and the forward FFT.

The ADC in a direct sampling SDR samples a lot of the HF spectrum that we don't want to display on our panadapters. In digital down conversion receivers, the data from the ADC is translated in frequency by the CORDIC in the FPGA, then decimated and filtered down to the panadapter bandwidth. The 24 bit IQ data for the narrow panadapter slices is sent to the PC at the panadapter sample rate and the DSP code in the PC software displays the panadapters and demodulates the signals. 'Thin client' radios like the FlexRadios reduce the Ethernet data requirement even further by doing the DSP in the radio as well.

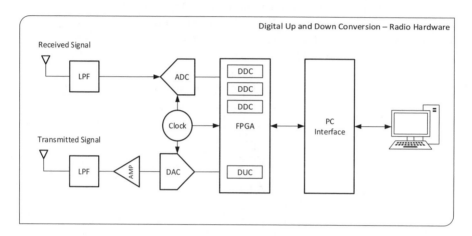

Figure 41: DDC / DUC transceiver – no on-board DSP

The DFC method achieves the frequency selection, decimation, and filtering functions in a different way. It also minimizes the functions performed in the radio board hardware and moves them into software running on a dedicated computer or the PC's video card.

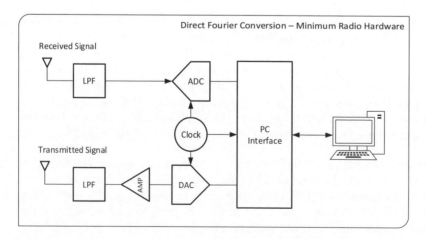

Figure 42: DFC transceiver – less hardware and no on-board DSP

When the sixteen bit ADC samples reach the DFC software running on the NVIDIA graphics processor, an 'overlap and store' process loads data into the input buffer for the forward FFT transformation. Overlapping the data stream in the input buffer, accounts for the time that it takes the GPU to do each FFT transform so that no input samples get missed. It is a common technique used when doing FFT on continuous data streams.

For a radio capable of receiving 0 to 30 MHz the FFT needs to work at a sample rate of at least 60 Msps. Once the signal has been converted into thousands of bins, it is relatively easy to select the ones that you want, for the panadapters that you want to display. The band selection, filtering, and decimation process involves calculations on the data in software buffers to select the wanted bandwidth. Then the data for each panadapter is converted back into the time domain using individual inverse FFT and the resulting time domain data streams are sent to the DSP running in the PC SDR software.

Performing the forward FFT calculation on such a fast data stream requires a very powerful computer. High speed calculations can be achieved by using parallel processing. For example, the code blocks for several panadapters can be run simultaneously on different CUDA cores, while the FFT process is running on other cores. The OpenHPSDR team has been experimenting with running DFC on an NVIDIA Jetson TK-1 computer board and also the graphics processor on NVIDIA PC video cards such as the GTX-750 Ti. The CUDA Cores in an NVIDIA GPU are parallel processors that are responsible for processing all the input data. The Jetson board has 192 CUDA cores and the GTX-750 Ti video card has 640 CUDA cores. Your PC CPU typically has two or four cores. Testing of FFT running on CUDA video card and on a PC CPU indicated that the video card can be up to sixteen times faster, although in the 'real world' this is reduced by memory access delays. These access delays can be reduced by using 'pinned' memory, so that the PC CPU does not have to manage data between the GPU and the computer memory.

Technical Tip: a Graphics Processing Unit is a specialized microprocessor designed to manage data for display on a computer monitor. They were introduced to speed up the display of high resolution images such as movies or computer games. Using a GPU reduces the processing load on the computer's main microprocessor, the CPU. GPU chips have many more processing cores than a standard microprocessor. They can manage large amounts of data very fast, by splitting the incoming signal into many paths and processing them all simultaneously.

CUDA is a parallel computing platform and application programming interface (API) model created by NVIDIA. It allows software developers to use a CUDA enabled graphics processing unit (GPU) for general purpose processing. (Source Wikipedia.com).

'Pinned' or 'page-locked' memory is a way of dedicating computer RAM to the video card rather than having to wait for the computer CPU to manage the data flow between the video card and the memory.

DFC RECEIVERS COMPARED WITH DDC RECEIVERS

Digital down conversion (DDC) receivers:	Direct Fourier conversion (DFC) receivers:
Frequency translation, decimation and band filtering is performed in the FPGA hardware on the radio board.	Frequency translation, decimation and band filtering is performed in software running on a NVIDIA GPU on a video card or a single board computer.
Sixteen bit data from the ADC is processed in the FPGA on the radio board.	Sixteen bit data from the ADC is sent directly to a PC video card graphics processor or to a standalone computer, (Jetson TK-1 or similar).
Each panadapter requires a separate DDC stage in the FPGA.	Each panadapter requires a separate DFC stage in the computer software.
DDC receivers work in the time domain. They use CORDIC mixers in the FPGA to mix the incoming data down for selection of the panadapter frequency band, then decimation and filtering, provides data to the DSP stage at the panadapter sample rate.	DFC works mostly in the frequency domain. A single very fast Fourier transform is performed on the incoming data stream. The output FFT buffer is copied to the input buffers for each of the DFC 'receivers.'
At each decimation stage, anti-alias filtering is performed in the time domain, using CIC filters. The final decimation stage uses a CFIR filter to correct roll off in the frequency response.	Anti-alias filtering is required because the signal is being decimated. The filter coefficients are converted into a frequency domain signal using FFT. The received signal bins are multiplied by the filter bins.
24 bit IQ data for each of the panadapters is sent to the PC for digital signal processing, panadapter display and demodulating.	Each DFC process consists of Rotate – Filter – Decimate – and Inverse FFT software blocks. After these processing stages the data, which has now been converted back into a time domain signal, is sent to the PC for digital signal processing, panadapter display and demodulating.

In the rest of the chapter, I explain more about the stages in the DFC process. This is followed by an example based on using a Hermes based radio as the hardware part of a DFC system. It does get a bit technical but it covers some of the rules and it illustrates DFC more fully. As I said above it is not just a matter of grabbing the frequency bins that you want. The buffer sizes and sample rates in the example come from work done by Steven Passe AD0ES. This was experimental work so the numbers may change, but the mathematics and the theory will stay true.

OVERLAP AND STORE

There is a continuous stream of 16 bit data arriving from the ADC. It is read into the FFT input buffer. When the buffer is full, the forward FFT transform can take place. However, the FFT needs time to process the calculations and we don't want to lose any of the ADC samples while that is happening. So the FFT input buffer is always preloaded with bytes from the preceding data frame. The overlap makes sure that the FFT output contains a frequency domain representation of all of the ADC data. The amount of overlap is made equal to the FIR filter length -1, so that the FFT input buffer does not need to be stuffed with zeros.

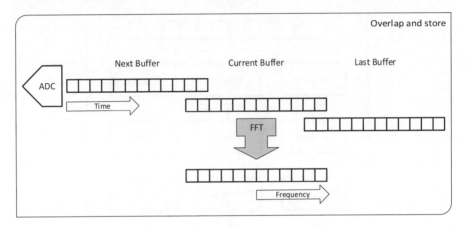

Figure 43: DFC process – overlap and store

FFT

A forward FFT transform is carried out on the data coming from the ADC. It takes a lot of computer power because the data rate is very fast and the input data buffer is very large. The data rate is at least 60 Msps and the FFT input buffer is more than a million bytes.

The actual FFT transform is done on a buffer large enough to contain the input data block plus the size of the FIR filter used later in the process. The extra space in the input buffer is filled with the overlap data, which gets discarded during and after the decimation process. The FFT output buffer is rearranged to place the 'zero' frequency in the centre with 'positive' frequencies to the right and 'negative' frequencies to the left.

The requirement to rearrange (flip) the data in each half of the output buffer depends on the actual FFT algorithm that is used. As with all FFT calculations, the output buffer contains 'complex' information. Frequencies above the nominal centre frequency are called 'real' or 'positive' frequencies and frequencies below the centre frequency are called 'imaginary' or 'negative' frequencies.

ONE FORWARD FFT – MULTIPLE PANADAPTERS

Each panadapter or 'DFC receiver' gets a copy of the FFT output data. The DFC receiver code blocks are; Rotate –> Filter –> Decimate –> IFFT.

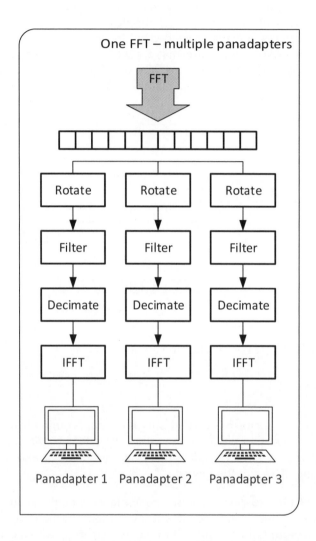

ROTATE

Each DFC receiver rotates the data in its input buffer to centre the wanted range of frequencies in the buffer. This does a coarse frequency translation, similar to the function of the CORDIC in a DDC receiver. The frequency translation is done to bring the wanted signal range into the filter passband. The filter is centred in the FFT coefficient buffer.

Rather than tediously left shifting data in the buffer and then moving the remainder back into the empty positions, the data is put into a 'circular' buffer, and then the pointer is simply moved to point at the wanted bins.

FILTER

The filter stage selects the wanted panadapter bandwidth. The rotation stage moves the bottom of the panadapter to the zero frequency and the FIR low pass filter, attenuates signals that are above the wanted panadapter.

The reason that you can't simply take the frequency bins that you want, without applying any filtering, is that you would in effect be applying a 'brick wall filter.' Very sharp filters cause problems. A signal completely outside of the filter will be OK and so would a signal completely within the filter. The problem is with signals, which contain energy in bins that have been selected as well as bins that are not selected. The wanted signals will be contained in several bins. For example if the bin width is 78 Hz an SSB signal may be spread across 30 or more bins. Cutting parts of these signals off will cause all sorts of transients and spurs. The filter also attenuates frequencies that would become aliased into the panadapter when the decimation is performed.

In a DDC receiver, the filtering is done on the time domain signal, but in a DFC receiver, it has to be done in the frequency domain. To achieve filtering, the (rotated) input signal is multiplied by a forward FFT of the wanted FIR filter coefficients. Multiplication of the data in the frequency domain is equivalent to 'convolution' of time domain signals i.e. filtering. The output of the filter multiplied by the (rotated) FFT data contains down-sampled components and aliased components. The decimate process averages out the aliased components leaving the down sampled wanted panadapter signals.

The input data for the filter is ¼ the size of the FFT size of the main forward FFT. The filter FFT is the same size as the main forward FFT. The rest of the input buffer is padded with zeros. Each DFC receiver has a separate filter, which can have different bandwidth and slope coefficients. If the number of coefficients is different, the input buffer can be padded with more zeros, but it is more likely that the designer will keep the number of coefficients the same in all cases and use different coefficient settings to create different filter shapes and roll off frequency. The filter FFT must be recalculated if the decimation ratio is changed because it has to have a narrower or wider bandwidth. But other than that, it remains fixed.

Technical Tip: for filtering in the frequency domain, the input signal is multiplied by the impulse response of the FIR filter. The buffer size for the output signal is equal to the input buffer size + the filter buffer size − 1. That is why the main FFT output buffer has to be big enough to hold the result of this calculation.

DECIMATE

The data rate is reduced to a rate appropriate to the wanted panadapter bandwidth by using decimation in the frequency domain. Actually, the filter stage has already broken the data up into wanted and aliased segments. To complete the decimation these segments must be added together. The output buffer is segmented into the same number of sections as the decimation ratio.

For example if we want the output data rate to be at 1/3 of the input data rate, with a corresponding bandwidth 1/3 of the original bandwidth, the output would be broken into three equal parts. In our Hermes example below the decimation is 256, so there are 256 segments to be added.

The segments are added byte for byte, i.e. byte 0 of segment 1 plus, byte 0 of segment 2 plus, byte 0 of segment 3.

The decimation ratio must be an integer and it is much easier mathematically if it is a 'power of 2' i.e. 2, 4, 8, 16, 32 etc. It is also related back to both the FIR filter FFT size and the main FFT size.

IFFT

The selected bins are converted back into a time domain signal using an Inverse FFT transform. This is calculated at the lower sampling rate that results from the decimation, i.e. the original ADC sampling rate divided by the decimation ratio. Not all of the output bytes are useable. Remember the bytes that were overlapped in the overlap and store stage? Decimation has eliminated some of them but the remainder must be removed from the IFFT output. Finally, the data can be read sequentially from the output buffer and to form a new time domain, data stream, which contains the panadapter information.

Data from all of the IFFT stages is combined and sent from the GPU to the software running on the PCs CPU. From there the normal DSP processing, spectrum and waterfall displays and demodulation occurs.

TRANSMITTING WITH DFC

You will note that I have not mentioned using DFC for the transmit part of the radio. That is because it has not been invented yet. But there is no reason why the process can't be utilised to create the signal required for the DAC on the radio board. It will involve a DFC up-conversion rather than a down conversion. The mathematics is similar and only one up-converter is required for transmitting. It will involve a low speed forward FFT, frequency up-conversion using interpolation and a high speed inverse FFT to provide the signal to the DAC. The inverse FFT will have to run at the approximately 60 Msps rate, but the buffer size will not have to be as large because the bandwidth of the transmitted signal is far smaller than the 30 MHz bandwidth of the receiver signal.

There still needs to be a path for microphone audio, filter switching commands, PTT and CW signals, and audio back to the radio from the PC. These signals could be managed by an FPGA on the radio board or by a microcomputer. In the Hermes and ANAN radios, the FPGA will probably still generate the ADC clock signal and perform CW modulation.

AN EXAMPLE OF THE DFC PROCESS USING A HERMES RECEIVER

The buffer sizes and sampling rates in this example come from experimental work done by Steven Passe AD0ES. By the time you get to play with a DFC radio, the numbers may change, but the mathematics and the theory will stay true. The theory behind this example comes from two excellent papers:

Turning Overlap-Save into a Multiband Mixing, Downsampling Filter Bank by Mark Borgerding, published in IEEE Signal processing magazine March 2006.

'Synchronous Sampling Rate Conversion using Frequency domain based techniques' by Chunduri SreenivasaRao, A. AroakiaRaj and Dhulipalla VenkataRao, published in the International Journal of Signal processing, 4th August 2013.

The example is relevant for DFC using the OpenHPSDR Hermes board, the Hermes Lite board, and the ANAN radios including the models using Angelia and Orion boards. For simplicity, I will refer to them all as 'Hermes'. To use the radio for DFC, the radio's FPGA firmware has to be modified to send ADC samples directly to the NVIDIA GPU via Gb Ethernet. You will be able to switch between the current DDC model and the DFC model by downloading the relevant firmware.

There is a small problem. The ADC on a Hermes board is clocked at 122.88 Msps resulting in a radio that can cover up to 61.44 MHz. To send data at that rate to the GPU we need a 'pipe' capable of 61.44 x 16 bits = 1.966 Gbits. That won't fit on a 1 GbE connection. To overcome this problem the FPGA does a 'decimate by two' function and sends every second sample to the GPU. This "only" needs a constant data rate of 983 Mbits, which is still pretty close to the speed limit. Unfortunately, this means that the Hermes radio can now only work up to 30.72 MHz. I don't see any reason why the CORDIC NCO and mixer in the FPGA code could not be used to translate the received frequencies in the time domain so that the 30 – 60 MHz band can be covered. But as far as I know this has not been attempted.

Here is a summary of the DFC process using the calculations below.

1. You have an input buffer (L) full of data from the ADC. The data is filled on a FIFO basis. When it is full a new FFT transform is done, and then the buffer is filled again.

2. The FFT buffer size (N) is large enough to hold the input data and it has additional space the same size as the FIR filter. This is so that there is room in the output buffer for the filter multiply operation. Note that the FFT input buffer does not hold the Filter coefficients it just has to be that big. You could fill the extra space in the FFT input buffer with zeros, but instead it is filled with the overlap bytes from the previous input block. The ratio of the total FFT size to the number of overlap and store bytes is called the 'overlap factor' (V). In our example the overlap is ¼ of the total FFT size so V = 4.

3. The filter FFT input and output buffers are the same size as the main FFT buffers. The input buffer contains the FIR filter coefficients (P). The maximum amount of space that these can take up is typically one byte larger than ¼ of the FFT size. The rest of the buffer, nearly three quarters of the space, is padded out with zeros. You can use fewer coefficients and pad the extra space with zeros. The filter has to be recalculated if the decimation ratio and hence the panadapter bandwidth and cut-off frequency are changed. Other than that, the same numbers in the Filter FFT output buffer are used over and over for each new block of input data. Usually each different filter uses the same number of coefficients, only the values are changed.

4. A forward FFT of the Filter buffer creates a frequency domain representation of the FIR filter impulse response.

5. A forward FFT of the input data block plus the overlap bytes creates a frequency domain representation of the spectrum being sampled by the ADC.

6. The FFT output is placed into a circular buffer and the start of buffer pointer is moved so that the data is effectively rotated. This is much quicker and easier than actually moving the bytes in a linear buffer. The rotation (Nrot) moves whole spectrum so that the bottom of the wanted panadapter is in the centre of the buffer i.e. at zero frequency.

7. Multiplying each frequency bin by its corresponding filter bin, applies a low pass filter. The filter is set so that its cut off frequency is at the high frequency of the wanted panadapter. It also removes signals from above the wanted panadapter so that they do not become aliased back onto the display when the decimation occurs.

8. At this stage, decimation is performed in order to create a spectrum that only contains the wanted panadapter bandwidth. The decimation factor is known as (D) in the calculations. The FFT output, which has by now been rotated and filtered, is broken into equal segments. The number of segments is the same as the decimation factor. In our example, that is 256. The 256 segments are added byte for byte. Byte 0 of segment 1 + byte 0 of segment 2 + byte 0 of segment 2 and so on. Each total can be divided by the decimation ratio, so that the result is in fact averaged. This process averages out noise and alias signals and leaves a clean panadapter sized spectrum. You can't just take the segment that contains the wanted signal i.e. the first one on the right of the centre of the buffer. Doing that would be equivalent to applying a brick wall filter and bad things would occur.

9. The decimation ratio controls the bandwidth (Fs/2) of the output panadapter and its sample rate. Because we need to filter out anything above the panadapter, if you change the decimation ratio, the filter needs to be changed and a new filter FFT must be performed.

10. Finally, at least for the DFC part of the receiver, the inverse FFT is applied. This turns the signal back into time domain samples. They are at a sample rate of Fs/D and they contain the data for the panadapter bandwidth, which is Fs/2/D in MHz if Fs is in Msps.

11. The IFFT buffer size is equal to the main FFT buffer size divided by the decimation factor. In our example, it is 4096 bytes.

12. Because the first ¼ of the input to the main FFT contained overlap bytes, ¼ of the IFFT output also contains overlap bytes. We have to dispose of the first 1024 bytes from every output frame.

13. The radio will probably have several DFC receiver stages all taking input data from the same forward FFT. So the IFFT outputs are combined into a frame structure and sent to the SDR software for the rest of the DSP.

Input Buffer (L):

L is the input buffer length. It is the number of ADC samples that are sent to the forward FFT at a time. It needs to be a big number because we want the FFT to break the spectrum into narrow bins. The bins need to be small enough to capture narrow band wanted signals such as digital mode tones and CW. To maintain a logical data frame structure, the L buffer size is also a multiple of the incoming data frames.

L = 786,432 bytes (192 x 4096 byte frames)

Fs = 61,440,000 sps (61.44 Msps is our ADC sample rate)

Bin = 78.13 Hz (Fs/L)

FFT size (N):

N is the number of bytes in the FFT input buffer and also the FFT output buffer. It has to be big enough to take the input data block plus additional bytes the same dimension as the FIR filter -1, so that there is room in the output buffer for the filter multiply function to occur. If we were not using 'overlap and store,' the input buffer would contain the input data 'L' and the rest would be padded with zeros. However, since we are using 'overlap and store,' the extra space is used to hold the overlap bytes.

N = L+P-1 $\qquad$ N = 1,048,576 bytes (2^{20} bytes).

The forward FFT buffer size must be a 'power of 2' because the algorithm needs it to be.

FIR Filter (P):

P is the FIR filter length. It is approximately ¼ the length of the main FFT buffer. The actual FIR FFT is the same size as the main forward FFT (N). The rest of the input buffer is filled with zeros.

$P = (0.25 \times N) +1$ $P = 262{,}145$ bytes

Buffer P contains the impulse response that will be convoluted with the data signal. In the frequency domain this is achieve by multiplying the FFT of the ADC samples by the FFT of the FIR filter coefficient.

Overlap (V):

V is the overlap factor. It is the main FFT size divided by the FIR filter length -1. Because the overlap factor is four, the number of overlap bytes in the overlap and store is exactly N/4. The system is designed for an overlap factor of four because there are 262,144 unused bytes in the FFT input buffer. Rather than padding the buffer with zeros, it makes sense to fill the space up with overlap bytes.

$V = N / (P-1) = 4$

V overlap $= N / 4$ $Vo = 262{,}144$ bytes (2^{18} bytes).

Rotation (Nrot):

How many bytes must the FFT output buffer be rotated to get the low end of the wanted panadapter to the zero frequency (centre of the buffer)?

The rule is that the amount of rotation must be a multiple of the Overlap factor. In other words, Nrot / V must be an integer. This means that your panadapter may not start at the exact frequency that you specify. It may be off by a few Hz. For example, Nrot could be 240636 or 240640 but not 240637, 240638, or 240639.

There are two way to look at this calculation. You may know the number of bytes that the buffer has been rotated and want to calculate the frequency that has ended up at the low end of the panadapter. Or, you may know the frequency and want to work out how many bytes to move the buffer pointer.

Fr = the wanted Receiver frequency (14.100 MHz)

Fs = the ADC sample rate (61.44 Msps)

V = overlap factor (4)

N = FFT size (1048576 bytes)

Nfr = N x Fr (the wanted Receiver frequency x FFT size) = 14784921.600

Vfs = V x Fs (the overlap factor x the ADC sample rate) = 245.760

- if Fs is in Msps then Fr should be in MHz
- if Fs is in ksps then Fr should be in kHz
- if Fs is in sps then Fr should be in Hz

Solving for the number of bytes to rotate the FFT buffer to reach a given Receiver frequency.

Nrot = round(Nfr/Vfs)*V   round(14784921.6 / 245.760,0) * 4 = 240640

Or you can do it this way.

Rotation per MHz = (N / Fs)   1048576 / 61.44 = 17066.66667

Nrot = Fr x Rotation per MHz   17066.66667 x 14.1000000 = 240640

Solving for the wanted frequency when you know the amount of rotation.

Fr = Nrot/V*round(Vfs,3)/N   240640/4*245.760/1048576 = 14.100000 MHz

Again, if Fs is in Msps the answer will be in MHz. If Fs is in sps the answer will be in Hz.

Decimation factor (D):

D is the amount that we want to decimate the input signal in order to get the desired panadapter width. The decimation factor must be an integer and it must be a 'power of 2,' so that the inverse FFT can function.

D = 256 (2^8 bytes).

The FFT length must be a multiple of the decimation rate, i.e. N/D must be an integer (so that IFFT can occur).

The FIR Filter order must be a multiple of the decimation rate, i.e. P-1/D must be an integer.

The number of Overlap bytes must be a multiple of the decimation rate, i.e. Vo/D must be an integer. (So that the remainder after decimation can be discarded).

IFFT:

The number of bytes in the inverse FFT input and output buffers must be a 'power of 2.' It is directly related to the decimation ratio.

IFFT size = N/D   IFFT size = 4096 bytes (2^{12} bytes).

The IFFT output contains wanted data and some of the unwanted overlap bytes (actually overlap bytes x the FIR filter).

Discarded bytes = (P-1)/D   Discarded bytes = 1024 bytes (2^{10} bytes).

Usable byes = IFFT - Discarded bytes   Usable byes = 3072 bytes.

Panadapter:

Now we can calculate the panadapter bandwidth and its sampling rate.

ADC sample rate   Fs = 61.44 Msps = 61,440,000 sps

IFFT sample rate = Fs/D   IFFT sample rate = 240 ksps

IFFT Bin = IFFT sample rate / Usable bytes

IFFT Bin = 240000 / 3072 = 78.13 Hz. This means that the bin size going into the IFFT is the same as the bin size coming out of the main FFT. ☺

The Panadapter bandwidth is equal to ½ of the sample rate. Of course if we used a smaller decimation ratio the bandwidth would increase.

Panadapter BW = 240 ksps / 2   Panadapter BW = 120 kHz.

Radio BW = 61.44 Msps / 2   Radio BW = 30.72 MHz.

VIDEO PROCESSORS FOR AMATEUR RADIO DSP

Using a video card to do digital signal processing for software defined radios is not a brand new idea. If an NVIDIA video card is available on your PC, the cuSDR (CUDA SDR) SDR software uses the graphics processor to speed up the FFT for the digital signal processing and the panadapter display. There seems to be quite a bit of commonality between the digital signal processing required to filter, demodulate and remove noise from digital video signals and the digital signal processing required to filter, demodulate and remove noise from the digital signals in our radios. The Texas DaVinci DSP chips that are used in many conventional amateur radio transceivers are actually designed for video signal processing.

DSP

Digital signal processing is the manipulation of analog signals using digital circuits, usually programmable digital circuits. To use digital signal processing the analog signal must first be converted into a digital data stream using an analog to digital converter. At the end of the DSP stage, the signal is normally converted back to analog using a digital to analog converter. Often the input to the DSP is at RF or at a low I.F frequency and the output is at audio frequencies. The primary advantage of DSP is the ability to filter, modulate, demodulate, amplify, and attenuate the signal without adding any significant noise or distortion. Other advantages are the ability to make extremely sharp filters without adding ringing distortion and being able to create various noise and notch filters. The performance of modern DSP is significantly better than using hardware filters and high quality hardware filters are more expensive to make.

In our receivers and transceivers, the digital signal processing is normally done using a software code block or .dll running within our SDR software. Other commonly options are the use of a dedicated DSP chip which is a specialized microprocessor running embedded firmware code. You can also use a microcomputer or a softcore computer running on an FPGA. The hardware or softcore computer arrangement is similar to using a dedicated DSP chip, in that the DSP is being performed using firmware code on hardware inside the radio box.

In a typical SDR, the ADC creates a series of digital words that represent the level of the sampled signal as a continuous stream of numbers. If it is a 16 bit ADC, each sample is represented by a 16 bit number. If the ADC samples at 100,000,000 samples per second (100 Msps), the DSP stage must handle 100,000,000, sixteen bit numbers every second, 1.6 Gbits.

Each DSP feature can be expressed as a set of mathematical operations applied to the numbers representing the signal. Some of the mathematics is very complex, particularly the FFT code. FFT is the mathematics that is used to convert signals from the time domain (like an oscilloscope) to the frequency domain (like a panadapter display) and back again. On the other hand, some of the DSP code is surprisingly simple, such as the single line of code that is used to demodulate an AM signal. The line of code calculates the magnitude or 'amplitude' of each IQ sample, [AM = the square root of I^2+Q^2].

Another simple DSP operation is making a signal louder. You just multiply all of the 16 bit samples by the same number. For example multiplying each sample number by two, will double the level of the data stream. To multiply a binary number by two all you have to do is move all of the bits one place to the left and add a zero into the least significant bit. E.g. 0111 x2 = 1110 or (7 x 2 = 14). You do have to be careful to avoid losing the most significant bit if it is a one.

DTTSP

DttSP is the DSP code module that is used in early versions of PowerSDR, GHPSDR, and cuSDR. Versions of PowerSDR mRX later than V3.2.7 use WDSP instead. It runs as a program under Linux or as a .dll file under Windows. PowerSDR and other Windows SDR programs call the DSP code blocks in the .dll file. DttSP in turn uses the FFTW .dll to do fast Fourier transformation mathematics.

DttSP is an open source project started by Dr.Frank Brickle and Dr. Robert McGwier of the DTTS Microwave Society to provide code to be used in various DSP projects with an emphasis on Software Defined and Cognitive Radio. DttSP implements the basic modulation, demodulation, signal conditioning, and synchronization processes required to operate a high performance transceiver using DSP as the detection and synthesis stages. While the development is done primarily on Linux, the code is also available for use as a Visual Studio 6 or Visual Studio 2003 project for Microsoft Windows®. It uses FFTW for much of the heavy lifting. http://dttsp.sourceforge.net/

FFTW = Fastest Fourier Transformation in the West – a software library used by many SDR programs. FFTW calculates the data that is used for the panadapter 'frequency domain' display. Some DSP filters are also applied to the frequency domain signal, rather than the standard 'time domain' samples.

WDSP

Wdsp is a DSP library written by Warren Pratt, NR0V. It replaced DttSP in recent versions of PowerSDR mRX and in the last Beta version of cuSDR.

SHARPDSP

SharpDSP was written by Phil Covington one of the pioneers of SDR for hams. It is the DSP code used in the Kiss Konsole SDR application.

HARDWARE DSP

Hardware DSP can be done inside the radio using code running on a microcomputer or a softcore in an FPGA. However, the most common choice is to use a dedicated DSP chip. They are the same as the ones used in conventional I.F. DSP radios. The DSP chips are firmware upgradable while installed in the radio. The FlexRadio 6000 radios use a Texas Instruments TMS320C6A8167 DaVinci chip for DSP. It incorporates an ARM Cortex-A8 microprocessor, which is used for control functions. The Texas DaVinci series are described as 'digital media processors.' They are actually designed for video signal processing but they are commonly used for digital signal processing inside amateur radio transceivers. The Elecraft KX3 uses the Analog Devices ADSP21479 SHARC chip. The SDR Cube uses a Microchip 'digital signal controller.' The Elad FDM Duo uses a pair of STM32F4 ARM floating point micro controllers, one for modulation and the other for demodulation. The Icom IC-7300 uses a Texas Instruments TMS320C6745 DSP chip.

RADIO PERFORMANCE TESTING

Much has been said about how well software defined radios work and sound. In most cases, the transmitter performance is about the same as a radio using a conventional architecture. The excellent receiver performance that you can expect from an SDR receiver is mostly due to the elimination of the sections in the receiver that cause noise and distortion to be added to the signal that you want to listen to. Software defined radios replace the mixers and oscillators that cause intermodulation with digital algorithms that don't.

Online comments and reviews can indicate whether a radio performs exceptionally badly, or is a low quality product, but much of the time, the reviews are very subjective. You only get people's opinions and that makes comparisons difficult. While there is, no substitute for actually using the radio 'on the air' it is valuable to be able to compare radios in an objective and repeatable way. The best way to do that is to compare the test results gathered by a lab. The ARRL lab performs tests on many transceivers and receivers and the results of these tests are published in QST magazine. Radcom, Sherwood Engineering and Adam Farson also publish top quality lab reports and reviews.

When I started this book, one of the questions I asked myself, was; "Do SDRs perform better than conventional Superhet architecture radios?" There is no clear answer to my question because there is a wide variance in the performance of both conventional and software defined radios. Some of it is related to the price you pay, the internal architecture of the radio, quality of components, and how recent it is. Many of the recent offerings from the 'big three' equipment suppliers have much better performance statistics than the radios they released ten years ago. SDR performance is affected by the PC and the SDR software as well as the radio hardware.

Based on the numbers published online and in QST lab tests, one or two conventional Superheterodyne receivers do outperform even the best SDR receivers. But if you compare radios at similar prices, the software defined radio is likely to beat the conventional radio in some of the key tests.

In the real world with many signals on the band, a software defined radio will usually have superior IMD (intermodulation distortion) performance because, within limitations, the IMD performance of an SDR improves when there are multiple signals. The signals you receive sound cleaner on a software defined radio, especially when the bands are full.

A big problem is that several of the tests that are traditionally used to compare radios on league tables like the Sherwood Engineering list and as the key measurements in Radcom and QST reports, are not as relevant to SDRs because of fundamental differences in technology.

For example the Sherwood Engineering list is sorted on the results of the, '3rd order dynamic range - narrow spaced', two tone IMD performance test. This is probably because that test indicates how well a receiver would perform when the band is busy such as during a contest. The problem in using this approach when comparing software defined receivers against traditional Superheterodyne receivers is that the causes and effects of intermodulation distortion is completely different in a software defined radio. In an SDR, the intermodulation distortion is not caused by oscillators and mixers but in preamplifiers and filters and as a product of the analog to digital conversion. As a result, software defined radio receivers often have very good 3rd order dynamic range and they often rank very high on the Sherwood list and in reviews. See http://www.sherweng.com/table.html.

TRANSMITTER PERFORMANCE TESTS

All of the common transmitter tests such as RF power, carrier and unwanted sideband suppression, two tone IMD, transmitter harmonics, and composite noise, are just as important in SDR transmitters as they are in conventional ones. In broad terms, you can expect that your SDR transmitter will work just as well as the transmitter in a conventional radio. The only real exception is software defined radios that can perform transmitter pre-distortion, which gives them exceptionally good transmitter IMD performance.

MINIMUM DISCERNIBLE SIGNAL (MDS)

Minimum discernible signal (MDS) is a measurement of the weakest signal, which can be heard from the receiver. When you connect your antenna to the radio, the noise level should rise indicating that the background noise being received at your QTH is higher than the noise being generated inside the receiver. As long as this is the case, you will be able to hear any signal that is above the received noise level. Having a good MDS figure is important for receiving weak signals when the band is quiet, or on 160m when using a low gain antenna like a Beverage.

RECEIVER INTERMODULATION DISTORTION

Intermodulation is the mixing of two signals resulting in unwanted distortion products. In a receiver, this can occur when two signals that are close together in frequency are received at the same time, or when an incoming signal mixes with the signal from an oscillator within the radio. Intermodulation distortion can happen in any active stage of a receiver or transmitter and even within filters. IMD is very typically generated within receiver mixer stages and in RF amplifiers. Bandpass filters and pin diode switches in the receiver front end can also cause problems. When a band is busy, the reception of many strong signals can result in so much intermodulation distortion that wanted signals are badly affected. Old timers who complain that contest weekends fill the band with unintelligible noise are likely to be hearing intermodulation distortion that is generated inside their own receivers. Contest grade receivers have excellent 'two tone IMD dynamic range' and 'RMDR' test results.

In order to test the 'many signals being received at once' problem we apply two unmodulated RF signals to the receiver at fixed offsets from the receiver frequency and measure the chaos that ensues. It is called a 'two tone IMD test.'

Receiver IMD testing is often performed at 2 kHz, 5 kHz and 20 kHz offsets from the nominal receiver frequency. The spacing between the two incoming signals is usually the same as the offset from the receiver frequency. If the receiver was tuned to 14.000 MHz USB, the test signals will be inserted at 14.002 MHz and 14.004 MHz, i.e. 2 kHz offset and 2 kHz spacing.

We also apply a single signal to test for intermodulation between the incoming signal and the oscillators within the radio. These tests are called 'blocking dynamic range' and 'RMDR'. In this case, only the test signal at the offset is applied.

TRANSMITTER INTERMODULATION DISTORTION

Intermodulation can also be generated within your transmitter and linear amplifier. The most common of transmitter intermodulation distortion is non-linearity in the RF amplifier. In a perfect amplifier, the ratio of the output power to the input signal would be constant at all input levels. i.e. the relationship is linear. Unfortunately, this never happens. The power amplifier in your transceiver may have a little less gain when the input signal is small and it might not put out as much power as it should when the input signal is large. This is usually due to the power supply voltage drooping under high current load. Components heat up under high current conditions. This can cause them to have more resistance or to change their capacitance or inductance, which might de-tune the transmitter slightly. All of these factors combine to introduce two kinds of nonlinearity. Amplitude nonlinearity where the gain of the amplifier does not remain the same for all input levels, and phase nonlinearity is when the phase of the output signal is being affected by the input level or frequency.

IMD can also be caused by overload of components especially the Toroid cores in the low pass filters. If the signal is over modulated or clipped, then severe intermodulation distortion will occur. You can see transmissions with this kind of distortion on the panadapter. The signals are far wider than they should be and the shape looks more like a triangle than the rectangular spectrum we desire.

To test a transmitter for IMD we measure the effect on the spectral purity of the transmitted signal when the transmitter is modulated with two tones. It is called the 'transmitter two tone IMD test.' The intermodulation causes harmonics of the spacing between the tones. On the transmitted RF spectrum, they appear both below and above the two test tones. The first set are called 3rd order IMD products, the next set are 5th order. It is common to record the products out to 9th order but the benchmark test is 3rd order IMD. A perfect transmitter would have no harmonics just the two test tones.

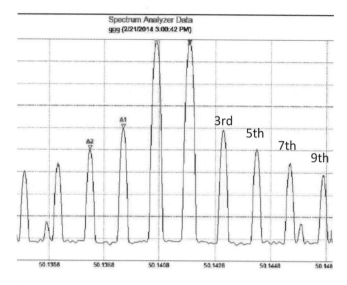

Figure 44: transmitter 'two tone IMD' test

3RD ORDER DYNAMIC RANGE (DR3)

This test is radically different when testing a software defined radio. In a Superheterodyne receiver, the non-linear process of mixing causes intermodulation distortion (IMD) products. Large signals near the receive frequency can cause interference on your receive frequency. This is a big problem on contest weekends when you want to hear weak signals operating on frequencies close to stronger stations. Direct sampling SDRs do not have mixers (in hardware) so they do not suffer from the problem of mixers causing IMD, however the ADC does cause some intermodulation distortion so the test is still useful if it is measured correctly, preferably with the results presented on a graph. The traditional practice of measuring the input level at the point that the intermodulation products become equal to the MDS level is not applicable to SDR receivers. It will produce unreliable and unpredictable results. Use the IFSS test instead.

In a 'normal' receiver, the IMD gets worse as the level of the two tone test signal is increased. In a software defined radio, it does not.

In the traditional test method you record the input level of the two tone test signal when intermodulation products become noticeable on the receive frequency, i.e. when you can just hear or measure the intermodulation level above the receiver noise floor. The distortion is measured in the same way as the wanted signal is in the MDS test. This point is a 'best case' scenario because as the two tone level is increased further, the IMD dynamic range continues to degrade in a linear fashion. The test is conducted in this way because it is easy to measure. You simply inject two test tone signals that are 2 kHz (or 5 kHz or 20 kHz) apart and increase their level until the resulting intermodulation distortion is 1 dB above the receiver noise floor.

In a software defined radio the IMD dynamic range does not degrade in a linear fashion, it stays the about same when the two tone test level is increased and at some input levels it actually improves. When the two tone test signal level reaches the receiver clipping level the IMD performance crashes.

In the real world, this means that a conventional receiver will suffer worse intermodulation distortion in the presence of several medium size signals like a contest going on, than a software defined radio will. The IMD performance of an SDR actually gets better when the band is busy!

Technical TIP: Because the 3rd order dynamic range of a conventional radio is usually worse when the interfering signals are close to the tuned receiver frequency, it is traditionally tested at a 'narrow' 2 kHz 2 tone spacing and also at wider spacing's of 5 kHz and 20 kHz. Software defined radios usually have the same 3rd order dynamic range at any spacing.

Unlike Superheterodyne receivers, The 3rd order IMD dynamic range of an SDR should not be measured at the MDS level, but at the level where there is the greatest difference between the two tone input level and the IMD product level. This is at a high level, usually just before clipping occurs.

To quote Leif Åsbrink, SM5BSZ in QEX Nov/Dec 2006, "Rather than measuring what level is required for getting IM3 equal to the noise floor, one should measure the largest difference (in dB) between the test tones and the intermodulation product. It will be close to saturation of the A/D converter on the SDR-14, while it will be at the noise floor for an analog receiver."

3RD ORDER INTERCEPT POINT (IP3)

The often quoted 3rd order IMD intercept point, or IP3, is never measured directly, because of the receiver's AGC action. It is usually calculated from the 3rd order IMD dynamic range. Calculated IP3 = (1.5 * DR3) − MDS (dBm).

With a conventional receiver, if you plot on a chart the RF input level against the receiver's output level. It is a straight line. The slope of the line is dependent on the gain of the receiver. Then add a plot of the 3rd order intermodulation relative to the RF input level (two tones). The 3rd order IMD is also a straight line which increases at three times the rate of the fundamental signal. Eventually, if there is no AGC action, the two lines cross on the chart. That point is the 3rd order IMD intercept point.

IP3 can't be measured for an SDR receiver because the relationship between the intermodulation products and the input tone levels is not linear. Plotted on a chart of RF input level vs receiver output level, the two lines diverge rather than crossing, so there is no IP3 point. However, this does not stop many SDR manufactures quoting an IP3 using a calculation based on the 3rd order dynamic range. I guess you can use IP3 as a point of comparison between receivers, but IP3 is actually meaningless for a software defined radio.

IFSS TEST

The IFSS (interference free signal strength) test was proposed by Adam Farson in order to replace the traditional 3rd order IMD dynamic range test which is no good for SDR receivers. It simply involves plotting the level of IMD distortion against the input level of the two test signals. You can see from the chart that the IMD response of the SDR receiver is nowhere near linear.

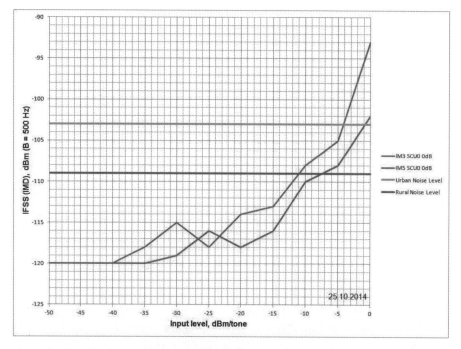

Figure 45: IFFS 3rd order IMD test by Adam Farson AB4OJ

It is important to note the horizontal lines at -103 dBm and -109 dBm. These values are the accepted local noise levels for an urban and rural environment respectively. If you have less local noise, you are lucky.

I don't really think that plotting the chart is necessary although it does demonstrate the difference between a SDR and a conventional Superheterodyne receiver, which would show a flat diagonal line. The key points are where the IMD products exceed the urban and rural noise thresholds. It does not matter what level the intermodulation products are if they are less than the noise level at your place when the antenna is connected. Therefore the critical numbers are the input level at which the intermodulation distortion products are higher than the noise floor, with your antenna connected. In this receiver the input signals need to reach at least -11 dBm before the intermodulation could even be seen at the bottom of the panadapter. It's a pretty good receiver!

The second line (to the right) is showing the 5th order IMD. It is, unsurprisingly, better than the 3rd order IMD performance.

RECIPROCAL MIXING DYNAMIC RANGE (RMDR)

The RMDR test measures how well a receiver can cope with a single large signal just outside the receiver's pass band. I call it a "Ham next door test" because it demonstrates how well your receiver works when the ham down the street transmits near your operating frequency. In a conventional receiver, reciprocal mixing noise is caused when noise from the LO (local oscillator) mixes with strong adjacent signals, generating noise and distortion at the output of the mixer. The generated noise can degrade a receiver's sensitivity and it is most noticeable when the offending signal is close to your receiver frequency, which is why RMDR is usually measured at a close offset of 2 kHz and also at a wider offset of 20 kHz.

In a direct sampling SDR, reciprocal mixing noise is caused when phase noise from the analog to digital converter mixes with the offending signal. So, in a software defined radio, the RMDR measurement is an indicator of the spectral purity of the ADC clock. In a software defined radio, the RMDR is usually completely independent of the offset from the receiver frequency. It is normally the same at the 2 kHz and at 20 kHz offset.

NOISE POWER RATIO (NPR)

Noise Power Ratio, sometimes called 'white noise testing' can be measured in either type of receiver and is a very good test of SDRs because they are wideband receivers. The idea of the NPR test is to load up the receiver with lots of signals. This is simulated by connecting a 4 or 8 MHz wide 'white' noise source to the receiver input. You increase the noise level until the signal is slightly under the clipping level. Then you cut a slot in the noise exactly 3 kHz wide using a very good band stop filter and measure the amount of noise caused by intermodulation products generated in the receiver that fall into the narrow quiet spot. Typically, you use a 2.4 kHz wide receiver bandwidth in the bottom of the slot since this is a typical bandwidth for SSB and it fits neatly inside the 3 kHz slot. The NPR is the ratio of the noise power inside the slot to the level of noise power in a channel the same bandwidth outside the slot. Since the SDR receiver has a spectrum display, the result can be read straight off the screen.

A 4 MHz wide noise signal, applied to the receiver input at just under clipping level is equivalent to more than 1200 SSB signals at S9 +30 dB. This is the ultimate test of how well the SDR will perform in a busy band.

RECEIVER DYNAMIC RANGE

Receiver dynamic range is the receiver's ability to handle a range from very weak signals near the receiver's internal noise floor to very strong signals like S9 +60 dB. The number of bits the ADC uses and the decimation ratio both affect the dynamic range of SDR receivers. Receiving very large signals can shrink the dynamic range due to ADC gain compression. Compared to conventional receivers the dynamic range of software defined radios is quite large. You can expect about 120 dB of dynamic range in a 2.4 kHz bandwidth.

Conventional Superheterodyne receivers use AGC to extend their dynamic range, but this is not necessary with software defined radios. The AGC in SDRs is used to limit the audio level rather managing the receiver's gain.

There is a great deal of misinformation on the Internet about the dynamic range of SDR receivers. It is due to a lack of understanding about the process gain arising from the ratio between the ADC sampling bandwidth and the actual receiver bandwidth. Superheterodyne receivers have process gain too, but it is less because the ratio between the RF bandwidth and the I.F. bandwidth is much smaller than the ratio of ADC bandwidth to receiver bandwidth in an SDR.

In an SDR the receiver's dynamic range is the difference between the MDS which is the weakest signal that the radio can 'hear' and the clipping level which is the largest signal that the ADC can sample. We normally back off the maximum input level to 1 dB below the clipping point. So the usable dynamic range is from MDS up to just under the clipping level.

One downside of SDR receivers is that the dynamic range of the ADC is affected by the sum power of all of the signals in the filtered range of frequencies that are being presented to it. If the ADC is sampling very large signals, the dynamic range shrinks. This can be demonstrated using the Noise Power test set which simulates a high loading of signals. In a test performed by Adam Farson a single tone injected into a FLEX-6700 demonstrated a clipping level in excess of +13 dBm, but a worst case white noise signal 8 MHz wide from the NPR test set reduced the clipping level to -2 dBm. This represents a 15 dB decrease in dynamic range, so it is lucky the receiver has a very large dynamic range to begin with. Of course, this level of reduction could never happen in the real world because the loading could never approach the white noise level. Eight bit SDRs, which have a limited dynamic range and don't have filters to reject the AM broadcast band, definitely suffer degraded dynamic range due to this effect. This is the reason that the RTL dongles and many of the experimenter's boards are not designed to work below 24 MHz.

BLOCKING DYNAMIC RANGE

In the Blocking Dynamic Range test, a wanted signal on the receiver frequency and an unwanted signal at either a 2 kHz or 20 kHz offset is input to the receiver. The unwanted signal is increased until the wanted signal measured at the receiver output decreases in level by 1 dB. The input level at which this occurs is the blocking level. The blocking dynamic range is the difference between the blocking level and the noise floor or MDS level.

SDRs don't normally suffer from this blocking de-sensitivity. The 'unwanted' test signal normally reaches clipping level with no effect on the wanted signal. So although BDR can be measured for a software defined radio but it may not mean much since you just record the ADC clipping level.

Some labs refer to this test as 'blocking gain compression dynamic range.'

BDR is more often measured in a different way, using only the unwanted offset signal with no signal present on the receiver frequency. In this case, the BDR is stated as the input level when the noise floor in a 2.4 kHz bandwidth at the wanted frequency rises by 1 dB. Instead of measuring a decrease in the wanted signal level, you measure an increase in noise within the 2.4 kHz bandwidth. The assumption is that a 1 dB increase in the noise level indicates that the signal to noise level of a wanted signal, if it was present, would have been reduced by 1 dB. A 1 dB decrease in the signal to noise ratio is considered to be equivalent to a 1 dB reduction of the wanted signal. BDR tested this way can be measured for an SDR due to the dynamic range compression noted above and the method is easier to perform since you only need one test tone.

IMAGE REJECTION

In a conventional Superheterodyne receiver, the image signal is related to the first I.F. frequency.

If the local oscillator frequency is greater than the receiver frequency, the image frequency is receiver frequency plus twice the intermediate frequency. For example if the receiver is tuned to 14.020 MHz and the receiver uses a 9 MHz I.F. then a test signal will be inserted at 32.020 MHz. It is increased until a signal is just noticed on the receiver frequency i.e. at the MDS level. The image rejection is the difference in dB between the image signal input level and the receiver's normal MDS level.

If the local oscillator frequency is less than the receiver frequency, the image frequency is receiver frequency minus twice the intermediate frequency.

Image rejection is not very relevant to HF digital down conversion software defined radios because they don't have hardware mixers. DDC receivers designed for VHF and above do have a down conversion mixer and oscillator so you can measure the image rejection. QSD (quadrature sampling detector) SDRs have imperfect IQ balancing so they are more prone to image signals.

SDRs use direct conversion receivers so the I.F. frequency is zero. This means that the image frequencies are spaced at the same offset from the local oscillator as the inserted signal. For example if the panadapter is centered on 28.3 MHz and you insert a signal at 27.3 MHz (Fo − 1 MHz) the image will show on the panadapter at 29.3 MHz (Fo + 1 MHz). If the IQ balance and phase relationship is good, the image signal will be small. The image rejection can be read directly off the panadapter. It is the difference in dB between the level of the inserted signal and level of the image signal at an equal frequency offset on the other side of the panadapter.

Some QSD receivers use an offset frequency of around 8 kHz to shift the whole panadapter. This is effectively creating a non-zero I.F. frequency. You still get images but they are no longer equidistant on the other side of the center of the panadapter. They get the same offset shift as the wanted signal.

ALIAS SIGNAL REJECTION

A better 'rejection' test for digital down conversion SDRs is to check the filtering used to prevent 'aliased' signals appearing in the receiver pass band. The biggest problem is usually interference from FM broadcast stations transmitting on frequencies in the 2nd Nyquist zone.

For the second Nyquist zone, a signal that is 1 MHz above the Fs/2 frequency will appear on the panadapter at 1 MHz below Fs/2. A signal that is 5 MHz above the Fs/2 frequency will appear on the panadapter at 5 MHz below Fs/2. So the reflected frequency order is backwards and the sidebands are inverted.

You can check spot frequencies but I have proposed a sweep test that can draw the alias response onto your panadapter.

Aliasing is not a fault. It is integral to the way an SDR works. But inadequate filtering can cause severe interference from above the Nyquist Fs/2 frequency. One radio that I tested suffered very bad interference from FM broadcast stations. The choice of ADC sampling frequency is important and so is the cut off frequency of the anti-alias filter. Some manufactures fail to realize that the sharpness of the alias filter's roll-off can be critical to the radios performance.

The effect of alias signals can be almost completely eliminated if the filter frequency is well below the Fs/2 frequency, because any interfering alias signals are well attenuated. Hopefully to a level below the noise floor. The Apache Labs ANAN radios have an Fs/2 of 61.44 MHz and a filter cutoff at 55 MHz. This limits the receiver to working below 55 MHz, but it also eliminates any alias image problems. Similarly, the FlexRadio series have an Fs/2 of 122.88 MHz but the radio is limited 77 MHz. The 2m reception is achieved using different front end filtering and undersampling.

If the alias filter is at the same frequency as the Fs/2 frequency, there is almost no alias rejection of signals just above Fs/s2 and the rejection gets better the further above Fs/2 that you go. The amount of alias rejection is directly proportional to the attenuation provided 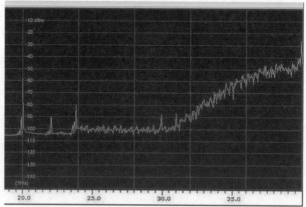 by the filter. If you apply a big sweep signal from Fs/2 up to Fs/2 + your maximum panadapter bandwidth, you will see a line of signal curve down from a maximum at the top right of the panadapter. The curve that is drawn is an exact representation of the roll off of the anti-alias filter and any other front end filtering. The displayed image level is also affected by preamplifiers and attenuators.

CATALOG OF SOFTWARE DEFINED RADIOS

This chapter is a list of some popular software defined receivers and transceivers used by listeners, hackers, experimenters, and amateur radio operators. It doesn't include very expensive, commercial, or specialist radios used by military and commercial users. It is not possible to list all of the software defined radios that are currently available. New models are appearing all the time and there are many variations of the same technology, particularly with small box receivers. The radios are listed approximately in order of the type of radio; 100 W transceivers, QRP transceivers, dongles, small box receivers, experimenter's cards and a few generation one radios.

The information provided is as accurate as my online research allows and I apologize in advance if any errors have been made. Placement, inclusion, or exclusion from this list in no way indicates any endorsement or criticism of any of the products mentioned or omitted. The listing is not ranked in any preferential order.

If you are buying an SDR radio, it is worth considering a few things:

- Make sure the radio suits your needs, particularly regarding the frequency range that it covers.

- If you buy a QRP transceiver but you want to run higher power, you need to factor in the additional cost of a linear amplifier.

- Don't expect a $20 RTL dongle to perform as well as a high end conventional or software defined radio. They are cheap and fun to play with, but they will not replace a real radio.

- SoftRock, dongle or small box receivers can be used as band scopes when connected to the IF output of a conventional receiver.

- In most cases, direct sampling HF receivers that use a 14 bit ADC will perform just as well as those using a 16 bit ADC. Although sometimes they cover less spectrum as they use a lower ADC sample rate.

- Receivers with front-end filters or pre-selectors offer more protection from overload and ADC gain compression.

- Receivers with a maximum panadapter bandwidth of 200 kHz or less are almost always QSD based receivers. Receivers with more than one, or wider, panadapters usually use direct digital synthesis or tuner chips. A panadapter of 192 kHz is adequate for use on the ham bands and listening to shortwave stations. Wider panadapters are more useful at VHF and UHF frequencies where the bands are bigger and wanted signals may be further apart. I find that a 48 kHz panadapter is a bit too small for general SSB or AM listening but it would be fine for CW and narrow digital modes where the band segments are smaller.

FLEX-6700 / FLEX-6700R (FLEXRADIO SYSTEMS)

The FLEX-6700 transceiver is the flagship model of the current FlexRadio Systems 'Signature' range. It has great technical performance and the SmartSDR software that is bundled with the radios has some excellent new features. The 6700R is a receiver only version of the FLEX-6700 transceiver. It has the same receiver specifications as the transceiver.

- Frequency range: 30 kHz – 77 MHz and 135 – 165 MHz
- Bands: LF, MF, HF +6m, +2m at very low power
- ADC resolution: 16 Bits, 245.76 Msps, two ADCs
- Panadapter bandwidth: up to 8x 14 MHz
- Class: direct sampling 100 W transceiver
- Interface: Ethernet
- Receive filters / pre-selector: yes (except 60m band)
- Transmit power: 100 W HF +6m (+7 dBm transverter output on 2m)
- Low latency CW generated in the radio FPGA firmware
- Two receiver ADCs (called Spectral Capture Units)
- Built in antenna tuner, eight channel DAX audio connectivity
- Eight slice receivers on up to eight panadapters
- Software: SmartSDR (supplied), dogparkSDR Beta (Mac)

FLEX-6600 / FLEX-6600M (FLEXRADIO SYSTEMS)

The FLEX-6600 and FLEX6600M models were announced at the 2017 Dayton Hamvention. They are an upgrade of the FLEX-6500 model. The M model has front panel knobs and a very high resolution 1920x1200 8" touchscreen display. The front panel has an identical layout to the Maestro external controller but the touchscreen has a higher resolution.

- Frequency range: 30 kHz – 54 MHz
- Bands: LF, MF, HF +6m
- Two ADCs. ADC resolution: 16 Bits, 245.76 Msps
- Panadapter bandwidth: up to 4x 14 MHz receivers
- Class: direct sampling 100 W transceiver
- Interface: Ethernet, HDMI 1920x1200 video output.
- Receive filters: 7th order on contest bands, 3rd order other bands
- Transmit power: 100 W HF +6m
- Low latency CW generated in the radio FPGA firmware
- Built in antenna tuner
- Four channel DAX audio connectivity, 4x IQ channels
- Four slice receivers on up to four panadapters
- Software: SmartSDR (supplied), dogparkSDR Beta (Mac)

FLEX-6500 (FLEXRADIO SYSTEMS)

The FLEX-6500 was the mid-range transceiver in the FlexRadio Systems 'Signature' range. It has been replaced by the FLEX-6600 and FLEX-6400. The FLEX-6500 only has one ADC. FlexRadio calls them 'spectral capture units' (SCU). The radio uses a different FPGA, DSP, and computer chips and unlike the FLEX-6700, it does not include coverage of the 2m band.

- Frequency range: 30 kHz – 77 MHz
- Bands: LF, MF, HF +6m
- ADC resolution: 16 Bits, 245.76 Msps
- Panadapter bandwidth: up to 4x 14 MHz
- Class: direct sampling 100 W transceiver
- Interface: Ethernet
- Receive filters / pre-selector: yes (except 60m band)
- Transmit power: 100 W HF +6m
- Low latency CW generated in the radio FPGA firmware
- Built in antenna tuner
- Four channel DAX audio connectivity
- Four slice receivers on up to four panadapters
- Software: SmartSDR (supplied), dogparkSDR Beta (Mac)

FLEX-6400 / FLEX-6400M (FLEXRADIO SYSTEMS)

The FLEX-6400 and FLEX6400M models were announced at the 2017 Dayton Hamvention. They are an upgrade of the FLEX-6300 model. The M model has front panel knobs and a very high resolution 1920x1200 8" touchscreen display. The front panel has an identical layout to the Maestro external controller but the touchscreen has a higher resolution.

- Frequency range: 30 kHz – 54 MHz
- Bands: LF, MF, HF +6m
- One ADC. ADC resolution: 16 Bits, 122.88 Msps
- Panadapter bandwidth: up to 2x 7 MHz receivers
- Class: direct sampling 100 W transceiver
- Interface: Ethernet, HDMI 1920x1200 video output.
- Receive filters: 3rd order filters
- Transmit power: 100 W HF +6m
- Low latency CW generated in the radio FPGA firmware
- Two channel DAX audio connectivity, 2x IQ channels
- Two slice receivers on up to two panadapters

Software: SmartSDR (supplied), dogparkSDR Beta (Mac)

FLEX-6300 (FLEXRADIO SYSTEMS)

The FLEX-6300 is the entry level transceiver in the FlexRadio Systems 'Signature' range. The main difference between the FLEX-6300 and the FLEX-6500 is that it supports only two receiver slices on up to two panadapters. It also has slightly less frequency coverage, the maximum panadapter size is reduced, but still huge, and the antenna tuner becomes an optional extra.

- Frequency range: 30 kHz – 54 MHz
- Bands: LF, MF, HF +6m
- ADC resolution: 16 Bits, 122.88 Msps
- Panadapter bandwidth: up to 2x 7 MHz
- Class: direct sampling 100 W transceiver
- Interface: Ethernet
- Receive filters / pre-selector: no
- Transmit power: 100 W HF +6m
- Low latency CW generated in the radio FPGA firmware
- Antenna tuner available as an option
- Two channel DAX audio connectivity
- Two slice receivers on up to two panadapters
- Software: SmartSDR (supplied), dogparkSDR Beta (Mac)

FLEX-5000A (FLEXRADIO SYSTEMS)

The FLEX-5000A is a 100 W SDR transceiver. It is no longer available new, but it is available on the second hand market. If you buy one, try to get one with the second receiver and antenna tuner, which were options. The Firewire interface that it uses is pretty much obsolete but you can still get PCI Firewire interface cards for desktop PCs. The FLEX-5000 was a very popular transceiver and was the 'top dog' amateur radio SDR until the new direct sampling HF transceivers became available.

- Frequency range: 10 kHz to 65 MHz
- Bands: HF +6m
- ADC resolution: 192 ksps. The ADC samples at audio frequencies
- Panadapter bandwidth: 192 kHz (built in audio CODEC)
- Class: QSD / QSE based 100 W transceiver
- Interface: Firewire
- Receive filters / pre-selector: yes, high and low pass filters
- SDR software: PowerSDR

The Flex-5000C is a variant that came in a larger case with a built in PC running the Windows XP operating system. It had an Intel Core 2 Duo processor, 1GB of RAM and a 160 GB hard drive. They are probably quite rare now and the PC, while still perfectly suitable for running the radio, is obsolete for general use.

FLEX-3000 (FLEXRADIO SYSTEMS)

The FLEX-3000 is a 100 W SDR transceiver. It is no longer available new, but it is available on the second hand market. The Firewire interface is pretty much obsolete but you can still get Firewire PCI cards for desktop PCs. The FLEX-3000 includes an internal antenna tuner as standard.

- Frequency range: 10 kHz to 65 MHz
- Bands: HF +6m
- ADC resolution: 96 ksps. The ADC samples at audio frequencies
- Panadapter bandwidth: 48 kHz or 96 kHz (built in audio CODEC)
- Class: QSD / QSE based 100 W transceiver
- Interface: Firewire
- Receive filters / pre-selector: no, just an anti-alias filter
- SDR software: PowerSDR

ANAN-100, 100D, 200D, 7000DLE, 8000DLE (APACHE LABS)

The ANAN-100 used an OpenHPSDR Hermes board manufactured by Apache Labs plus a 100 W power amp and filter board designed and manufactured by Apache Labs. The filters on it are based on the OpenHPSDR Alex design and they are still referred to as 'Alex filters.'

The ANAN-100D used the Angelia board, which was designed by Apache Labs. It is similar to the Hermes board, but it has two ADCs, which allows for features like diversity reception and using two antennas at the same time, for receiving different bands.

The ANAN-200D used a further upgraded design called the Orion. It has two ADCs with the option of adding a third (off board) and it has a faster and larger FPGA chip.

The ANAN-7000DLE and 8000DLE models use an upgraded Orion MKII board.

- Frequency range: 10 kHz to 54 MHz (60 MHz maximum)
- Bands: LF, MF, HF +6m
- ADC resolution: 16 Bits, 122.88 Msps
- Panadapter bandwidth: up to 7x 384 kHz depending on software
- Class: direct sampling 100 W / 200W transceiver
- Interface: Gb Ethernet
- Receive filters / pre-selector: HPF and LPF Alex filters on PA board
- Transmit power: 100 W, 8000DLE 200W
- Low latency CW generated in the radio FPGA firmware
- PureSignal transmit pre-distortion – best transmit IMD in class
- Diversity reception – impressive noise reduction using a reference 'noise' antenna, (100D, 200D, 7000DLE, 8000DLE only).
- SDR software: PowerSDR mRX PS, cuSDR, Hetrodyne, Kiss Konsole, GHPSDR3, and others.

- The 7000DLE and 8000DLE models feature 0.1ppm TXCO with an exceptionally low -149 dB phase noise at 10kHz spacing.
- 7000DLE has world class third order IMD typically -68dB below PEP @ 100W output on 20M
- 8000DLE has exceptional third order IMD typically -72dB below PEP @ 200W output on 20M

ANAN-100B (APACHE LABS)

The ANAN-100B was a short lived 100 W version of the ANAN-10E. It has a slightly lower specification than the other 100 Watt models with a 14 bit ADC and a smaller FPGA. Unlike the ANAN-10E 10 Watt version, the ANAN-100B includes the Alex high pass and low pass filter bank.

The receiver performance of the ANAN-100B is substantially the same as the ANAN-10E. You can use the same SDR software as the rest of the ANAN range, usually PowerSDR mRX or cuSDR. The ANAN-100B can use transmit 'pre-distortion' to dramatically improve the transmitter intermodulation distortion.

- Frequency range: 10 kHz to 54 MHz
- Bands: LF, MF, HF +6m
- ADC resolution: 14 bits
- Panadapter bandwidth: up to 2x 384 kHz depending on software
- Class: Direct sampling 100 W transceiver (Full Duplex)
- Interface: Ethernet
- Receive filters / pre-selector: uses the HPF and LPF Alex filters on the PA board.
- Transmit power: 100 W
- Low latency CW generated in the radio FPGA firmware
- PureSignal transmit pre-distortion – best transmit IMD in class
- SDR software: PowerSDR mRX, cuSDR, Hetrodyne, Kiss Konsole, GHPSDR3, others

Note that ANAN transceivers sold by European distributers often have an E suffix attached to the model name. So the ANAN-100B becomes the ANAN-100BE.

DX-SR9T (ALINCO)

The DX-SR9T 100 W transceiver is marketed as an 'All Mode + SDR Transceiver,' meaning that it includes some SDR capability. The receiver is a double conversion Superheterodyne receiver that can output an audio frequency IQ signal from its DSP stage. The panadapter bandwidth that you can display on your PC is limited by the sampling frequency of the PC sound card that you use. This is usually 48 kHz or 96 kHz. Alinco offers its own KG-TRX SDR software, which includes full control of the transceiver. Or you can use other 'sound card' type SDR software if you just want a band scope. The SDR capability can be used for both receive and transmit so this may be an option if you want to operate the radio as a remote station. There is a note on the KG-TRX web page that states that CW operation via SDR is not very practical, probably due to latency issues. This is a conventional architecture radio with DSP not a digital conversion or QSD / QSE based software defined radio. It has about the same SDR capability, as an Elecraft KX3 or a generation one, 'sound card' type software defined radio.

IC-7300 (ICOM)

The IC-7300 was the first software defined radio to be released by one of the 'big three' amateur radio manufacturers. It uses direct digital synthesis with on board DSP. It has significantly better RMDR and transmitter phase noise, than the Icom IC-7100 and IC-7200. The Icom IC-7300 is a stand-alone 100 W transceiver with knobs. No computer connection is required. It looks very much like other recent Icom HF transceivers, with the same controls as the older models and a 4.3 inch TFT touch screen display. Part of the display is used as the band scope (panadapter) with the option to show a waterfall or an audio scope.

- Frequency range: 30 kHz to 74.8 MHz
- Bands: HF +6m and 4m
- ADC resolution: 16 bits, 150 Msps
- Panadapter bandwidth: built in band scope 5 kHz to 1 MHz
- Class: direct sampling HF and VHF transceiver – built in DSP
- Interface: USB for CI-V, audio, remote control, and RTTY decode
- Receive filters / pre-selector: band pass filters
- Transmit power: 100W (50W on 4m band)
- Automatic antenna tuner
- 240(W)×238(D)×95(H) mm, 4.1 kg

IC-7610 (ICOM)

In 2017 Icom released the IC-7610 a higher specification SDR to replace their IC-7600 conventional architecture model.

- Frequency range: 30 kHz to 60 MHz
- Bands: HF +6m
- 7" touchscreen 800x480 pixel display
- Dual reception on different bands
- Two band scopes, mouse click tune
- On screen decode RTTY, PSK31, and PSK63
- Class: direct sampling HF and VHF transceiver – built in DSP
- Receive filters / pre-selector: band pass filters
- Transmit power: 100W
- IQ output via USB and DVI-D video output
- Automatic antenna tuner

MB1 (EXPERT ELECTRONICS)

The MB1 is a fully standalone 100 W SDR transceiver. Unlike 'hybrid' transceivers, which include some very limited SDR functionality, the MB1 is a genuine, high performance, direct sampling software defined radio that includes a built-in Intel Core i5 Windows PC to perform the DSP, display, and control functions. You can even use the internal PC for other functions such as digital mode programs, a station log, or web browsing and email.

The radio's internal PC runs Expert Electronics proprietary SDR software. An antenna tuner is available as an option. The front panel and display looks very impressive, rather like a top end conventional ham radio transceiver.

The MB1 seems to be basically a 100 Watt version of the SunSDR2 pro QRP transceiver with the addition of the internal computer and the 100 W PA for HF and 50 W PA for VHF.

- Frequency range: 90 kHz to 62 MHz and 95 MHz to 148 MHz
- Bands: LF, MF, HF, VHF (6m + 2m)
- The radio can receive FM broadcast band in WFM mode
- ADC resolution: 16 bits, 160 Msps
- Panadapter bandwidth: 2x 312 kHz, wideband display to 80 MHz
- Class: direct sampling HF and VHF transceiver with built in PC
- Interface: Ethernet and HDMI presumably for an external monitor, also 2x USB, 1x RS232, and four PTT connectors
- Receive filters / pre-selector: band pass filters
- Transmit power: 100 W HF and 50 W VHF
- Four HF antenna jacks, plus two for VHF and two BNC connectors for 'UHF' and 'SHF' (presumably for transverters)
- CW transmission performed in 'hardware', (this is probably coded into the FPGA for low latency), 10ms delay
- SDR software: Expert SDR2

SUNSDR2 (EXPERT ELECTRONICS)

The SunSDR2 is QRP SDR transceiver covering HF and the 6m band. This transceiver is a good choice for QRP CW operators because the CW signal is created in hardware, which means that the radio has a low CW latency, allowing for full QSK operation. The free Expert SDR2 software supports CAT (remote transceiver control) and VAC (virtual audio cable) operation.

- Frequency range: 90 kHz to 55 MHz
- Bands: LF, MF, HF, VHF (6m)
- ADC resolution: 14 bits, 125 Msps
- Panadapter bandwidth: 2x 312 kHz, wideband display to 60 MHz
- Class: direct sampling HF and 6m QRP transceiver
- Interface: Ethernet

- Receive filters / pre-selector: band pass filters
- Transmit power: 5 W
- CW generation is performed in 'hardware', (this is probably coded into the FPGA for low latency), 10ms delay
- SDR software: Expert SDR2 (supplied)
- Dimensions: 65 x 100 x 35 mm, weight 0.5 kg

SUNSDR2 PRO (EXPERT ELECTRONICS)

The SunSDR2 Pro is QRP SDR transceiver covering HF and the VHF 6m and 2m bands. This transceiver is a good choice for QRP CW operators because the CW signal is created in hardware, which means that the radio has a low CW latency, allowing for full QSK operation. The free Expert SDR2 software supports CAT (remote transceiver control) and VAC (virtual audio cable) operation. The higher ADC sampling speed means better protection from FM broadcast interference (except on 6m).

- Frequency range: 90 kHz to 66 MHz (max 80 MHz) and 95 MHz to 148 MHz (max 160 MHz)
- Bands: LF, MF, HF, VHF (6m + 2m)
- Can receive FM broadcast band in WFM (not stereo)
- ADC resolution: 16 bits, 160 Msps
- Panadapter bandwidth: 2x 312 kHz, wideband display to 80 MHz
- Class: direct sampling HF and VHF QRP transceiver
- Interface: Ethernet
- Receive filters / pre-selector: band pass filters
- Transmit power: 20 W HF and 8 W VHF
- CW generation is performed in 'hardware', (this is probably coded into the FPGA for low latency), 10ms delay
- SDR software: Expert SDR2 (supplied)
- Dimensions: 165 x 165 x 35 mm, weight 1.5 kg

SDR20 (SIRU INNOVATION)

This radio it is a sub QRP stand-alone transceiver with frequency coverage from a few kHz up to 2.5 GHz. It has a Cyclone FPGA, which includes dual 950 MHz ARM processors. The system has a 7 inch touch screen display and runs the Linux operating system. It has 1 GbE Ethernet interface. A 10 GbE interface is planned. Operating software, usually GNU Radio is loaded onto a 32 Gb SD card.

This is an expensive serious radio intended for commercial applications. I believe that the SDR20 is the first stand-alone SDR that will work into the microwave radio region.

- Frequency range: DC to 2.5 GHz
- Bands: LF, MF, HF, VHF, UHF, SHF

- Class: standalone sub QRP transceiver
- ADC resolution: 200 Msps, 14 bits
- Display 1024 x 600 pixels
- Transmit power: 100 mW

ANAN-10 / ANAN-10E (APACHE LABS)

The ANAN-10 uses an OpenHPSDR Hermes board manufactured by Apache Labs plus a 10 W power amp. It does not include the pre-select high pass filter bank that is included with the 100 W transceivers. The ANAN-10E has a slightly lower specification, using a 14 bit ADC and a smaller FPGA.

The receiver performance of the ANAN-10 is substantially the same as the ANAN-100, since it uses the same transceiver board, although the lack of receive filters makes the radio slightly more prone to overload and ADC gain compression. For most users this will never be a problem and if it does occur, a simple filter can be easily connected via the rear panel BNC connectors.

Similarly, the receiver performance of the ANAN-10E is substantially the same as the ANAN-100B, since it uses the same transceiver board. Again the lack of receive filters makes the radio slightly more prone to overload and ADC gain compression

You can use the same SDR software as the 100 Watt transceivers, usually PowerSDR mRX PS or cuSDR. The ANAN-10 and ANAN-10E radios can use transmit 'pre-distortion' to dramatically improve the transmitter intermodulation distortion, making them 'best in class.'

- Frequency range: 10 kHz to 54 MHz
- Bands: LF, MF, HF +6m
- ADC resolution: 16 Bits, 122.88 Msps (10E is 14 bits)
- Panadapter bandwidth: up to 4x 384 kHz depending on software, (the ANAN-10E supports 2x 384 kHz panadapters).
- Class: Direct sampling 10 W QRP transceiver (Full Duplex)
- Interface: Ethernet
- Receive filters / pre-selector: no
- Transmit power: 10 W (actually 15-20 W on HF)
- SDR software: PowerSDR mRX PS, cuSDR, Hetrodyne, Kiss Konsole, GHPSDR3, and others.

Note that ANAN transceivers sold by European distributers may have an E suffix attached to the model name. So, rather confusingly, the ANAN-10 becomes the ANAN-10E and the ANAN10E becomes the ANAN-10EE.

US / International models ANAN10, 10E, 100, 100B, 100D, 200D
European models   ANAN10E, 10EE, 100E, 100BE, 100DE, 200DE

I am not sure why Apache didn't call the ANAN-10E the ANAN-10B. It is possible that they will rename it now that the ANAN-100B model has been released. The

ANAN-100B uses the same transceiver board as the ANAN-10E. The ANAN-100 uses the same 'Hermes' transceiver board as the ANAN-10. The ANAN-100D uses the 'Angelia' transceiver board. The ANAN-200 uses the 'Orion' transceiver board.

KX3 (ELECRAFT)

The Elecraft KX3 is a standalone QRP transceiver, which is available as a 'no solder kit' or completely assembled. I recommend buying the kit as it is very easy to assemble. All of the boards are complete and there is no soldering required. Nevertheless, it is immensely satisfying to know that you 'built it yourself.' The KX3 has one of the best receivers available in any amateur radio, at any price. Yes, it really is that good! Check out the QST review and other benchmarking web sites.

The KX3 has several options which can all be fitted inside the radio; these include; an antenna tuner, 2m transverter, roofing filters (at digital audio), batteries, NiCad charger, and a CW paddle (mounted on the radio). There is also a companion 100 W linear amplifier that can include a 100 W antenna tuner, and the Elecraft PX3 external panadapter. The radio has some features that you usually only get on very expensive 'top end' radios; these include a voice keyer, CW memory keyer, and a BPSK / RTTY / CW decoder. Weirdly you can use the CW paddle or an external key to send RTTY or BPSK. The radio can convert Morse code to the digital modes. This allows you to send and receive BPSK or RTTY from a 'mountain top' or holiday location with just the radio and an antenna. The radio front panel is quite similar to the Elecraft K3 transceiver, but the internal architecture is completely different.

The IQ output for SDR software is at audio like a generation one SDR, even though the radio itself is a generation three SDR with the ADC and DSP on board. The radio was designed for portable 'SOTA' type operation, so it is unfair to criticize its capabilities as a home station, or as a software defined radio. But I wish it had a USB interface for the audio and control interface to the PC. It would mean that there would only be one cable instead of three and it would eliminate the earth loop, hum problems that many people experience with the audio cables.

The KX3 has a CAT control interface and DSP filters (I.F. width and shift, or high and low cut). It also has a CW keyer and most of the other functions that you would expect from a top end transceiver.

- Frequency range: 31.8 kHz – 50 MHz
- Bands: HF +6m, (+2m with optional internal transverter)
- ADC resolution: the ADC samples at audio frequencies
- Panadapter bandwidth: 48-192 kHz (depending on PC sound card) 200 kHz on PX3 panadapter
- Class: standalone QRP 10 W transceiver (QSD / QSE)
- On board DSP and MCU
- Interface: audio and a serial to USB adapter for CAT control

- Receive filters / pre-selector: band pass filters and low pass filters used for both receive and transmit.
- SDR software: NaP3, HDSDR, Win4K3 and others.

MCHF (DESIGNED BY CHRIS ATANASSOV, M0NKA)

The mcHF is a very interesting SDR transceiver project. It is not available assembled or as a fully documented kit, but the bare pc boards and components, excluding the RF power transistors, are available online. This is a radio for serious constructors who are able to solder hundreds of smd components. All of the construction information and software is available online, for free. There is a design file for a '3D' printed case as well.

The radio is a bit of an odd mix because it is a standalone transceiver with built in DSP and a very nice 2.8 inch LCD screen display, which includes a spectrum scope panadapter. But the performance is limited by the processing power that is available. The panadapter can only display a 48 kHz bandwidth. It is a new product and is under development so the specifications are likely to evolve. The mcHF transceiver is a generation three SDR with quite a sophisticated interface and display. Like many other generation three transceivers, the radio uses an SI570 programmable oscillator as its VFO.

- Frequency range: 3 MHz – 30 MHz
- Bands: HF
- ADC resolution: the Codec samples at audio frequencies
- Panadapter bandwidth: 48 kHz (on built in display)
- Class: standalone QRP transceiver (QSD / QSE)
- Interface: USB for control & programming
- Receive filters / pre-selector: four band pass filters and four low pass filters, used for both receive and transmit.

SKY-221 (DOBRI COMMERCE - LZ2TU)

There is very little information online about this little QRP transceiver. It has a Si570 oscillator, so I assume that it is a QSE /QSD design, with a 10 W RF power amplifier and a built in sound card.

- 10 W transceiver
- 48 kHz panadapter (built-in sound card)
- Probably a generation two QSD/QSE type of radio
- SDR software: PowerSDR IQ (recommended) and others
- Interface: USB

FLEX-1500 (FLEXRADIO SYSTEMS)

The FLEX-1500 is a QRP SDR transceiver. It is a bit dated now, but it is still a great low cost introduction to HF SDR. The radio costs about the same as some of the small box SDR receivers but you get a 5 Watt QRP transceiver, not just a receiver. The downside is that the radio only offers a single 48 kHz wide panadapter. Unlike the FLEX-3000 and FLEX-5000 radios, the FLEX-1500 uses a USB interface for both control and the audio IQ connection to the PC.

I used one of these radios to drive a 100 W linear amplifier for a couple of years and it was great. It was used for digital mode operation, contesting, and general rag chewing and it worked well in all of those roles. The FLEX-1500 was a big step up from the SoftRock kit that it replaced. After using the FLEX-1500 as my primary radio, I can't imagine not having an SDR transceiver in my radio shack. After I became hooked on SDR, I traded up to a 100 W SDR transceiver, which gave me another big step up in performance.

- Frequency range: 490 kHz to 54 MHz
- Bands: HF +6m
- ADC resolution: 48 ksps, the ADC samples at audio frequencies
- Panadapter bandwidth: 48 kHz (built in audio CODEC)
- Class: QSD / QSE based 5 W QRP transceiver
- Interface: USB
- Receive filters / pre-selector: band pass and low pass filters
- SDR software: PowerSDR and others

Note: The Flex-1550 has too much latency for high speed CW operation. It is not popular with keen CW operators. If you want to operate CW with full break-in, you should buy one of the newer designs, which have CW generated within the radio.

SDR CUBE (MIDNIGHT DESIGN SOLUTIONS)

The SDR Cube is quite unique as it uses any of the SoftRock radios as an RF front end. The SDR Cube hardware adds on-board DSP and control circuitry to create a stand-alone receiver or transceiver, on whatever bands the SoftRock card can cover; (usually one or two ham bands). There is also a receiver board available, which can cover 2 MHz - 30 MHz.

The SDR Cube can be provided either; assembled and tested, or in kit form. You end up with a sophisticated interface to a basic radio front end, making the radio a generation three SDR.

The performance will be much the same as any other QSD / QSE based SDR but you do not need a PC to use it. A 20 W linear amp based on the OpenHPSDR Pennywhistle design is also available.

As far as I can tell, there is no facility to output IQ to an external panadapter and the internal display is too small to be of any real use, so this is an SDR for people who want a QRP radio but don't want a panadapter.

- Frequency range: 2 MHz – 30 MHz (depends on the front end used)
- Bands: HF
- ADC resolution: the ADC samples at audio frequencies
- Panadapter bandwidth: 8 kHz (on the tiny internal display)
- Class: standalone sub QRP transceiver (QSD / QSE)

- Interface: USB for control & programming
- Receive filters / pre-selector: yes, with new receiver board
- Transmit power: 700 mW to 1 W (depends on the SoftRock used)

HIQSDR (DESIGNED BY JIM AHLSTROM N2ADR)

The HiQSDR is based on a design by Jim Ahlstrom N2ADR and developed by Helmut Goebkes, DB1CC and others. It is a direct sampling HF SDR QRP transceiver with a Cyclone III FPGA. I am not sure of the current status of this project since the web site has not been updated since June 2014.

The radio seems to be a build it yourself project although a very nice fully cased version is shown on the website.

Stefan DL2STG, built a very professional looking standalone transceiver using a Raspberry Pi. He uses his own raSDR software with the HiQSDR boards. Power amplifier and filter boards are apparently available.

- Frequency range: 30 kHz to 62 MHz
- LF, MF, HF +6m
- ADC resolution: 14 Bits, 122.88 Msps
- Panadapter bandwidth: 48 – 960 kHz
- Class: Direct sampling QRP transceiver board, plus case
- Interface: Ethernet
- Receive filters / pre-selector: yes, on a separate board
- Transmitter power +17 dBm (50 mW)
- SDR software: Quisk (Linux or Windows), GNU Radio, raSDR (Raspberry Pi Linux)

ODYSSEY TRX (DAVID FAINITSKI)

The Odyssey is a small box direct sampling transceiver with sub QRP output power. It uses a 122.88 MHz clock and is software compatible with a wide range of SDR software. You can buy the radio via a Kickstarter website with either a USB 3.0 or an Ethernet interface. There is also a Wi-Fi + LAN option.

- Frequency range: 100 kHz – 55 MHz
- Bands: HF +6m
- ADC resolution: 16 bits, 122.88 Msps
- Panadapter bandwidth: two receivers (panadapters) 48 – 960 kHz may be less with some software.
- Class: small box direct sampling sub QRP transceiver
- Interface: USB 3.0 or Ethernet, Wi-Fi option.
- Receive filters / pre-selector: no band pass filters, only a 55 MHz anti alias filter.
- Transmit power: 10 mW (48 kHz transmit baseband)
- Built in sound codec

- SDR Software: Zeus, QUISK, QUISK VNA, PowerSDR mRX, CuSDR, Kiss Konsole, Studio1, and others via extIO.dll.

ZEUS ZS-1 AND ZS-400 (SSB ELECTRONICS)

The Zeus ZS1 is a small box, direct sampling QRP transceiver. It comes with its own proprietary software, which gives it some quite advanced features. The radio supports transmit pre-distortion to improve transmitter IMD and the software can decode and display RTTY and BPSK signals. Another novel feature called 'Time Machine,' allows you to listen to signals down the waterfall. This means that you can listen again to a call sign that you missed or copy a missed contest exchange. You can look back as far as 2 ½ minutes.

A 400W version called the Zeus ZS-400 is scheduled for release late in 2016. The 400W transmitter features transmit pre-distortion, achieving an IP3 of better than 40 dB.

- Frequency range: 300 kHz – 30 MHz
- Bands: HF
- ADC resolution: 16 bits, 100 Msps
- Panadapter bandwidth: 10 to 100 kHz and wideband from 160 kHz to 4 MHz. (Time machine feature only works in narrow band mode.)
- Class: small box direct sampling QRP transceiver
- Interface: USB
- Receive filters / pre-selector: six switchable band pass filters, used on transmit as well.
- Transmit power: 10-15 Watts, (400 W version planned)
- SDR Software: Zeus SDR and Zeus IQ recorder (supplied) also Ham Radio Deluxe, SDR.com and SDRmax III
- Internal decode of RTTY and BPSK (no native transmit yet)

POCKET SDR / PORTABLE SDR / PDSDR (MICHAEL COLTON)

The Pocket SDR, also known as the Portable SDR or PSDR, takes yet another unique approach. As I write this, it is still in development and there has been very little technical data published. The radio is designed to be a rugged, ultra-portable, stand-alone, sub QRP transceiver small enough to pop in your pocket. It has one knob, which also has a push to click function. This single control is used to change all of the adjustable parameters. There is a built in paddle for CW operation and a tiny two inch color LCD display.

The screen can display a waterfall, as well as the mode, frequency and filter settings. But wait there's more in this little miracle! The radio also includes a GPS receiver, and it can work as a vector network analyzer (VNA) to check out your antenna.

It can work as a standalone radio as it has on board DSP and an ARM processor to manage the control and display functions. I am very impressed with the innovation demonstrated in this little transceiver. The PSDR is an open source project funded by a Kick Starter campaign.

- Frequency range: up to 35 MHz
- Transmit power: modulated exciter only. It needs external low pass filters and a power amplifier – hopefully under development
- Internal GPS receiver – could in future work as an emergency locator beacon on HF, or display your location on the display
- VNA mode – antenna analyzer
- Built in CW paddle
- Receives AM and SSB, and transmits SSB (either USB or LSB)
- Standalone SDR for SOTA or ultra QRP operation

FDM-S1 / S2 (ELAD)

Elad makes two small box direct sampling SDR receivers, the FDM-S1, which has a 14 bit 61.44 Msps ADC and the FDM-S2, which has a 16 bit, 122.88 Msps ADC, the same as their Duo transceiver.

The FDM-S2 can deliver 192 ksps, 384 ksps, 768 ksps, 1536 ksps, 3072 ksps, or 6144 ksps panadapters. It can receive HF +6m, the FM broadcast band, and VHF from 135-160 MHz using ADC under-sampling.

- HF: 9 kHz – 52 MHz
- MDS: -132 dBm @ 14 MHz
- FM: 74-108 MHz. Sensitivity <2uV 12 dB SINAD @ 98 MHz
- VHF: 135-160 MHz MDS -137 dBm @ 145 MHz
- The FDM-S1 can decode DRM broadcast signals

RTL DONGLES

RTL dongles is a collective term used to describe a range of USB stick software defined radios. They are usually based on the RTL2832U and R820T / R820T2 chips. RTL dongles were designed to be cheap receivers for digital TV and FM broadcast signals, but they can be used as general purpose receivers for the upper HF, VHF, and UHF bands. There are many models. NooElec sells RTL dongles and an up-converter plus dongle combo. KN0CK sells RTL dongles modified for HF reception. DX Patrol sells a 100 kHz – 2GHz SDR that is a boxed combo RTL chip plus up-converter. It seems to be similar to the Watson W-SDRX1. The Soft66RTL is another RTL variant with an up-converter.

These devices are incredibly cheap and they are fun to play with. There are options to extend the range down to the HF bands by using a hardware modification or an up-converter.

- Frequency range: varies with model. 24 MHz – 1766 MHz or 52 MHz to 2200 MHz are typical for the most common models
- Bands: VHF – UHF (and HF with modification or up converter)
- ADC resolution: 8 Bits

- Panadapter bandwidth: 2.8 MHz typical
- Class: USB dongle receiver (tuner / receiver chip)
- Interface: USB
- Receive filters / pre-selector: none
- Limited dynamic range and overload performance
- SDR software HDSDR, SDR# and others

FUNCUBE DONGLE PRO+ (FUNCUBEDONGLE.COM)

The FCD pro+ is a USB stick 'dongle' style receiver designed by Howard Long G6LVB. It has automatically switched front end filters to protect the receiver from overload. You can select a low noise pre-amplifier as well. It was developed specifically to create a cheap high performance receiver that schools could use as a part of the educational goals of the FUNcube satellite program. One source states that the FCD pro+ uses the Mirics MSi001 tuner chip, which is also used in the SDRplay receiver. The radio features a power injector to supply 5 Volts DC to a remote low noise amplifier (LNA) over the antenna feeder coax.

- Earlier models include the original FCD and the FCD Pro
- Frequency range: 150 kHz to 260 MHz and 410 MHz to 2.05 GHz
- Bands: LF to L band (LF, MF, HF, VHF, UHF)
- ADC resolution: 32 Bits (at audio frequencies). Decimated to 16 bits before being sent to the PC.
- Panadapter bandwidth: 192 kHz (96 kHz on FCD Pro and FCD)
- Class: USB dongle receiver
- Interface: USB
- Receive filters / pre-selector: 11 filters, SAW filters on 2m and 70cm
- SDR software SDR#, HDSDR and others

AIRSPY (AIRSPY.COM)

The Airspy receiver was created by the same developer as the excellent SDR# software. It uses an R820T2 chip, the same as some of the RTL dongles, but it has I.F. filters which helps to avoid overload. This receiver is really for VHF and UHF, although it does cover the 10m HF amateur radio band.

- Frequency range: 24 MHz – 1.8 GHz
- Bands: 10m plus VHF - UHF
- ADC resolution: 12 Bits, 20 Msps
- Panadapter bandwidth: 9 MHz
- Class: USB small box receiver
- Type: small box receiver (tuner / receiver chip)
- Interface: USB
- Receive filters / pre-selector: no, but it has an I.F. tracking filter in the tuner chip
- SDR software SDR# and others.

TITAN / TITAN PRO (ENABLIA)

This receiver has some rather unique features that are better suited to commercial users for surveillance and monitoring than amateur radio operators and shortwave listeners. It is designed to monitor up to 40 demodulated channels at the same time, or 8 on the basic Titan model, which is not really something your average ham needs to do. The radio displays a panadapter between 9 kHz and 32 MHz wide, so you can display the whole of the HF spectrum. You then select between one and four wideband slots, which can be 312 to 2187 kHz wide. Then you can demodulate eight 'narrow band' signals on the Titan model or up to 40 'narrow band' signals on the Titan Pro within the chosen wideband slots. The radio can manage 40 outputs via VAC or straight audio connections. It has sixteen pre-selector band pass filters, but they are probably not very useful unless you want to monitor many channels very close together.

- Frequency range: 9 kHz – 32 MHz
- Bands: LF, MF, HF
- ADC resolution: 16 Bits, 80 Msps
- Panadapter bandwidth: four slots 312 kHz to 2187 kHz wide, and a wideband display to 32 MHz
- Class: direct sampling (see note below) small box receiver
- Interface: USB (the Titan Pro has a LAN port for the audio outputs)
- Receive filters / pre-selector: 16 switchable band pass filters
- Useful for monitoring, interference investigations, propagation analysis, beacon monitoring
- SDR Software: TitanSDR (includes special recording features)

Technical note: the manufacture states that; *"Innovative pre-processing (based on filters banks) was implemented on FPGA, instead of conventional DDC (Digital Down Conversion), allowing for flexible partitioning of the acquisition bandwidth into WB channels and permitting tens of NB channels with reduced impact on CPU, even during replay of WB channels."* I am not aware of this innovative technique being used on other small box receivers, although it may be used on commercial and military radios.

MATCHSTIQ S10 (EPIQ SOLUTIONS)

The Matcstiq SDR is an advanced transceiver, covering 70 MHz to 6 GHz. It has a 12 bit ADC and a 50 MHz bandwidth. The Matchstiq crams a lot of capability into a small box 4.5" x 1.6" x 1.1" (114 x 41 x 28 mm). It includes a Spartan 6 FPGA, a Linux microcomputer, and a GPS receiver. The radio is an engineering marvel, but it is much too expensive for most amateur enthusiasts. It has Ethernet, micro HDMI, and USB 2.0 interfaces.

The Matchstiq is a complete stand-alone sub QRP transceiver with an output power below 2 GHz of +13 dBm (20 mW), +10 dBm (10 mW) above. Configure as two phase coherent receivers or a single receiver with full duplex transmit.

COLIBRIDDC (EXPERT ELECTRONICS)

The ColibriDDC is a small box, direct sampling receiver that uses an Ethernet connection to the PC rather than a USB connection. This enables the receiver to be controlled over a LAN, or it can be connected directly to your PC. It has seven programmable open collector digital outputs for controlling antenna switches or filters etc. This interface also provides a 'mute' input, which allows the ColibriDDC SDR to be used in conjunction with a transmitter.

- Frequency range: 10 kHz – 55 MHz (works up to at least 61 MHz)
- Bands: LF, MH, HF +6m
- ADC resolution: 14 bits, 125 Msps
- Panadapter bandwidth: 2x 312 kHz panadapters (4 VFOs)
- Wideband scope to 62 MHz
- Class: small box direct sampling receiver
- Interface: Ethernet
- Receive filters / pre-selector: no, just a 55 MHz anti alias filter
- Switch out 55 MHz to under-sample zones up to more than 900 MHz
- SDR Software: ExpertSDR2 (supplied), or GNU radio
- 10 MHz SMA connector for optional external clock input
- SMA antenna connector
- TXCO +- 0.5 ppm
- DC 5V plug pack supplied

CR1A (COMMRADIO)

The CR1a is a small standalone receiver with a modern looking design. I quite like it; maybe it's the big knobs or the big feet. It covers HF, VHF, and UHF frequencies, but it misses out the 6m ham band and the bottom 7 MHz of the 70 cm band.

The radio is a Superheterodyne +SDR receiver, with an IQ output from the 32 bit IF DSP stage. It is not really for SDR enthusiasts, but it can display a limited band scope.

- Frequency range: 0.5 – 30 MHz, 64 – 260 MHz, 437-512 MHz
- Bands: HF, VHF, UHF
- Dual conversion Superheterodyne receiver for HF. Single conversion at VHF and UHF, with 32-bit I.F. DSP and an audio CODEC
- Modes: AM, CW, LSB, USB, FM
- Demodulation is performed by DSP firmware
- ADC resolution: the IQ output is from the audio codec
- Panadapter bandwidth: no internal band scope or panadapter but it can display a 200 kHz panadapter via the IQ audio output, sent over the USB port

- Class: small box receiver with limited SDR capability
- Interface: USB (for control and IQ audio for a band scope)
- Powered by USB or 6-18 Volts DC
- SDR Software: CommRadio 'Spectrum View,' which includes some radio control. Or you can use other 'sound card' SDR software
- 64 memories
- Can receive the FM broadcast band – mono only
- Internal Lithium battery for portable operation

SDR-IQ (RF SPACE)

The SDR-IQ is a direct sampling small box receiver with a USB interface. The radio is powered from the USB port. It has a RS232 serial port to interface with other radios. The SDR-IQ is no longer available. It has been replaced by the NetSDR and Cloud-IQ SDR radios.

- Frequency range: 500 Hz – 30 MHz, (usable down to 100 Hz)
- Bands: MF, HF
- ADC resolution: 14 Bits at 66.67 Msps
- Panadapter bandwidth: 196 kHz
- Class: direct sampling small box receiver
- Interface: USB
- DC 5 Volts from the USB port
- Receive filters / pre-selector: yes
- SDR software: SDR Radio and Moetronix SpectraVue (supplied), GNU radio, SDR#, OsmoSDR

NETSDR (RF SPACE)

The NetSDR is a direct sampling small box receiver. There are several variants offering ultra-low noise reference VCXO or OCXO clocks. The radio can be operated remotely over a LAN. There is a mute control line on the RS232 serial connector, for use in conjunction with a conventional HF transmitter.

- Frequency range: 10 kHz – 32 MHz
- Bands: LF, MF, HF
- ADC resolution: 16 Bits at 80 Msps
- Panadapter bandwidth: 10 kHz up to 1.6 MHz
- Class: direct sampling small box receiver
- Interface: Ethernet, USB for setup, and RS232
- Receive filters / pre-selector: 10 sub-octave filters
- External 10 MHz reference clock input
- Phase noise at 15 MHz: -152 dBc/Hz at 10 kHz

CLOUD-IQ (RF SPACE)

'The Cloud-IQ offers two modes of operation. The IQ mode, offers 24 bit, IQ streaming to the PC over Ethernet. This mode uses SpectraVue software or third party programs like SDR-Radio, SDR#, or GNU radio. The stand-alone "Cloud" mode includes a built-in Internet server. In this mode, the radio performs the tuning and demodulation of signals and transmits the demodulated information back to a PC, OS-X, Linux or Android client anywhere in the world.' (http://www.rfspace.com/RFSPACE/CloudIQ.html).

- Frequency range: 9 kHz – 56 MHz
- Bands: LF, MF, HF+ 6m
- ADC resolution: 12 Bits ENOB (probably 14 or 16 bit) at 122.88 Msps
- Panadapter bandwidth: Up to 1.8 MHz
- Spectrum analyzer wideband mode up to 56 MHz
- IQ output stream: up to 1.288 MHz bandwidth at 24 bits
- Class: direct sampling small box receiver
- Interface: Ethernet
- Built in TXCO: <2.5 ppm
- DC supply: 5V at 0.8A, USB plug pack supplied
- Two antenna ports
- Receive filters / pre-selector: yes
- SDR software: On board demodulation or SDR Radio and Moetronix SpectraVue (supplied), GNU radio, SDR#
- The software used with the on board demodulated mode of operation has several spectrum analyzer specific modes.

CLOUDSDR (RF SPACE)

The CloudSDR receiver has not been released yet, but has been included because it represents another approach. The radio was specifically designed to be accessed over the Internet. *"The built-in remote server allows the CloudSDR to be placed anywhere in the world. A PC running Windows, Linux, Android or MacOS is able to access the radio with very low latency."*

The CloudSDR features two RF inputs. The low frequency port operates from 9kHz to 56 MHz. The high frequency port uses a wide-band silicon tuner down converter to cover the 56 MHz to the 1 GHz range.

- Frequency range: 9 kHz – 56 MHz plus 56 MHz to at least 1000 MHz
- Bands: LF, MF, HF +6m (input 1), VHF, UHF, SHF (input 2)
- Panadapter bandwidth: Up to 10 MHz, wideband scope 56 MHz
- ADC resolution: 122.88 Msps (HF), silicon tuner for high bands
- Interface: Ethernet
- Software has several spectrum analyzer modes.

SDR-NET (AFEDRI)

The Afedri SDR-Net is a direct sampling small box receiver with both Ethernet and USB interfaces. It is compatible with a large range of open source and commercial SDR software and it is very reasonably priced. The 12 bit ADC may result in some performance compromises such as a slightly reduced dynamic range. It is unusual to have an Ethernet port on a low cost SDR receiver and it is very unusual to have both Ethernet and USB interfaces.

This radio uses an AFEDRI8201 chip, which includes a preamp and the ADC as well as performing functions that are normally performed by an FPGA in other direct sampling receivers. This includes the numerically controlled oscillator (NCO), a quadrature mixer, and decimating CIC and FIR filters.

- Frequency range: 100 kHz – 36 MHz
- Bands: LF, MF, HF
- ADC resolution: 12 Bits, 80 Msps
- Panadapter bandwidth: 2 MHz (Ethernet) or 230 kHz (USB)
- Class: direct sampling HF receiver
- Interface: Ethernet and USB (power over USB or external 7-10 V DC according to the specifications, but the front panel says 12.6 Volts)
- Receive filters / pre-selector: no, only a low pass anti alias filter
- SDR software: SDR#, HDSDR, Linrad, Winrad, Quisk, PowerSDR mRX, Studio 1, SDR Console and others. There is software plugin, called 'SDR Network Control Box' for control of the radio when you are using SDR software that does not support the radio natively.

AFE822X (AFEDRI)

The Afedri AFE822x SDR-Net is a direct sampling small box receiver with two phase coherent RF front ends. This allows for diversity reception and diversity noise cancellation. It is available boxed or unboxed. Like the SDR-Net it includes both USB and Ethernet connectivity.

- Frequency range: 100 kHz – 30 MHz
- Bands: LF, MF, HF
- ADC resolution: 12 Bits, 72 Msps, (AFE8220 dual channel receiver)
- Panadapter bandwidth: 1x 2 MHz or 2x 1 MHz (Ethernet)
- Panadapter bandwidth: 1x 250 kHz or 2x 125 kHz (USB)
- Class: direct sampling HF receiver
- Interface: Ethernet and USB (power over USB or external 7-10V DC)
- Receive filters / pre-selector: no, only a low pass anti alias filter
- SDR software: Linrad, Winrad, HDSDR, Studio1, SDR#, SDR-Console v.2, Cute SDR, SDR DX, PowerSDR mRX and others
- Order with either 2x SMA connectors or 2x BNC connectors

SDR-USB-HS (AFEDRI)

The Afedri SDR-USB-HS is a direct sampling small box receiver with HF and VHF to SHF coverage. The radio has two receiver front ends and two antenna connectors, one for HF and one for VHF-SHF. It is available as an uncased board or in a case.

Like the SDR-Net, the SDR-USB-HS model uses an AFEDRI 8201 chip made by Texas Instruments. For frequencies above 35 MHz, this is preceded by the R820T2 VHF/SHF receiver front end, (the same as used in most RTL dongles).

- Frequency range: 100 kHz – 35 MHz and 35 MHz – 1700 MHz
- Bands: LF, MF, HF, VHF, UHF, SHF
- ADC resolution: 12 Bits, 70.656 Msps
- Panadapter bandwidth: 920 kHz
- Class: direct sampling HF and VHF-SHF using a down converter
- Interface: USB
- DC power: 5 Volts over USB at up to 550 mA
- Receive filters / pre-selector: low pass filter on HF, HPF on VHF-SHF
- SDR software: Linrad, websdr, Winrad, HDSDR, Studio1, SDR#, SDR-Console v.2, Quisk, PowerSDR mRX, and others.

Q1SR (QUICKSILVER)

The QS1R receiver was designed by SDR guru Phil Covington. He wrote the companion software as well. It is a high performance direct sampling receiver. There is an optional exciter board, so with the addition of a few external elements the radio can be configured as a transceiver. The exciter output power is +3 dBm (around 2 mW), which could be used for a transverter, or to feed an external power amplifier. There is no transmit / receive (TR) switching or low pass filters included in the radio.

- Frequency range: 10 kHz – 62 MHz
- Bands: LF, MF, HF +6m
- ADC resolution: 16 Bits, 125 Msps
- Panadapter bandwidth: 20 to 2,000 kHz
- Class: direct sampling small box receiver
- Interface: USB
- Exciter board option
- Receive filters / pre-selector: switched filters
- FPGA: Altera Cyclone III
- SDR software: SDR Max V (Windows, Linux, OS X), HDSDR with extio.dll

PERSEUS (MICROTELECOM)

Perseus is one of the earliest direct sampling SDR receivers. It comes with its own SDR software. The 14 bit ADC used in this radio offers very similar performance to a 16 bit ADC (almost the same ENOB), but the lower sampling rate means that the Perseus receiver does not include coverage of the 6m band. A separate (not in the same box) 'FM+' down converter can be purchased to add coverage of the FM broadcast band, 87.5 to 108 MHz. But it is rather expensive when compared to the cost of an average FM broadcast receiver, so it would only appeal to listeners looking for FM broadcast DX.

- Frequency range: 10 kHz – 40 MHz
- Bands: HF
- ADC resolution: 14 bit, 80 Msps
- Panadapter bandwidth: 125 kHz to 1.6 MHz, a 40 MHz spectrum display is available using the separately bundled HFSpan software
- Class: direct sampling small box HF receiver
- Interface: USB
- FPGA: Xilinx Spartan IIIE
- Receive filters / pre-selector: yes 10 switched band pass filters
- Software: proprietary Perseus software, LinRad, HDSDR and others.

MK1.5 ANDRUS (SATRIAN)

The MK1.5 Andrus receiver is another small box HF SDR. There is a new daughter board in development that dramatically extends the frequency range and adds an exciter for transmit. Like other models with an exciter, you need to add your own transmit / receive switching, a power amplifier and low pass filters. There is a fairly limited amount of technical information available online. The radio has two independent front ends, so it can probably be used for diversity reception and noise cancellation.

- Frequency range: 5 kHz – 30 MHz
- Bands: LF, MF, HF
- ADC resolution: bits unknown, sample rate 64 Msps
- Panadapter bandwidth: 400 kHz to Ethernet port or 234 kHz to USB port, or 2x 117 kHz to USB port
- Class: direct sampling small box receiver, (exciter card option)
- Interface: Ethernet and USB
- TX8M exciter board option increases receiver range to 2 GHz and includes sub QRP power transmit up to 450 MHz (or higher with external filters)
- Audio is via USB connection to the PC
- SDR software: Linrad, HDSDR, Cute SDR and others.

SIGNAL HOUND BB60C

The Signal hound BB60C SDR is marketed as a 'real time' spectrum analyzer and long term recorder for industrial and scientific applications, rather than as a general use receiver. But it can be used as a receiver. It covers a very wide frequency range.

- Frequency range: 9 kHz – 6 GHz
- Bands: LF, MF, HF, VHF, UHF, SHF
- ADC resolution: 14 Bits, 312.5 ksps - 40 Msps
- Panadapter bandwidth: 27 MHz
- Class: USB small box receiver, USB powered
- Interface: USB 3.0
- Streams 140 MB / second to the PC
- Wide dynamic range -158 dBm to +10 dBm
- Receive filters / pre-selector: switched filters

SIGNAL HOUND SA124B

The Signal hound SA124B SDR is marketed as a spectrum analyzer for industrial and scientific applications. It has the highest maximum frequency and the widest range of all of the radios listed in this chapter. It is cheaper than the BB60C model and it can be used as a general purpose receiver.

- Frequency range: 100 kHz – 12.4 GHz
- Bands: LF, MF, HF, VHF, UHF, SHF
- Class: USB small box receiver, USB powered
- Interface: USB 2.0
- IQ output up to 240 kHz bandwidth
- Wide dynamic range -151 dBm to +10 dBm
- Internal demodulation of AM/FM/SSB/CW
- Free API for software development

SIGNAL HOUND SA44B

The Signal hound SA44B SDR is marketed as a spectrum analyzer for industrial and scientific applications. It is considerably cheaper than the SA124B model and it can be used as a general purpose receiver.

- Frequency range: 1 Hz – 4.4 GHz
- Bands: LF, MF, HF, VHF, UHF, SHF
- Class: USB small box receiver, USB powered
- Interface: USB 2.0
- Wide dynamic range -151 dBm to +10 dBm
- IQ output up to 240 kHz bandwidth
- Internal demodulation of AM/FM/SSB/CW
- Free API for software development

SDRPLAY RSP (SDRPLAY.COM)

The SDRplay 'Radio Spectrum Processor' is a small box receiver. It covers a very wide frequency range.

The receiver uses a Mirics MSi001 RF tuner and MSi2500 'digital interface' chip. The Mirics RF tuner chip contains five low noise amplifiers for several bands, the frequency synthesizer, and a quadrature mixer producing I and Q streams at an I.F. frequency. The digital interface chip performs the ADC and the DSP functions. This is the same chipset as used in the Mirics MSi3101 USB TV dongle, but with the SDRplay you get front end filters and established ham radio / general listening software compatibility.

This radio has similar frequency coverage to the FUNcube Dongle Pro+ but it has a much wider panadapter bandwidth.

- Frequency range: 100 kHz – 2 GHz
- Bands: LF, MF, HF, VHF, UHF
- ADC resolution: 12 Bits, (2 – 10.66 Msps)
- Panadapter bandwidth: up to 8 MHz
- Class: USB small box receiver (tuner / receiver chip)
- Interface: USB
- Receive filters / pre-selector: eight switched filters
- Includes DAB, DVB-T, and FM receiver software
- SDR software HDSDR, SDR#, SDR Console, and others.

AR-2300 / AR-5001D (AOR)

The AOR-2300 is a 'black box' no knobs version of the AOR AR-5001D receiver. They are quite complex receivers employing both direct sampling technology to receive frequencies below 25 MHz and conventional receiver architecture above 25 MHz. They have limited SDR capability about the same as a generation two SDR, using I and Q audio signals at a 12 kHz I.F. from the DSP stage. You can also buy an optional 'digital board', which provides a digital IQ output when the receiver is tuned to frequencies between 25 MHz and 3.15 GHz.

- Frequency range: 40 kHz – 3.15 GHz
    - 40 kHz – 25 MHz direct conversion SDR
    - 25 MHz – 220 MHz double conversion Superheterodyne
    - 220 MHz – 360 MHz triple conversion Superheterodyne
    - 360 MHz - 3.15 GHz double conversion Superheterodyne
- Bands: LF, MF, HF, VHF, UHF, SHF
- ADC resolution: Audio IQ at 12 kHz I.F. or 14 bits at 65 Msps from the optional digital board (25 MHz to 3.15 GHz only)
- Panadapter bandwidth: 24 kHz or 1 MHz with the digital board
- Class: dual/triple conversion super heterodyne receiver with SDR direct conversion below 25 MHz only. (Hybrid SDR)

- Interface: USB
- Receive filters / pre-selector: none below 25 MHz
- SDR software: proprietary AR-IQ software supplied with the digital card, or typical sound card SDR software for the audio IQ output.

WR-G305E/I (WINRADIO BY RADIXON)

WiNRADiO makes a range of 'no knob' conventional architecture receivers designed to be installed as add on PCI cards inside a PC. There are also models like the WR-G305e/i that are small box, no knobs, radios. The WR305e/i radio has very limited SDR capability about the same as a generation two SDR, using IQ audio signals out of the DSP stage.

- Frequency range: 9 kHz – 1.8 GHz
- Bands: LF, MF, HF, VHF, UHF
- ADC resolution: not applicable, (sound card radio)
- Panadapter bandwidth: sound card dependent, 48, 96, or 192 kHz
- Class: dual-conversion Superheterodyne receiver with a software-defined last IF stage and demodulator. (Hybrid SDR)
- Interface: USB
- Receive filters / pre-selector: tracking pre-selector
- Expandable to 3500 MHz using an optional down converter
- SDR software: proprietary G305 software

WR-G31DDC 'EXCALIBUR' (WINRADIO BY RADIXON)

Unlike the G305 model, the Excalibur is a direct sampling SDR. But it is LF to HF only and does not include coverage of the 6m amateur band. There is a PCI version for installation inside a desktop PC and also a 'professional' version. The software has the ability to schedule recording of either demodulated audio or the entire 2 MHz wide IQ spectrum to the PC hard drive. Within the 2 MHz wide panadapter, the radio supports the reception and demodulation of three narrow band receiver channels at the same time.

- Frequency range: 9 kHz – 49.99 MHz
- Bands: LF, MF, HF
- ADC resolution: 16 bits, 100 Msps
- Panadapter bandwidth: 20 kHz – 2 MHz plus a low resolution wideband display up to 50 MHz
- Class: direct sampling HF receiver
- Three demodulated channels
- Interface: USB
- Receive filters / pre-selector: no, apart from a filter for the MF broadcast band
- SDR software: proprietary G31DDC software

HACKRF ONE (GREAT SCOTT GADGETS)

HackRF One is an experimenter's radio. It may be of interest to radio amateurs operating on the 23cm, 12cm, 9cm, and 5cm microwave amateur bands. It has very wide frequency coverage and transmitting capability. HackRF One is an open source project initially backed by Kickstarter funding. The hardware was designed by Michael Ossmann. It is able to receive and send wideband signals like WFM and Wi-Fi. You can synchronize several HackRF One radios so that they work as a diversity reception system or as a MIMO radio. The radio runs off power supplied by the USB connection.

- Frequency range: 10 MHz to 6 GHz
- Bands: upper HF, VHF, UHF, SHF
- ADC resolution: 8 Bits, (2 - 20 Msps)
- Panadapter bandwidth: 20 MHz
- Class: sub QRP low power transceiver (Half Duplex)
- Interface: USB and USB powered
- Receive filters / pre-selector: none
- On board Arm Cortex M4 microcontroller and a CPLD for DSP experimentation
- Transmitter power -10 dBm to +15 dBm (0.1 to 31 mW) depends on frequency of operation
- SDR Software: GNU Radio, SDR#, SDR Radio.

BLADE RF (NUAND)

The bladeRF is an experimenter's board, which may be of interest to radio amateurs operating on the 23cm or 12cm microwave amateur bands. It has very wide frequency coverage and transmitting capability. A transverter board can be added to enable HF and VHF coverage.

The radio uses USB 3.0 format for higher data speed, which allows for a very wide output 'panadapter' bandwidth. It can also work at lower bandwidth with a USB 2.0 port. It uses a LimeMicro LMS6002D RF transceiver chip.

- Frequency range: 300 MHz to 3.8 GHz
- Bands: UHF, SHF
- ADC resolution: 12 Bits, 40 Msps
- Panadapter bandwidth: 28 MHz
- Class: Uncased PCB - sub QRP transceiver (Full Duplex)
- Separate receive and transmit SMA antenna connectors
- Interface: USB 3.0, USB or 5V DC powered
- Receive filters / pre-selector: none
- On board Arm9 and a Cyclone 4 E FPGA for DSP experimentation
- bladeRF x115 uses 115KLE Cyclone 4 FPGA, bladeRF x40 uses 40KLE
- Transmitter power +6 dBm (4 mW) typical

USRP B200 (ETTUS RESEARCH)

Ettus Research makes a large range of professional SDR transceivers and receivers, both cased and un-cased. Of these the B200 and B210 are the most accessible to amateur operators and experimenters. The B200 is really an experimenter's board, but it may also be of interest to radio amateurs operating on the microwave amateur bands. It has very wide frequency coverage and sub QRP transmitting capability. The radio uses a USB 3.0 interface to carry the high data load required for it's very wide output 'panadapter' bandwidth.

- Frequency range: 70 MHz to 6 GHz
- VHF, UHF, SHF
- ADC resolution: 12 Bits, 61.44 Msps
- Panadapter bandwidth: 56 MHz
- Class: Uncased PCB - low power transceiver (sub QRP)
- Type: Transceiver (Full Duplex)
- Interface: USB 3.0 and USB powered
- Receive filters / pre-selector: none
- On board Xilinx Spartan 6 FPGA for DSP experimentation
- Transmitter power +10 dBm (10 mW) maximum
- SDR software: GNU Radio

USRP B210 (ETTUS RESEARCH)

The B210 is really an experimenter's board, but it may also be of interest to radio amateurs operating on the microwave amateur bands. It is similar to the B200 but it has two receivers and two transmitters, allowing the radio to work in MIMO mode. The twin receivers could be used for diversity or beam steering applications. The radio uses a USB 3.0 interface to carry the high data load required for it's very wide output 'panadapter' bandwidth.

- Frequency range: 70 MHz to 6 GHz
- VHF, UHF, SHF
- ADC resolution: 12 Bits, 61.44 Msps
- Panadapter bandwidth: 56 MHz (or 30.72 MHz in two transmit, two receiver mode)
- Class: Uncased PCB - low power transceiver (sub QRP)
- Type: Transceiver (single or 2x full duplex)
- Interface: USB 3.0, separate 6V DC powered
- Receive filters / pre-selector: none
- On board Xilinx Spartan 6 FPGA for DSP experimentation
- Transmitter power +10 dBm (10 mW) maximum
- SDR software: GNU Radio
- USRP = Universal Software Radio Peripheral

USRP 2900 AND 2901 (NATIONAL INSTRUMENTS)

The National Instruments USRP 2900 and 2901 are small box radios designed primarily for educational use and for experimenters. The 2901 has two receiver and transmitter front ends and the 2900 only has one. National Instruments owns Ettus Research, which explains why these radios have essentially the same specifications as the Ettus radios.

- Frequency range: 70 MHz to 6 GHz
- VHF, UHF, SHF
- ADC and DAC resolution: 12 Bits, 61.44 Msps (or 30.72 MHz in two transmit, two receiver mode)
- Panadapter bandwidth: 56 MHz (max)
- Class: small box - low power transceiver (sub QRP)
- Type: Transceiver (single or 2x full duplex)
- Interface: USB 3.0, separate 6V DC powered
- Receive filters / pre-selector: none
- Transmitter power +20 dBm (100 mW) maximum
- USRP 2901 1-channel single input single output (SISO)
- USRP 2901 2-channel multiple input multiple output (MIMO)
- SDR software: LabVIEW, GNU Radio

HERMES (OPENHPSDR / APACHE LABS)

The Hermes transceiver board was developed as an open source project by the OpenHPSDR group. It is now manufactured by Apache Labs. The transmitter has a maximum output power of 500 mW, so it is normally used in combination with a linear amplifier and the Alex filter board.

The Hermes transceiver board is used in the Apache Labs ANAN-10 and ANAN-100 models, which gives you the advantages of on-going firmware support and compatibility with the latest releases of PowerSDR mRX. Hermes (and Angelia) boards are available from Apache Labs. They also sell the ANAN-10 case for you to house your Hermes board.

- Frequency range: 10 kHz to 54 MHz
- Bands: LF, MF, HF +6m
- ADC resolution: 16 Bits, 122.88 Msps
- Panadapter bandwidth: up to 4x 384 kHz depending on software
- Class: Direct sampling low power transceiver (sub QRP)
- Type: Transceiver (Full Duplex)
- Interface: Ethernet
- Receive filters / pre-selector: none – use the Alex board.
- Transmit power: 0.5 W
- Software: PowerSDR, Hetrodyne, Kiss Konsole, GHPSDR3, others.

NOCTAR (PER VICES)

The Noctar is primarily an industrial and scientific board, but may be of interest to radio amateurs operating on the microwave amateur bands. It has very wide frequency coverage and transmitting capability.

- Frequency range: 100 kHz to 4.4 GHz
- Bands: LF, MF, HF, VHF, UHF, SHF
- ADC resolution: 12 Bits, (2 x 125 Msps)
- Panadapter bandwidth: 250 MHz
- Class: sub QRP low power transceiver
- Type: Transceiver (Full Duplex), dual ADCs
- Interface: PCI card (installed inside PC)
- FPGA: Altera Cyclone IV FPGA
- Receive filters / pre-selector: none
- On board Cyclone IV FPGA for DSP experimentation
- Transmitter power +15 dBm (31 mW) maximum
- SDR software: GNU Radio

QUADRUS DRU-244A (SPECTRAFOLD TECHNOLOGIES)

The Quadrus board is not an SDR receiver on its own. It is described as an 'SDR phase coherent hardware digitizer'. It can be purchased with one, two or four ADCs operating at a sample rate of 80Msps, so it can provide up to four 0-40 MHz receivers. I expect it would be more commonly used at much higher frequencies, using external front end filters and down converters.

- Frequency range: Up to 40MHz (Nyquist zone 1)
- LF - HF, (higher with outboard down converters or undersampling)
- ADC resolution: 16 Bits at 80 Msps (per ADC)
- Panadapter bandwidth: 25 – 400 kHz (per channel)
- Class: PCI card
- Type: Phase coherent receiver
- Interface: PCI card (installed inside PC)
- Receive filters / pre-selector: none
- On board FPGA for DSP experimentation
- External 10 MHz clock and synchronization inputs and outputs
- Can be stacked to 16 inputs using four cards
- The Quadrus is designed for commercial applications. The phase coherent receivers could be used for diversity and beam steering applications.

RED PITAYA (REDPITAYA.COM)

The Red Pitaya SDR is a small card with an on-board FPGA and a softcore processor, which can run Linux. It has two RF receiver ports and two transmitter ports, as well as the usual digital i/o pins. It is really a development board with RF functionality, but it can certainly be used as an SDR transceiver.

The board is marketed for use as a two-channel 50 MHz digital oscilloscope. I expect that it could be used as a vector network analyzer or an antenna analyzer as well.

- Frequency range: 50 kHz – 500 MHz
- Bands: LF, MF, HF, VHF - UHF
- ADC resolution: 14 Bits at 125 Msps
- Panadapter bandwidth: 50-500 kHz
- Class: uncased PCB – sub QRP transceiver (1x or 2x full duplex)
- Interface: Ethernet and USB (power 5V micro USB)
- On board FPGA for DSP experimentation
- Receive filters / pre-selector: none
- SDR software SDR#, HDSDR, GQRX and others

PMSDR SDR KIT (IW3AUT.ALTERVISTA.ORG)

The PMSDR is a small, low-cost, HF band receiver that uses a computer USB port for control of the radio and the PC sound card for A/D conversion. It was designed by Martin Pernter IW3AUT. The radio is supplied as a kit and there are several other kits to go with it. All smd integrated circuits are pre soldered, so it should not be too difficult to build.

- Frequency range: 100 kHz – 72 MHz
- Bands: LF, MF, HF, Some VHF
- ADC resolution: not applicable - PC sound card
- Panadapter bandwidth: depends on PC sound card 48 kHz to 192 kHz
- Class: QSD based HF receiver with Si570 oscillator
- Interface: USB (for control) plus IQ at audio
- Receive filters / pre-selector: three selectable band pass filters (or optional filter board)
- SDR software: typical sound card based SDR software
- Onboard PIC microcontroller
- Optional kits: case, display board, filter and TR changeover board, VHF/UHF down converter board

The optional filter and TR changeover board is interesting because it adds filters that are switched automatically by the PIC microcontroller according to the frequency of operation. It can also use a PTT signal from your transceiver to switch the SDR receiver out of the antenna circuit while you are transmitting. The down converter option adds the ability to receive signals between 90 and 500 MHz, so you can receive signals on the 2m and 70cm amateur radio bands.

HERMES-LITE (GITHUB.COM/SOFTERHARDWARE/HERMES-LITE)

Hermes-Lite is an open source SDR project for those who want to experiment with building a low cost HF transceiver. It is a collection of small circuit boards, which can be combined to form a direct digital synthesis sub QRP HF transceiver. A major plus is that it uses the same FPGA firmware as the OpenHPSDR Hermes board, which means that you can use PowerSDR mRX and other SDR software that is compatible with Hermes. The hardware prototype uses a BeMicro SDK FPGA board for DSP processing. A V2 version is in development. It will use an on-board Altera MAX 10 FPGA instead of the BeMicro card.

Currently, the easiest way to obtain a Hermes-Lite is to buy one of the partially assembled kits. They are made available when there is enough interest. The partially assembled kits have the most difficult to solder surface mount components pre-soldered. You must complete the kit including soldering of the larger 0805 size SMT components and winding the baluns.

FIFI SDR KIT (BOX73.COM)

The FiFi SDR was introduced as a construction project for the youth camp at the Fichten Field Day (FiFi) 2010. It is a generation two QSD receiver using a Si570 oscillator. It can be controlled via the USB interface and it includes a built in 192 kHz sampling sound card. The FiFi is supplied as a kit, which includes the case. All smd integrated circuits are pre soldered, so there are actually only a few connectors to solder on to the board.

- Frequency range: 100 kHz – 30 MHz (usable to 54 MHz)
- Bands: LF, MF, HF
- ADC resolution: not applicable, sampling is at audio frequencies
- Panadapter bandwidth: 192 kHz
- Class: QSD based HF receiver with Si570 oscillator
- Internal 192 kHz sound card chip
- Interface: USB
- Receive filters / pre-selector: no
- SDR software: Genesis Radio's 'GSDR' and other sound card based SDR software
- Onboard ARM Cortex M3 microcomputer.

PEABERRY, OMNIA, GENESIS G59, SOFT66LC4, SDR 4+, SOFTROCK

I have included notes on a few generation one and generation two QSD based receivers. There are many, many others available. Most of them use the PC sound card as the A/D converter, but some have a built in sound card with a USB interface. Some cover all of the HF bands and the Genesis G59 covers 6m as well. Others are single band or only cover a couple of HF bands. They generally offer a single panadapter with a 48 kHz or 96 kHz bandwidth. A few can manage a 192 kHz panadapter, depending on the sound card.

- The Peaberry (Omnia SDR basic) SDR is a kit that includes an inbuilt sound card and provides a USB connection to the PC. It can be configured to cover selected bands: 160/80m, 80/75/60/40m, 60/40/30/20m, 30/20/17/15m, or 17/15/12/10m.

- Genesis G59 is a kit transceiver with many additional components and filters. It covers HF and 6m with 10 mW output power. There is an optional 10 W power amplifier available.

- The Soft66LC4 has a USB interface for control. It works from 500 kHz to 70 MHz and has a band pass filter.

- Soft66Lite is a fixed tuned generation one SDR with band pass filters.

- Cross Country Radio SDR 4+ is a generation two SDR receiver, using a Si570 VFO and an internal USB sound card. It covers 850 kHz to 70.5 MHz. It has switched band pass filters. The panadapter display is 48 kHz using the internal sound card and up to 192 kHz using an external PC sound card.

- The SoftRock kits are based on the QSD Tayloe detector design (Dan Tayloe N7VE).

In many ways, the SoftRock is the design that started SDR for radio amateurs*. The SoftRock kits have been the first introduction to software defined radio for thousands of people, including me. They are available from http://fivedash.com/. These little kits have surprisingly good performance and they are excellent value for money. But, these days the equally cheap and more versatile RTL dongles are more popular. SoftRock kits are still ideal if you want to create a band scope for an older ham transceiver or receiver, or if you want to "build it yourself."

Another early pioneer of SDR for radio hams is Gerald Youngblood AC5OG, the founder of FlexRadio, who brought the first commercial SDR transceivers to market. He wrote the early code for PowerSDR and the excellent, 'A software-defined radio for the masses' series of articles for QEX.

GLOSSARY OF ABBREVIATIONS AND ACRONYMS

ABBREVIATIONS, ACRONYMS AND OTHER TERMS	
Term	*Description*
2m, 6m, 10m	144 MHz, 50 MHz, and 28 MHz amateur radio bands
15m, 20m, 40m, 80m	21 MHz, 14 MHz, 7 MHz, and 3.5 MHz amateur radio bands
59	Standard (default) signal report for amateur radio voice conversations. A report of '59' means perfect readability and strength.
599, 5NN	Standard (default) signal report for amateur radio CW conversations. A 599 report means perfect readability, strength, and tone. The 599 signal report is often used for digital modes as well. The 5NN version is faster to send using CW. It is often used as a signal report exchange when working contest stations.
73	Morse code abbreviation 'best wishes, see you later.' It is used when you have finished transmitting at the end of the conversation.
A/D	Analog to digital.
ADC	Analog to digital converter or analog to digital conversion.
AF	Audio frequency - nominally 20 to 20,000 Hz.
algorithm	A process or set of rules to be followed in calculations or other problem-solving operations, especially by a computer. In DSP it is a mathematical formula, code block, or process that acts on the data signal stream to perform a particular function, for example a noise filter.
ANF	Automatic notch filter – filter that eliminates the effect of long term interference signals such as carrier signals that are close to the wanted receiving frequency. Not effective against impulse noise.
ARM	Advanced RISC Machine. A type of microprocessor that works faster because it has a reduced list of possible instructions.
Band scope	A band scope is a spectrum display of the frequencies above and below the frequency that the radio is tuned to. The center of the display is generally the frequency that you are listening to. This is different to a panadapter where you can listen to any frequency across the display.
BDR	Blocking dynamic range receiver test.
Bin	Narrow band of frequencies. The FFT process creates thousands of narrow bins.
Bit	Binary value 0 or 1.
Bus	The lines on a computer mainboard that connect key devices together. You can think of a bus as a data highway. It carries parallel data signals usually 32 bits or 64 bits wide.
Byte	Eight binary bits.

C#	C Sharp – computer language (a development of C, C+, and C++).
Carrier	Usually refers to the transmission of an un-modulated RF signal. It is called a carrier because the modulation process modifies the un-modulated RF signal to carry the modulation information. A carrier signal can be amplitude, frequency, and / or phase modulated. Then it is referred to as a 'modulated carrier.' An oscillator signal is not a carrier unless it is transmitted.
CAT	Computer aided transceiver. A computer sends predefined text strings to the radio to control and read information from the radio. Icom calls it CI-V.
CC	Command and Control bytes.
CFIR	ιpensating finite impulse response – a filter type with a rise at the high frequency end to compensate for the roll off created by the 'eding CIC filters in the FPGA.
CI-V	Icom version of CAT control. A computer sends predefined text strings to the radio to control and read information from the radio.
CIC	Cascaded integrated comb filters used in the FPGA to remove alias frequencies during the decimation process.
CISC	Complex instruction set computing – Standard microprocessor.
CODEC	Coder/decoder - a device or software used for encoding or decoding a digital data stream.
COTS	Commercial off the shelf – a component you can buy from a dealer. For DSP this means that the chips are provided already configured for digital signal processing applications.
CPU	Central processing unit - usually the microprocessor in a PC or other computer.
CQ	'Seek You' an abbreviation used by amateur radio operators when making a general call which anyone can answer.
CW	Continuous Wave – the transmission mode used to transmit Morse Code.
D/A	Digital to analog.
DAC	Digital to analog converter or digital to analog conversion.
dB, dBm, dBc, dBV	The Decibel is a way of representing numbers using a logarithmic scale. dB is used to describe a ratio, i.e. the difference between two levels or numbers. Decibels are often referenced to a fixed value such as a Volt (dBV), a milliwatt (dBm), or the carrier level (dBc). Decibels are also used to represent logarithmic units of gain or loss. An amplifier might have 3 dB gain. An attenuator might have 10 dB loss.
dBFS	Signal level compared to the full scale level, expressed in dB.
DDC	Digital down conversion - the receiver part of a direct sampling SDR.
DDS	Direct digital synthesis. SDR that uses digital down or up conversion, or an oscillator that uses software code to generate frequencies (DSP).

digital modes	Amateur radio transmission of digital information rather than voice. It can be text, or data such as video, still pictures, or computer files.
digital voice	Amateur radio mode where speech is coded into a digital format and sent as tone sequences or phase shift keying.
.dll	Dynamic link library – reusable software block - can be called from other programs.
DR3	3rd order dynamic range receiver test - needs to be tested differently for an SDR.
DSP	Digital signal processing – a dedicated integrated circuit chip usually running internal firmware code, or a software program running on a computer. DSP uses mathematical algorithms in computer software to manipulate digital signals in a ways that are equivalent to functions performed on analog signals by hardware mixers, oscillators, filters, amplifiers, attenuators, modulators, or demodulators.
DUC	Digital up conversion - the transmitter part of a direct sampling SDR.
DX	Long distance, or rare, or wanted by you, amateur radio station.
EME	Earth - Moon – Earth, communications using signals 'bounced' off the moon back to Earth. These days usually using the JT65 digital mode.
ENOB	Effective number of bits of an ADC. The ADC can't describe very small input signals due to its internal noise performance. ENOB is the number of bits that contain real usable information.
FFT	Fast Fourier Transformation – conversion of signals from the time domain to the frequency domain (and back).
FFTW	Fastest Fourier Transformation in the West – a software library used by many SDR programs.
FIFO	First In First Out – a type of data buffer.
FPGA	Field Programmable Gate Array – a chip that can be programmed to act like logic circuits, memory, or a CPU.
Frame	Data packet structure – usually includes synchronization, control, and payload information in bytes.
Fs	Signal frequency
GHz	Gigahertz – unit of frequency = 1,000,000,000 cycles per second.
GPU	Graphics Processing Unit – a specialized microprocessor designed to manage data for display on a computer monitor. They were introduced to speed up the display of high resolution images such as movies or computer games. Using a GPU reduces the processing load on the computers main processor, the CPU.
GUI	Graphical user interface – the form on the PC software that allows you to interact with the radio. The GUI is the knobs and display of an SDR.
HF	High Frequency (3 MHz - 30 MHz).
Hz	Hertz – unit of frequency = 1 cycle per second.
I data or stream	The non-phase shifted part of the IQ audio signal or data stream.

I.F.	Intermediate frequency i.e. the Fs – LO or Fs + LO output of a mixer. (Fs = Signal frequency LO = local oscillator frequency.)
Imaginary	Part of the complex signal in a buffer - often holds the Q signal or frequency bins below the LO frequency.
IMD	Intermodulation distortion - interference / distortion caused by non-linear devices like mixers. There are IMD tests for receivers and transmitters. IMD performance of linear amplifiers can also be tested.
IQ	Refers to the I and Q data streams treated as a pair of signals.
JT65	Slow digital mode used for extremely weak signal communications. Designed for EME but also used for some terrestrial communications.
kHz	Kilohertz – unit of frequency = 1 thousand cycles per second.
KK	Kiss Konsole – SDR application for Windows used as an example of PC software.
ksps	Thousands of samples per second.
L band	Amateur radio 1296 MHz band (1,240 to 1,300 MHz) also known as the 23cm band.
latency	Latency is the delay caused by using computer software or DSP chips to process the audio signal. In the SDR receiver, it is the delay between the time the receiver detects a signal and the time that you hear it from the speaker or see it on the panadapter. In the SDR transmitter, it is the delay between your speech going into the microphone or the Morse key or bug is depressed until the signal is transmitted. It is a particular issue for CW operators where it can cause an annoying delay before the side tone is heard.
LF	Low Frequency (30 kHz - 300 kHz).
LO	Local Oscillator frequency of a Superheterodyne receiver. In an SDR with a 'zero I.F.', it is the same as the frequency that the SDR is tuned to. It is usually the frequency that is displayed at the center of the panadapter spectrum display.
LSB	Lower sideband transmission. When talking about data streams or frames it is the least significant byte – lower 8 bits of a 16 bit word.
MDS	Minimum discernible signal – measurement of receiver sensitivity.
MF	Medium Frequency (300 kHz – 3 MHz).
MHz	Megahertz – unit of frequency = 1 million cycles per second.
MIMO	Multiple input multiple output
MOX	Microphone operated switch (in KK this is PTT from the PC software).
MSB	When talking about data streams or frames it is the most significant byte – higher 8 bits of a 16 bit word.
Msps	Millions of samples per second.
Multicore	A cable containing several wires.
mW	Milliwatt = 1/0000th Watts

m, 2m, 6m	Meter (US) or Metre. Often used to denote an amateur radio or shortwave band; e.g. 2m, 6m, 30m, 10m, where it denotes the approximate free space wavelength of the radio frequency. Wavelength = 300 / frequency in MHz. A frequency range of 3 to 30 MHz has a corresponding wavelength of 100 to 10m.
NB	Noise blanker – filter used to eliminate impulse noise
NCO	Numerically controlled oscillator - the local oscillator in a DDS type SDR (CORDIC software code in the FPGA).
Net	An on air meeting of a group of amateur operators.
Non linearity	Is when the ratio between the input to a device and the output signal is not linear. For example, an amplifier that puts out less power at full drive because the supply voltage droops.
NPR	Noise power ratio or 'white noise' receiver test.
NR	Noise Reduction – filter used to eliminate continuous background noise
Panadapter	Panadapter is short for panoramic adapter. It allows us to see a panoramic display of the band. The panadapter is sometimes confusingly referred to as a 'receiver.' It often can display a spectrum display and / or a waterfall picture. You can usually adjust the size, speed, and width of the display with a mouse or touch screen device. You may be listening to one or more signals anywhere within the displayed spectrum of frequencies. This is different to a band scope.
Payload	The part of a digital data frame that contains the wanted data signal. The rest of the bits in the data frame are used to carry synchronization and control information.
PC	Personal computer - usually with a Windows, Mac, or Linux operating system. In this book, it could include a tablet or even a smart phone running the Android operating system.
PSK, BPSK, QPSK	Phase shift keying / binary phase shift keying / quadrature phase shift keying. Some of the amateur radio and commercial digital modes used for sending text.
PTT	Press to talk - the transmit button on a microphone – The PTT signal sets the radio and software to transmit mode.
Q data or stream	The 90 degree phase shifted part of the IQ audio signal or data stream.
QRP	Q code - amateur radio low power operation (usually < 5 Watts).
QSD	Quadrature sampling detector - SDR receiver front end (often a Tayloe detector).
QSE	Quadrature sampling exciter - SDR transmitter front end (often a Tayloe detector working in reverse).
QSO	Q code - amateur radio conversation or "contact".
QSY	Q code - request or decision to change to another frequency.

RDS	Radio data system – system for sending brief test strings over the FM broadcast radio. It usually includes station ID and sometimes the song title and artist currently playing.
Real	Part of the complex signal in a buffer - often holds the 'I' signal or frequency bins above the LO frequency.
RF	Radio frequency.
RISC	Reduced instruction set computing – special microprocessor usually used for embedded systems or for fast digital processing.
RMDR	Reciprocal mixing dynamic range – a receiver performance test.
RS232	A computer interface used for serial data communications.
SAM	Synchronous amplitude modulation.
SAW	SAW (surface acoustic wave) filters are electromechanical devices commonly used in radio frequency applications. They are usually ceramic or crystal filters.
SDR	If you don't know this one you haven't been paying attention!
+ SDR	A conventional radio with some basic SDR functionality, usually the ability to display a band scope of up to 200 kHz bandwidth.
SFDR	Spurious free dynamic range – a performance measurement of the dynamic range of an analog to digital converter (or other device).
SHF	Super High Frequency (3 GHz - 30 GHz).
SINAD	Signal-to-Noise Plus Distortion Ratio in dB.
Sked	A pre-organized or scheduled appointment to communicate with another amateur radio operator.
Slice	The part of the spectrum that is within the selected audio bandwidth i.e. the part that you can listen to.
smd	Surface mounted device. Very small integrated circuit packages, chip capacitors and resistors that are designed to sit on top of the circuit board and are not through hole mounted.
SNR	Signal-to-Noise Ratio in dB.
softcore	An emulation of a microprocessor running as a firmware program on another device such as an FPGA. Can be used like a hardware microprocessor.
SSB	Single sideband transmission mode.
Superhet	Superheterodyne receiver – conventional, non-SDR, receiver architecture that uses oscillators and mixers to convert ('heterodyne') the incoming RF signal to an intermediate frequency.
SWL	Short wave listener.
TR	Transmit / Receive. Usually refers to the antenna change over relay, or the signal that controls the, transmit to receive switching.
TU	Morse code abbreviation meaning 'to you.' Used when you have finished transmitting and wish the other station to respond.

UHF	Ultra High Frequency (300 MHz - 3000 MHz).
USB	Universal serial bus – serial data communications between a computer and other devices. USB 2.0 is fast, USB 3.0 is very fast.
USB	Upper sideband transmission.
VHF	Very High Frequency (30 MHz - 300 MHz).
VNA	Vector network analyzer - mode to use the SDR as a tracking spectrum analyzer to test antennas, coax feeder cables, or RF filters.
W	Watts – unit of power (electrical or RF).
Word	A digital word is one or more bytes used to carry a particular piece of information. For example, the Q signal between the ANAN or Hermes radio and the PC software is a stream of 24 bit (3 byte) words. The microphone signal is 16 bit (2 byte) words.
Zadig	Zadig is a program that installs Windows USB drivers, which allow the RTL dongle to communicate with the SDR software. In some cases, you have to run Zadig as well as installing the SDR program. But SDR# installs Zadig as a part of its installation. Your RTL dongle might not work in a different USB port. You might have to run Zadig for each USB port that you plan to use. It is easier if you use the same SDR port every time you use your RTL dongle.

DRAWINGS AND IMAGES

ABOUT THE AUTHOR

Hi, I live in Christchurch, New Zealand. I am married to Carol who is very understanding and tolerant of my obsession with amateur radio. She describes my efforts as "Andrew playing around with radios." We have two children and a cat. One son is studying Commerce at Canterbury University and the other is studying Medicine at Otago University. The cat stays mostly at home.

I am a keen amateur radio operator who enjoys radio contesting, chasing DX, digital modes, and satellite operating. But I am rubbish at sending and receiving Morse code. I write extensively about many aspects of the amateur radio hobby, mostly for our national amateur radio magazine, 'Break-in.' Some of my articles are available at my website at http://qsl.net/zl3dw/.

Thanks for reading my book!

73 de Andrew ZL3DW

Other books by Andrew Barron

An Introduction to HF Software Defined Radio
ISBN: 9781 5001 1993 5 Published July 2014

Index

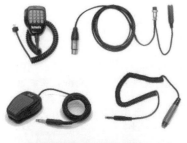